# CURRENT TOPICS
# IN RADIATION RESEARCH

## VOLUME II

EDITED BY

## MICHAEL EBERT

AND

## ALMA HOWARD

*Paterson Laboratories, Christie Hospital & Holt Radium Institute,
Withington, Manchester*

1966

NORTH-HOLLAND PUBLISHING COMPANY - AMSTERDAM

PUBLISHERS:

NORTH-HOLLAND PUBLISHING CO. - AMSTERDAM

PRINTED IN THE NETHERLANDS

# FOREWORD TO VOLUME I

It is the inspiration and experience of individuals which leads to progress in science. In radiation research a general advance relies also on a variety of disciplines and their interrelation. We felt that a real contribution to radiation research could be made by inviting individual workers to summarize their subjects from their own point of view, free from the requirements of handbook or review articles. We believed that this would help authors to cut across the traditional frontiers of their parent disciplines, and would encourage a measure of spontaneity.

*Manchester*, August 1964.


The success of the first Volume suggested that Volume 2 of the series should follow fairly soon. We felt that our policy of asking the authors to write about their field of interest without restrictions or limitations had been fully justified. The selection of topics again emphasizes some of the more recent and far reaching developments in radiation research.

We wish to thank our contributors for their work and their prompt delivery of manuscripts.

*Manchester*, November 1965. The Editors

# CONTENTS

# I

# RADIATION CHEMISTRY OF SYNTHETIC MACROMOLECULES IN SOLUTION, LET EFFECTS

A. HENGLEIN and W. SCHNABEL

*Hahn-Meitner-Institut für Kernforschung Berlin*
*Berlin-Wannsee, Germany*

# CONTENTS

# 1. Fundamental aspects and experimental methods

In recent years, considerable research on the radiation chemistry of macromolecular substances has been devoted to changes which occur in polymers when they are irradiated by $\gamma$-rays, fast electrons or mixed $\gamma$- and fast neutron radiations [CHARLESBY, 1960; CHAPIRO, 1962]. In these studies fundamental processes such as degradation of the main chain and crosslinking as well as decomposition of side groups, formation or disappearance of double bonds and the effects of additives have been investigated. In addition, the corresponding changes in the physical and technological properties of the polymers have been examined carefully. Relatively little research concerning the effects of ionizing radiation on macromolecules in solution has been carried out. The few investigations in this field have revealed that polymers in solution undergo changes similar to those in solid state irradiations such as degradation and intermolecular crosslinking. However, the mechanisms responsible for these changes are rather complex since they may result from either the direct or indirect action of radiation or both, depending on the concentration of the polymer and the nature of the solvent. Two new phenomena have been observed in the irradiation of polymers in solution, namely intramolecular crosslinking or microgel formation and co-crosslinking of two polymers present in the same solution.

Studies on LET effects in the irradiation of solid and dissolved polymers have only occasionally been reported. Most of this work seems to have been carried out on polymers in solution. The linear dimensions of a polymer coil in either the solid state or in solution are often comparable or larger than the diameter of the cylindrical volume in which a high (linear energy transfer) LET particle dissipates its energy when passing through matter. It can therefore occur that different parts of a macromolecule—even base units close to each other—are ionized or excited at practically the same time. In other words, the ionized and excited intermediates may differ from those produced by the passage of a fast electron through the coil. LET effects in macromolecules have therefore in part to be explained by other concepts than those usually applied in LET studies with low molecular

weight compounds. The effects of LET are of special interest to radiation biologists since LET effects probably very often are caused by
differences in the response of biologically active macromolecules to
the passing of an electron and a high LET particle. The study of LET
effects in synthetic polymers is still an underdeveloped field of the
radiation chemistry of polymeric systems. Our description of this
field and the theory given in this article should therefore be regarded
more as a stimulus for further work than as a final answer to the
question.

Before treating the radiation induced reactions of macromolecules
in solutions, it seems useful to review briefly some fundamentals of
polymer chemistry and the radiation chemical reactions of macromolecules in the solid state. This will constitute the material of the next
subsections. Reactions which occur in solutions of polymers under the
influence of radiations of low LET are described in sections 2, 3 and 4.
These parts will begin with a theoretical examination of the problem
followed by descriptions of the behaviour of macromolecules in aqueous
and non-aqueous solutions. Such a distinction with respect to the solvent seems to be useful, firstly, because one would predict pronounced
differences in reactions in aqueous and non-aqueous solutions, and
secondly, because aqueous solutions are of special interest to radiation
biologists. Finally, in section 5 a comparison will be made of the effects
produced by low and high LET radiations on polymers and some
theoretical considerations will be presented.

## 1.2. MOLECULAR WEIGHT AND SHAPE OF MACROMOLECULES

A polymeric substance generally contains macromolecules of different chain lengths. The average molecular weight may be calculated
by weighing the macromolecules of different size either by their relative
abundance $n_{(M)}$ (number average $\bar{M}_n$) or by their abundance and their
weight (weight average $\bar{M}_w$):

$$\bar{M}_n = \frac{\sum n_{(M)} M}{\sum n_{(M)}} \tag{1}$$

$$\bar{M}_w = \frac{\sum n_{(M)} M^2}{\sum n_{(M)} M}. \tag{2}$$

The various methods for the determination of the molecular weight yield the number or weight average or some value between these two. If a polymeric substance has an uniform (monodisperse) molecular weight distribution, i.e. if all macromolecules are of equal size, $\bar{M}_n$ is equal to $\bar{M}_w$ and all methods of determination give the number average. Polymers of practically uniform molecular weight distribution are obtained by suitable fractionation of polydisperse samples. A more usual distribution is a random or exponental distribution, as it may be obtained by random fragmentation of an infinite chain. Most polymers which are formed by the polymerization of monomers have a random molecular weight distribution. Polymers that are degraded by radiation, generally have this distribution. It can be shown that for a random distribution the weight average molecular weight is equal to twice the number average.

The number average molecular weight is determined by osmotic measurements. Since experiments of this type are rather sensitive to low molecular weight impurities and until recently were rather time consuming they have scarcely been carried out in radiation chemical studies. Industrial laboratories recently developed high speed methods for osmotic measurements which are based on the detection of the movement of the solvent through the membrane (separating solvent from solution) together with automatic application of a pressure to counterbalance the osmotic pressure. It might therefore be expected that osmotic measurements will more frequently be carried out in the future.

The weight average molecular weight can be determined by light scattering experiments. An average molecular weight close to $\bar{M}_w$ is obtained by viscosity measurements. The intrinsic viscosity of a polymer depends on $M$ according to

$$[\eta] = kM^a, \tag{3}$$

where $k$ and $a$ are constants that depend on the nature of the polymer as well as of the solvent. This is the simplest method for determining the molecular weight. It is, however, an indirect method which must first be standardized by one of the direct methods. The exponent $a$ in eq. (3) usually lies between 0.6 and 1.0. If the polymer is monodisperse, the molecular weight $\bar{M}_v$ (viscosity average) determined by viscosity measurements is equal to $\bar{M}_n$. In the case of a random distribution, $\bar{M}_v$ lies close to $\bar{M}_w$; the exact value of $\bar{M}_v$ depends on the exponent $a$ in eq. (3) (for $a = 1.0$, $\bar{M}_v = 2\bar{M}_w$, while for $a = 0.8$, $\bar{M}_v = 1.908\ \bar{M}_n = 0.954\ \bar{M}_w$).

It should be noted that the relationship according to eq. (3) is only valid for a homologous series of a polymer of linear structure. The intrinsic viscosity of a branched polymer is lower than that of a linear polymer having the same molecular weight. The intrinsic viscosity therefore is not an unequivocal measure of the molecular weight. This must always be kept in mind, if radiation induced effects are studied, since changes may occur not only in the molecular weight but also in the structure of a polymer. On the other hand, the difference $\bar{M}_w - \bar{M}_v$ in the molecular weights determined by light scattering and viscosity measurements, respectively, may indicate the amount of branching in a polymer. This difference will become larger as the amount of branching increases.

Light scattering experiments also give information about the shape of the macromolecules in solution. They can exist as statistical coils of more or less ellipsoidal shape enlarged by solvent intrusion. The macromolecules may also have a spherical or rodlike shape. Synthetic polymers in which the base units are arranged in a linear way generally form statistical coils in solution while certain biological molecules such as glycogen and some viruses have the shapes of a sphere or of a rod, respectively. In the case of a coil, the root mean square of the end to end distance can be calculated from the light scattering diagram. In concentrated solutions the coils are largely entangled. The expansion of a coil or its end to end distance is larger in the better solvent. In dilute solutions the entanglement of the molecules becomes smaller with decreasing concentration. There exists a certain polymer concentration where the individual coils just touch each other, i.e. where there is but little entanglement. This concentration in general is lower in the better solvent. The shape of polyelectrolytes strongly depends on the degree of ionization and this varies with the $p$H of the solution and the concentration of added ions. The coils expand as the degree of ionization increases, because of the mutual repulsion of the charged groups within a macromolecule. The intrinsic viscosity of a polymer also depends on the interaction between the solvent and the polymer. The exponent $a$ in eq. (3) in general is larger for better solvents, i.e. the stronger the interaction between solute and solvent.

## 1.3. CROSSLINKING AND DEGRADATION OF SOLID POLYMERS

Polymers can be classified into two groups according to their behaviour when exposed to $\gamma$-radiation or fast electrons. Two processes may be observed: 1) crosslinking of the polymer chains leading first to an increase in molecular weight and, at high enough doses, to the formation of a three-dimensional and insoluble network, or 2) scission of the main chains resulting in a decrease in molecular weight. Both processes occur simultaneously in many polymers and the classification depends upon which is predominant. In general, all vinyl polymers in which chain scission predominates have the structure

$$
\begin{array}{c}
R_1 \\
| \\
-CH_2-C- \\
| \\
R_2
\end{array}
$$

where $R_1$ or $R_2$ may be $CH_3$, $Cl$, $F$ etc. If either $R_1$ or $R_2$ or both are hydrogen atoms, crosslinking can be achieved. Accompanying the scission and crosslinking reactions are other processes. The splitting off of hydrogen, which is the chief volatile product from most polymers, and the formation of double bonds are perhaps the most important processes of this kind. Appreciable quantities of methane, ethane, carbon monoxide, carbon dioxide, and other small molecules also may be evolved. The number of crosslinks and of scissions generally is proportional to the absorbed dose. The yields of crosslinking and degradation are often given as densities $q_0$ and $p_0$, by which are designated the fractions of base units in the irradiated sample that are respectively crosslinked or degraded per unit of absorbed radiation. If the molecular weight of the base unit is designated by $m$, the following relations between the $G$-values and densities exist:

$$G(\text{crosslinked units}) = 9.6 \times 10^5 \frac{q_0}{m}, \tag{4}$$

$$G(\text{crosslinks}) = 4.8 \times 10^5 \frac{q_0}{m}, \tag{5}$$

$$G(\text{fractured units}) = 9.6 \times 10^5 \frac{p_0}{m}, \tag{6}$$

$q_0$ and $p_0$ are expressed here in $Mrad^{-1}$.

The number and weight average molecular weights of a polymer that initially had a random molecular weight distribution depend in the following way on the absorbed dose $D$ [CHARLESBY, 1960]:

$$\frac{1}{\overline{M}_n} = \frac{1}{\overline{M}_{n_0}} + (p_0 - \tfrac{1}{2}q_0)\frac{D}{m}, \tag{7}$$

$$\frac{1}{\overline{M}_w} = \frac{1}{\overline{M}_{w_0}} + (\tfrac{1}{2}p_0 - q_0)\frac{D}{m}. \tag{8}$$

If $p_0/q_0 > 2$, the average molecular weight decreases with increasing dose. The whole sample of the irradiated polymer remains soluble since no network will be formed. If $p_0/q_0 < 2$, the average molecular weight increases with dose. At a certain dose (gel dose), a three dimensional network is formed in part of the polymer. At still higher doses, more and more macromolecules are connected to the network, i.e. a larger part of the irradiated material becomes insoluble. A complete network

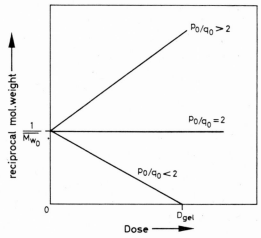

Fig. 1. The reciprocal weight average of the molecular weight as a function of the absorbed dose for different ratios $p_0/q_0$.

throughout the whole sample can finally be obtained, if there is no degradation of the main chain at all. However, if scission occurs to even a small degree, part of the polymer will always be soluble even at much higher doses than the gel dose. As the molecular weight is practically infinite at the gel point, it follows from eq. (8):

$$D_{gel} = \frac{m}{\overline{M_{w_0}}} \frac{1}{(q_0 - \frac{1}{2}p_0)}.$$ (9)

Finally, if $p_0/q_0 = 2$, no change in the avarage molecular weight of the polymer should occur when it is exposed to radiation, although some branching may be expected. The three cases, i.e. $p_0/q_0 \gtreqless 2$, are illustrated by fig. 1. where the reciprocal average molecular weight is plotted versus the absorbed dose. The difference $(\frac{1}{2}p_0 - q_0)$ can be obtained from the slope of the straight lines and, in the case of network formation, the gel dose is found by extrapolating the straight line down to $1/\overline{M}_w$ equal to zero.

If degradation of the main chain is predominant, the intrinsic viscosity of a polymer will continuously decrease with increasing dose. If $p_0/q_0$ is smaller than 2.0, the viscosity may pass through a minimum

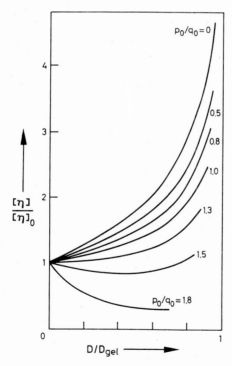

Fig. 2. The ratio of $[\eta]$ after dose $D$ to the initial $[\eta]_0$ *versus* $D/D_{gel}$ according to KILB [1959]. The curves are given for several values of the ratio $p_0/q_0$ and for a value of 0.68 of the exponent $a$ in eq. (3).

before undergoing a rapid increase as the gel dose is approached. The average molecular weight, of course, continuously increases at all values of $p_0/q_0$ smaller than two. The dependence of the ratio $[\eta]/[\eta]_0$ on the ratio $D/D_{gel}$ is shown by fig. 2 for various values of $p_0/q_0$ (all values being smaller than two). In the case of intramolecular cross-linking the viscosity often at first increases with dose, reaches a maximum and then falls off continuously as in the case of degradation. This effect has not yet been observed in the irradiation of solid polymers but may be encountered with dissolved macromolecules.

In studies on polymers in solution, the same methods may be used to determine $p_0$ and $q_0$ as in the case of the irradiation of solid polymers:

If the degradation of the main chain occurs to a negligible extent, $q_0$ is obtained from the slope of the straight line in the plot of $1/\overline{M_w}$ versus dose or is calculated from the gel dose according to eq. (9). If crosslinking is minor, $p_0$ is again easily calculated from the slope of the corresponding straight line in fig. 1. In the more general case, where degradation and crosslinking simultaneously occur, the ratio $p_0/q_0$ and the absolute value of $q_0$ can be obtained by measuring the soluble fraction $s$ from samples that have been irradiated with doses beyond the gel point. According to the equation [CHARLESBY and PINNER, 1959]

$$s + s^{\frac{1}{2}} = \frac{p_0}{q_0} + \frac{m}{q_0 \overline{M_{w_0}} \cdot D} \tag{10}$$

a plot of $s + s^{\frac{1}{2}}$ versus the reciprocal dose leads to a straight line which intercepts the ordinate axis at the point $p_0/q_0$ and has a slope equal to $m/q_0 \overline{M_w}$. The ratio $p_0/q_0$ may also be obtained from the dependence of the intrinsic viscosity on the dose at doses below the gel point [KILB, 1959]. $[\eta]/[\eta]_0$ is plotted here as a function of $D/D_{gel}$ and the experimental curve is compared with theoretical curves for various values of $p_0/q_0$ such as are shown in fig. 2.

In the case of $p_0/q_0 > 2$, a combination of osmotic pressure and light scattering measurements by which $\overline{M_n}$ and $\overline{M_w}$ are determined, makes it possible to calculate the ratio $p_0/q_0$. If $k_n$ and $k_w$ are the experimentally obtained values of the differences $(p_0 - \frac{1}{2}q_0)$ and $(\frac{1}{2}p_0 - q_0)$ in eqs. (7 and 8), respectively, $p_0/q_0$ is calculated according to,

$$\frac{p_0}{q_0} = \frac{k_w - 2k_n}{2k_w - k_n}. \tag{11}$$

If no gelation occurs, there does not exist a definite point such as $D_{\text{gel}}$, and so one cannot construct plots like fig. 2. However, similar plots can be constructed, if viscosity and light scattering measurements are combined. The ratio $[\eta]/[\eta]_0$ is plotted here versus the ratio $D/D^*$

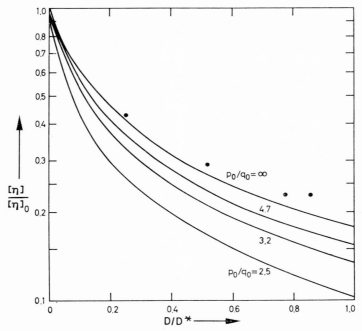

Fig. 3. The ratio $[\eta]/[\eta]_0$ *versus* $D/D^*$ according to KILB [1959]. $D^*$ is the dose needed to reduce the molecular weight $M_{\text{w}}$ to one tenth of its original value. The curves are calculated for a value of 0.75 of the exponent $a$ in eq. (3). (The experimental points correspond to data obtained in the irradiation of polymethylmethacrylate. They follow the curve for $p_0/q_0 = \infty$ quite well, i.e. there is very little crosslinking in this polymer).

where $D^*$ is the dose needed to decrease $\overline{M_{\text{w}}}$ (measured by light scattering) to a given fraction of the initial value $\overline{M_{\text{w}_0}}$. The experimental curve is then compared with theoretical curves that have been calculated for different values of the ratio $p_0/q_0$. Fig. 3 shows as a typical example.

## 2. Theory

2.1. GENERAL MECHANISM OF INTERMOLECULAR CROSSLINKING

The following reaction scheme contains all of the elementary processes which may occur during the irradiation of a polymer in solution [HENGLEIN, 1959a; SCHNABEL and HENGLEIN, 1961]:

direct effects of radiation

$$P \longrightarrow P* \begin{cases} \longrightarrow \cdots\cdot + \cdot\cdots & (12) \\ \longrightarrow \cdots\cdot + R_1^{\cdot}. & (13) \end{cases}$$

$$S \longrightarrow S* \longrightarrow 2R_2^{\cdot}. \qquad (14)$$

energy transfer

$$P*+S \longrightarrow P+S* \qquad (15)$$
$$S*+P \longrightarrow S+P* \qquad (16)$$

macroradical combination

$$\text{---}\overset{\cdot}{\text{---}} \longrightarrow \overset{}{\underset{|}{\text{---}}} \qquad (17)$$

spontaneous decay of side group macroradicals

$$\text{---}\cdot \longrightarrow \text{---}\cdot + \text{---} \qquad (18)$$

deactivation of macroradicals by solvent radicals

$$\text{---} + R_2^{\cdot}\cdot \longrightarrow \text{---} \qquad (19)$$

formation of macroradicals by solvent radicals

$$R_2^{\cdot} + \text{---} \longrightarrow R_2H + \text{---} \qquad (20)$$

deactivation of macroradicals by solvent molecules

$$\text{---} + S \longrightarrow R_2^{\cdot} + \text{---} \qquad (21)$$

The primary reactions are the excitation (or ionization) and dissociation of both the polymer P and the solvent S by the direct action of radiation. P* and S* designate electronically excited or ionized macromolecules in eqs. (12–16). Dissociation in the main chain of P leads to two "end group" macroradicals eq. (12) while decomposition of a side group yields a free "side group" macroradical and a free radical $R_1$ of low molecular weight eq. (13). Dissociation in the main chain and in side groups may occur from the same or from different excited states of P*. Protection of the polymer will occur if energy is transferred from the polymer to the solvent eq. (15). Energy (or charge) transfer in the opposite direction will result in a sensitization of the decomposition of the polymer eq. (16). The formation of inter-molecular crosslinks is attributed to the combination of side group macroradicals eq. (17). Combinations between side group and end group macroradicals lead to branching and may also contribute to network formation. In all cases studied to date, intermolecular cross-linking in solution could always be inhibited by small amounts of radical scavengers (iodine, tetranitromethane, oxygen) which clearly shows that crosslinking proceeds via a free radical mechanism. Eq. (18) describes the spontaneous conversion of a side group macroradical into an end group macroradical of lower chain length and a stable long fragment. This decay is known to occur in certain polymers even when they undergo conventional chemical changes. For example, poly-vinylacetate degrades in the main chain when exposed to chlorine:

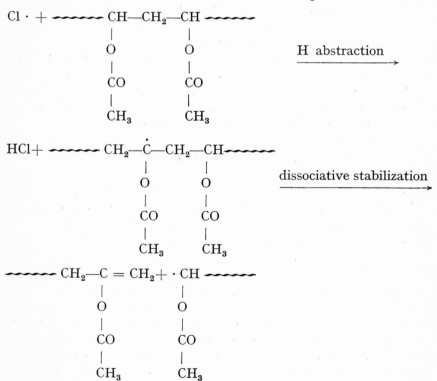

The deactivation of macroradicals by free radicals from the radiolysis of the solvent is described by eq. (19). This process must lead to a decrease in the rate of crosslinking since it competes with the combination of side group macroradicals. On the other hand, a sensitization may occur if free radicals $R_2$ attack the polymer and abstract hydrogen as is shown by eq. (20). The competition between the reactions described by eqs. (19 and 20) is very important to an understanding of the sensitizing or inhibiting effect of the solvent. Macroradicals may also be deactivated by their reaction with intact solvent molecules as is indicated by eq. (21).

Because of this complex mechanism, it is not possible to make a safe prediction about the overall effect of the solvent. Network formation is favoured if the rates of reactions 13, 17, and 20 are high while it is retarded or inhibited if reactions 12, 18, 19, and 21 are too fast. The rate of reaction 14 depends on the radiation sensitivity $[G(R)$ value] of the solvent. Reaction 14 retards or sensitizes crosslinking depending on whether the following reactions 19 or 17 and 20 are fast. In certain polymer-solvent mixtures, a few of the reactions mentioned in the scheme are very fast while the others occur to a negligible extent. In these special cases, which will be discussed in subsections 2.3 and 2.4, certain aspects of the general reaction mechanism can be studied quantitatively. Our consideration of the general scheme will now be completed by a discussion of the viscosity effects that have to be expected since the scheme contains diffusion controlled reactions eqs. (17 and 19).

In a polymer solution, the mobility of macromolecular species is much more strongly decreased by the viscosity than is the mobility of small molecules. This is well known from the ordinary polymerization of vinyl monomers in which the rate goes up after a certain degree of conversion is reached. When the viscosity of the solution increases during a polymerization, the rate of termination, in which two growing macroradicals are generally involved, decreases. However, the rate of chain propagation, in which swiftly diffusing monomer molecules participate, is only slightly influenced by viscosity changes in the system. An effect similar to this "gel effect" is to be expected in the irradiation of a polymer in solution at different concentrations. In our case, the desired reaction 17 becomes slower at higher viscosities while the competing process according to eq. (19), in which a reactant of low molecular weight participates, will be favoured. It is therefore to be expected that the dose required for gelation decreases with decreasing polymer concentration in concentrated solutions since the intermediate macroradicals become more mobile. This decrease is shown in fig. 4. On the other hand, more free radicals of the type $R_2$

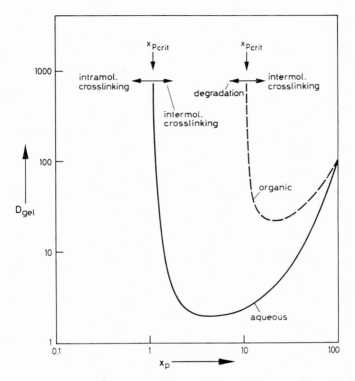

Fig. 4. The generally expected dependence of the gel dose on the mole fraction of the polymer in aqueous and organic solutions (the molecular weight of the solvent and a base unit of the polymer were assumed to be equal). $x_p$ is expressed in per cent.

are produced at lower polymer concentrations which favors the deactivation of macroradicals by reaction 19 (if reaction 20 is slow). The gel dose is therefore expected to increase again at low polymer concentrations and this is also shown in fig. 4. At a "critical" polymer concentration, the gel dose will become infinite, i.e. below that concentration a network can no longer be formed. This is because the efficiency of main chain degradation (eq. 12) is not decreased by the dilution as is the efficiency of crosslink formation according to eq. (17). The ratio

$p_0/q_0$ will therefore increase with decreasing polymer concentration. At the critical concentration, this ratio surpasses its critical value of 2.0.

## 2.2. MICROGEL FORMATION BY INTRAMOLECULAR CROSSLINKING

Intramolecular crosslinking cannot be explained by the simple reaction scheme of eqs. (12–21), in which the size and shape of the macromolecules have not yet been considered. As long as the macromolecules are strongly entangled in the more concentrated solutions, the distribution of macroradicals produced by either direct or indirect action of radiation can practically be regarded as uniform in the irradiated solution. If two radical spots are simultaneously produced in the same chain, they very probably interact with radical spots of other chains instead of reacting among themselves to form an intramolecular crosslink. In dilute solutions, however, the polymer molecules are less tangled, and the radical spots introduced into different chains have a larger average distance from each other. The combination of radical spots produced simultaneously in the same macromolecule may now be favoured over intermolecular combination. This effect will mainly occur with the largest macromolecules in the solution since they have the highest probability of acquiring more than one radical spot at the same time during irradiation. Large macromolecules, however, are produced by intermolecular crosslinking between two or perhaps several polymer chains in the first stages of irradiation [HENGLEIN, 1959b]. In other words, intramolecular crosslinking is expected to occur preferentially in those areas in the solution where a few macromolecules have already been connected by some bridges. The introduction of more and more internal crosslinks into these large species by continued irradiation will lead to microgels that become less soluble and less swollen. Under these conditions, the molecular weight of the polymer as measured by light scattering experiments is expected to increase rapidly at low doses and approach a limiting value at high doses. The viscosity of the solution may first increase because of the increase in molecular weight and then decrease because of the smaller hydrodynamic volume of the microgels. Microgel formation at higher doses has therefore the same effect on the intrinsic viscosity of a polymer as the degradation of the main chain. This should always be kept in mind if only viscosity measurements are carried out to study radiation effects in dissolved polymers.

If microgels are preferentially formed, the whole solution cannot be gelated. Intramolecular crosslinking will lead to an increase in the gel dose with decreasing polymer concentration in dilute solutions until a critical concentration is reached where more intra than intermolecular crosslinks are formed. A critical concentration at which the gel dose becomes infinite has been found for all solutions studied up to date. The reasons for the critical concentrations, however, may be quite different since both preferential intramolecular crosslinking and preferential degradation of the main chain lead to this phenomenon. In most cases, the transition from inter to intramolecular crosslinking occurs in aqueous polymer solutions, while the transition from inter-molecular crosslinking to degradation takes place mainly in organic solvents.

## 2.3. WATER AND ORGANIC SOLVENTS

Water has some unique properties as a solvent for the irradiation of dissolved polymers. Energy transfer effects between solvent and solute probably do not complicate the reaction scheme. Macroradicals that are produced will not react with the solvent because of the high strength of the bonds in the water molecule. On the other hand, very reactive free radicals such as OH radicals and H atoms are formed in the radiolysis of the solvent. Hydrated electrons which are also pro-duced either react with solutes or are converted into hydrogen atoms by the reaction $e_{aq}^- + H_3O^+ \rightarrow H + H_2O$. The abstraction of an H atom from an organic solute by an OH radical

$$\cdot OH + RH \rightarrow H_2O + R \cdot$$

generally is very fast and occurs as a diffusion controlled reaction [HART, 1964]. For example, if RH is an alcohol or the formate ion, bimolecular rate constants of the order of $10^9 M^{-1} sec^{-1}$ are observed. The corresponding abstraction reactions for H atoms have rate con-stants between $10^6$ to $10^8$ $M^{-1}$ $sec^{-1}$. It can therefore be expected that all free radicals from the decomposition of the solvent will imme-diately attack dissolved macromolecules and be completely converted into free side group macroradicals. In other words, macroradical formation by indirect action of radiation will be very effective and the dominating process in dilute solutions. The reaction scheme of eqs. (12–21) can be simplified now since reactions 15, 16, 19, and 21 may be omitted.

Several conclusions may be drawn from these considerations: a) The dose required for gelation in aqueous solutions will be rather low, b) Degradation of the main chain by direct action of radiation will be nearly negligible as compared to the formation of side group macroradicals by indirect action. The critical concentration will therefore not be determined by the rate of degradation but by intramolecular crosslinking, c) Intramolecular crosslinking is very probable at concentrations of about one weight per cent of the polymer, where the macromolecules become less entangled, d) In principle, every polymer soluble in water should be crosslinked in aqueous solutions, if its side group macroradicals do not spontaneously decompose according to eq. (19) and are able to combine with high efficiency (the efficiency of combination would be low if disproportionation between macroradicals often occurs), e) Because of its unique properties mentioned above, water should be the most efficient solvent for the crosslinking of polymers in solution.

The free radicals that are formed in the radiolysis of organic solvents are generally less reactive than the radicals from water. Organic radicals will only rarely attack intact macromolecules to produce side group macroradicals. Instead, they will mainly deactivate macroradicals which have been formed by direct action of radiation. The gel dose will therefore be much higher than for aqueous solutions. A simple calculation gives the order of magnitude of the critical concentration: The fraction of macroradicals which combine to form crosslinks is equal to

$$f = \frac{2k_{17}[\mathrm{P}\cdot]^2}{k_{17}[\mathrm{P}\cdot]^2 + k_{19}[\mathrm{P}\cdot][\mathrm{R}\cdot]} \sim x_{\mathrm{p}}, \qquad (22)$$

where $[\mathrm{P}\cdot]$ and $[\mathrm{R}\cdot]$ are the stationary concentrations of macro- and small radicals and the $k$'s are the bimolecular rate constants of the corresponding reactions. (The factor of 2 in eq. (22) appears since two macroradicals are consumed per crosslink formed.) If the same number of free radicals is formed in the polymer and in the solvent per unit absorbed dose and if the two rate constants are assumed to be equal, the concentrations $[\mathrm{P}\cdot]$ and $[\mathrm{R}\cdot]$ may be substituted by $x_{\mathrm{p}}$ and $(x_{\mathrm{p}} + 2x_{\mathrm{s}})$

$= x_p + 2(1-x_p)$ where $x_p$ and $x_s$ are the mole fractions of the polymer and the solvent, respectively. (The number of low molecular weight radicals is proportional to $2x_s + x_p$, since two radicals are formed per elementary process according to eq. (14), and one is produced by the reaction of eq. (13).) Under these conditions, the fraction $f$ becomes equal to $x_p$, i.e. the crosslinking density $q_0'$ of the dissolved polymer depends on the polymer concentration according to $q_0' = q_0 \cdot x_p$, where $q_0$ is the crosslinking density in the pure polymer. If it is further assumed that the density of degradation by direct action eq. (12) does not change upon dilution, the following relationship between the ratios $(p_0/q_0)$ and $(p_0'/q_0')$ of the polymer in the solid state and in solution is obtained:

$$\left(\frac{p_0'}{q_0'}\right) = \left(\frac{p_0}{q_0}\right)\frac{1}{x_p} . \tag{23}$$

For a value of $p_0/q_0 = 0.3$, a critical mole fraction of 0.15 is calculated, above which $p_0'/q_0'$ becomes equal to 2.0. Intramolecular crosslinking is not expected to be important at such high concentrations. The critical concentration is therefore determined by the transition from intermolecular crosslinking to degradation and is more than ten times as large as in the case of aqueous solutions. An exception to this rule may be found in the case of organic solvents that are only slightly decomposed under irradiation. For example, liquid carbon disulfide is radiolysed with a small yield of 0.8 molecules per 100 eV of absorbed energy and the resulting intermediates such as CS and S particles are not very reactive [JANSSEN et al., 1964]. The solvent may now simply play the role of a diluent and not significantly influence the reactions of the dissolved polymer. The ratio $p_0'/q_0'$ may still be low at concentrations below about 10 weight per cent of the polymer under these conditions, i.e. intermolecular crosslinking may still be observed at lower concentrations and intramolecular crosslinking may even be achieved.

## 2.4. OLIGOMERS AS SOLVENTS

Oligomers of small chain lengths are ideal solvents for the irradiation of polymers from the following points of view. Energy transfer can be neglected since the rates of reactions 15 and 16 are equal at all concentrations of the polymer. Similarly, abstraction reactions according to eqs. (20 and 21) will occur with the same rate in both directions and therefore cancel each other with respect to the overall effect. The chemical nature and 100 eV yield of the radicals formed from the solvent and the polymer are equal. The conditions which have been assumed in section 2.3 to estimate the ratio $(p_0'/q_0')$ are therefore fulfilled in a solution of a polymer in its own oligomer. Substitution of $q_0$ by $q_0 \cdot x_p$ in eq. (9) leads to the following dependence of the reciprocal gel dose upon the mole fraction of the polymer:

$$\frac{1}{D_{gel}} = \frac{\bar{M}_{w_0}}{m} \cdot q_0 x_p - \frac{\bar{M}_{w_0}}{m} \cdot \frac{p_0}{2}. \tag{24}$$

Fig. 5 shows the straight line which is obtained in a plot of $1/D_{gel}$ versus $x_p$. The absolute values of $q_0$ and $p_0$ can be calculated from the slope of the line and its intercept with the $1/D_{gel}$-axis. The critical polymer mole fraction, where $1/D_{gel}$ is equal to zero, is equal to

$$x_{p_{crit}} = \frac{p_0}{2q_0} \tag{25}$$

and is independent of the initial molecular weight. In these considerations, we have completely neglected the viscosity effect which tends

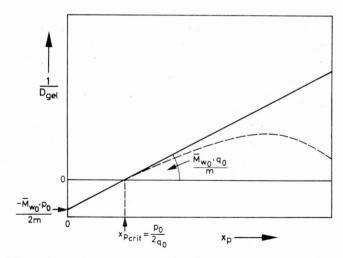

Fig. 5. The reciprocal of the gel dose versus the mole fraction of the polymer [Schnabel and Henglein, 1961] (full line: no viscosity effect; dotted line: effect of increase in viscosity with increasing $x_p$ taken into consideration).

to increase the gel dose at higher polymer concentrations because of the reduced mobility of the macroradicals. One therefore expects in most cases that the straight line of eq. (24) will bend more and more toward the abscissa at higher concentrations as is indicated by the dotted line in fig. 5.

As the oligomer molecules are rather large, the solvent radicals may not be very mobile. Under these conditions, the homogeneous reactions kinetics which have tacitly been assumed in the discussion above may not prevail. For example, it has been shown by scavenger techniques that reactions in a silicon polymer of short chain length do not occur homogeneously in the irradiated solution but in small volumes where radical pairs are produced [CHARLESBY and LLOYD, 1960]. It is interesting to note that under these conditions a straight line is still expected if $1/D_{gel}$ is plotted *versus* $x_p$. For, if a macroradical pair is formed in the pure polymer according to the reactions

$$\text{\textasciitilde\textasciitilde\textasciitilde} \longrightarrow \text{\textasciitilde\textasciitilde} + R \cdot \qquad (26)$$

$$R \cdot + \text{\textasciitilde\textasciitilde} \longrightarrow \text{\textasciitilde\textasciitilde} + RH \qquad (27)$$

where R is a low molecular weight radical which attacks an intact polymer chain in the immediate neighbourhood of its formation, the probability of abstraction from an intact chain in the presence of an oligomer solvent is equal to $x_p$. Combinations of the radical pairs will often not lead to crosslinks between two long chains but between a long chain and an oligomer molecule, i.e. will be unavailable for the network formation in the dissolved polymer. The relation $q_0' = q_0 x_p$ is therefore still valid and eq. (24) can be applied. Since the viscosity effect is already extremely large in the pure solvent, deviations from the straight line are not expected to occur in a plot according to fig. 5.

Experiments with oligomers as solvents have been carried out only with polydimethyl-siloxane (section 4.1), although many other examples are conceivable. Polyethylene could be irradiated in a higher n-alkane or polyisobutylene in a correspondingly branched saturated hydrocarbon.

## 2.5. CO-CROSSLINKING AND OTHER MACRORADICAL REACTIONS

When two polymers $A_n$ and $B_n$ are present in a solution, macroradicals of both solutes are expected to be formed at the same time

[HENGLEIN, 1959c]. If a macroradical $A_n^\cdot$ combines with a macro-radical $B_n^\cdot$, graft or block copolymers are formed depending on whether $A_n^\cdot$ and $B_n^\cdot$ carry their radical spots at side groups or at their ends. These processes will occur at low doses until a complete "co-network" is produced:

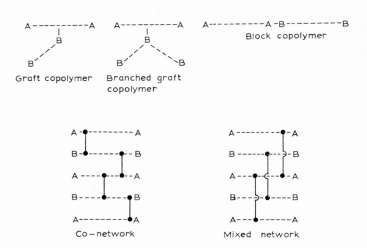

Graft copolymer    Branched graft copolymer    Block copolymer

Co–network    Mixed network

In such a co-network, chemical bonds between macromolecules of the same kind probably also exist. However, if macroradicals of the type $A_n^\cdot$ only combine with $A_n^\cdot$, and radicals of type $B_n^\cdot$ only with $B_n^\cdot$, a mixed network will be formed, i.e. two networks which are mechanically entangled. The two kinds of networks cannot be distinguished since the chemical bonds in the co-network probably have the same effect on its swelling power and on other properties as the mechanical entanglement in the mixed network. However, in certain cases it can be concluded from the kinetics of network formation that chemical bonds exist between the two constituents (section 3.2). Two polymers generally are compatible in a solution only at concentrations below a few weight per cent since they repel each other (in this respect polymers behave completely different from solutes of low molecular weight which can be present in large number in the same solution). Practically, this means that co-crosslinking can only be achieved in aqueous solutions where the critical concentration for intermolecular crosslinking in most cases is lower.

Intermediate macroradicals can undergo many other chemical reactions with dissolved radical scavengers [HENGLEIN and SCHNEIDER, 1959; HENGLEIN and BOYSEN, 1956] Iodine reacts according to

$$\sim\!\!\sim\!\!\sim\cdot + I_2 \longrightarrow \sim\!\!\sim\!\!\sim\!\!\underset{I}{|} + I \qquad (28)$$

One atom of iodine is incorporated into the polymer per radical spot produced. If radioactive iodine ($I^{131}$) is used and if the irradiated polymer is purified by several precipitations, the amount of iodine incorporated may be determined by measuring the specific activity of the polymer. Diphenylpicrylhydrazyl (DPPH) is also incorporated to give yellow coloured polymers that can readily be oxidized to form violet coloured products. Macroradicals can also initiate the polymerization of a vinyl monomer present in the solution to form graft and block copolymers [CHAPIRO, 1962; HENGLEIN et al., 1958].

## 3. Aqueous solutions

### 3.1. INTER- AND INTRAMOLECULAR CROSSLINKING

Most polymers which are crosslinked in the solid state form a gel when exposed to γ-rays in aqueous solution [CHARLESBY and ALEXANDER, 1955; ALEXANDER and CHARLESBY, 1957]. Typical examples are polyvinylalcohol [BERKOWITSCH et al., 1957; DANNO, 1958; SHINOHARA et al., 1958; KHENOKH et al., 1960; DIEU, 1960; DIEU and DESREUX, 1959; MATSUMOTO, 1963a, b; MATSUMOTO and DANNO, 1959; NARASAKI and FUJIWARA, 1963; SAKURADA et al., 1958; SAKURADA and IKADA, 1961, 1963, 1964a, b], polyvinylpyrrolidone [HENGLEIN, 1959c; DIEU, 1960; SCHNABEL, 1964], polyacrylamide [HENGLEIN, 1959c, BONI, 1961; RAJU and MERRILL, 1964], polyvinylmethylether [SAKURADA and IKADA, 1962a], polyacrylic acid [SAKURADA and IKADA, 1963a], and polyethylene oxide [CHARLESBY et al., 1962; CHARLESBY and KOPP, 1962; CROUZET and MARCHAL, 1962]. The gel dose always depends on the polymer concentration as has been shown by fig. 4. If the concentration is higher than about one weight per cent, the viscosity steadily increases with dose and after a given dose the solution forms a stiff gel. Upon further irradiation the degree of swelling decreases until the gel pulls away from the walls of the reaction vessel and floats freely in the solution. Below the critical concentration, the solutions often become turbid during irradiation and less viscous.

The curves in fig. 6 allow to compare the effects of water and of organic solvents on the crosslinking of polyvinylmethylether [SAKURADA and IKADA, 1962]. In aqueous solutions, the gel dose is much

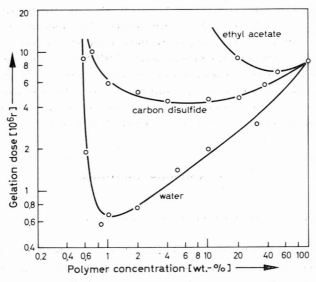

Fig. 6. Gelation dose as a function of polymer concentration for polyvinylmethylether in various solvents [SAKURADA and IKADA, 1962a].

smaller than for the solid polymer. This agrees with the expectations from the theory discussed in section 2. A minimum in gel dose is reached at about one weight per cent of the dissolved polyvinylmethylether. It is followed by a steep increase in gel dose at lower concentrations. In carbon disulfide, intermolecular crosslinking can still be obtained at rather low polymer concentrations as is expected from the theory in section 2.3. The dose for gelation, however, is much higher than for the aqueous solutions because of the absence of indirect action of radiation. In the case of ethylacetate, the minimum gel dose is not significantly lower than the gel dose for the solid polymer and no gelation occurs at concentrations below about 10 weight per cent.

Fig. 7 shows that the gel dose and the critical concentration of poly-vinylalcohol decrease with increasing degree of polymerization. The straight line obtained in plotting the data of fig. 7, according to fig. 8 proves that there exists a linear relationship between $1/D_{gel}\bar{P}$ and $1/c$ in the concentration range where intermolecular crosslinking occurs.

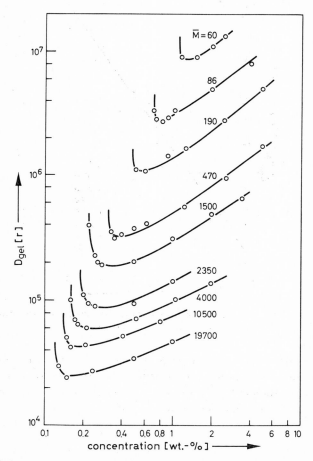

Fig. 7. Gel dose versus concentration of polyvinylalcohol in water at different degrees of polymerization [SAKURADA and IKADA, 1964a].

This relationship can be understood by making simple assumptions about the contributions of the direct and indirect action of radiation on the dissolved polymer [SAKURADA and IKADA, 1964a]. The lower critical concentrations at higher degrees of polymerization are explained by assuming that intermolecular links are only formed if the macromolecules are in contact with each other. If the statistical coils exist

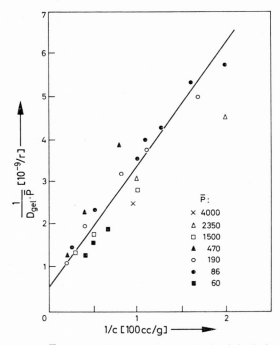

Fig. 8. Plot of $1/D_{gel} \cdot \bar{P}$ against $1/c$ for various polyvinylalcohol samples [Saku-
rada and Ikada, 1964a].

in dilute solutions in a closely packed structure (i.e. if the coil diameter does not increase upon further dilution), the average distance $R$ between two molecular centers at a polymer concentration $c$ (in g/100 cc) and for a molecular weight $M$ is:

$$R = \left(100 \frac{M}{cN} \sqrt{2}\right)^{\frac{1}{3}}, \qquad (29)$$

where $N$ is Avogadro's number. For $c = c_{crit}$ and $R = 2r$, where $r$ is the radius of a coil, it follows

$$c_{crit} = \frac{100\sqrt{2}M}{8Nr^3}. \qquad (30)$$

Rewriting eq. (30) and applying it to polyvinylalcohol, one obtains

$$r = 10.89 \left(\frac{\bar{P}}{c_{\text{crit}}}\right)^{\frac{1}{3}}. \tag{31}$$

The radius $r$ of the macromolecular spheres may therefore be calculated from the critical concentration. Fig. 9 is a double logarithmic plot of $r$ calculated from eq. (31) against the degree of polymerization $\bar{P}$.

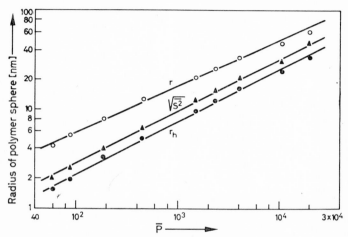

Fig. 9. Radius of the polymer sphere calculated from the data of crosslinking by $\gamma$ rays ($r$) and from viscosity data [SAKURADA and IKADA, 1964a] ($\sqrt{\overline{S^2}}$: radius of gyration. $r_{\text{h}}$: hydrodynamic effective radius).

For comparison, the radius of gyration $\sqrt{\overline{S^2}}$ and the effective hydrodynamic radius, $r_{\text{h}}$, which were calculated from viscosity data of the polymer, are also plotted. As can be seen from the figure, $r$ has the same order of magnitude as that of $r_{\text{h}}$ and $\sqrt{\overline{S^2}}$ [SAKURADA and IKADA, 1964a].

The changes in viscosity which can be observed in the irradiation of various polymers in aqueous solutions are illustrated by figs. 10, 11a, and 11b. In the case of polyvinylalcohol [SAKURADA and IKADA, 1964b] and of polyacrylamide [HENGLEIN, 1959c] the viscosity continuously increases with dose if the polymer concentration is higher than the critical concentration. It steadily decreases if the concentration is far below $c_{\text{crit}}$. As can be seen from figs. 10 and 11b, it first goes through a maximum and then decreases if the concentration is just below the critical concentration. Other authors [SHINOHARA et al., 1958; DIEU, 1960; DIEU and DESREUX, 1959] found an initial decrease before the maximum occurred which probably was due to oxygen

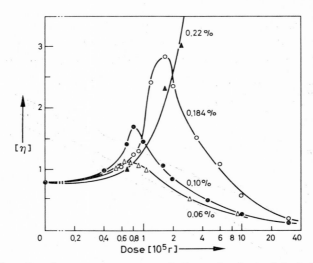

Fig. 10. Viscosity changes of aqueous solutions of polyvinylalcohol irradiated at various concentrations [SAKURADA and IKADA, 1964b].

impurities in their solutions [SAKURADA and IKADA, 1964]. In the case of polyvinylpyrrolidone, such a maximum in viscosity has not been observed [HENGLEIN, 1959c; DIEU, 1960]. The sedimentation constant of polyvinylalcohol was found to increase rapidly at low doses and to approach a limiting value at high doses if the concentration was below the critical concentration [DIEU, 1960; DIEU and DESREUX, 1959]. Similar evidence for an increase in the molecular weight was obtained from light scattering experiments [BERKOWITSCH et al., 1957; SAKURADA and IKADA, 1964b]. These results, together with the observed changes in viscosity, show that microgels are formed as has been described in section 2.2.

## 3.2. CO-CROSSLINKING

The formation of a graft copolymer and of a co-network was first detected in the irradiation of dilute aqueous solutions containing both polyacrylamide and polyvinylpyrrolidone [HENGLEIN, 1959c]. Solubility measurements can be used to prove the production of a graft copolymer at low doses since pure polyacrylamide is precipitated from an aqueous solution by methanol. Table 1 shows the amount of precipitate after irradiation of a solution containing both polymers at 0.25 weight per cent. Ninety per cent of the dissolved polyacrylamide is precipitated from the unirradiated solution. After irradiation with a small dose, no precipitation occurs, the solutions becoming only turbid after the addition of methanol. Apparently, the polyacrylamide becomes soluble in methanol when it is irradiated in the presence of polyvinylpyrrolidone. This is explained by crosslinks between the two polymers (see section 2.5). Doses near to the gel dose, a voluminous precipitate is obtained, the amount of which exceeds the amount of polyacrylamide present in the solution. At such high doses, the polyacrylamide component of the graft copolymer apparently determines the solubility and pulls the polyvinylpyrrolidone component out of the methanol containing solution. The reason for this effect probably is a slower swelling power of the polyvinylpyrrolidone component at high doses since it may already in part carry several crosslinks per macromolecule.

TABLE 1

$\gamma$-Irradiation of aqueous solutions of polyacrylamide and polyvinylpyrrolidone (0.25 weight per-cent) [HENGLEIN, 1959c]

| Time of irradiation [min] | Specific viscosity of the solution [$g^{-1} \cdot 100$ cc] | Precipitation with methanol | |
|---|---|---|---|
| | | Amount of precipitate [% of dissolved polyacrylamide] | Remarks |
| 0 | 1.7 | 90 | full precipitate |
| 12 | 1.8 | 10 | very turbid solution |
| 22 | 2.8 | — | slightly turbid solution |
| 33 | 4.1 | — | slightly turbid solution |
| 45 | 5.1 | — | slightly turbid solution |
| 50 | 7.0 | 120 | voluminous precipitate |
| 70 | 14.8 | 150 | voluminous precipitate |
| 90 | very high (gel point) | 165 | voluminous precipitate |

The viscosity-dose curves in figs. 11a-c also show that chemical bonds between polyacrylamide and polyvinylpyrrolidone molecules are formed. Solutions of polyvinylpyrrolidone at different concentrations (fig. 11a), of polyacrylamide (fig. 11b) and common solutions

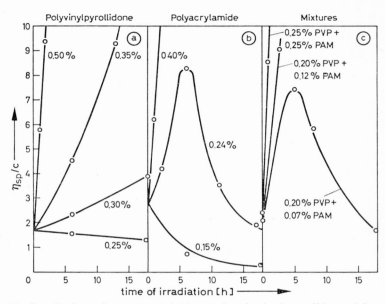

Fig. 11. Irradiation of aqueous solutions of polyvinylpyrrolidone (a), polyacrylamide (b) and of common solutions (c) at various concentrations [HENGLEIN, 1959c] (concentrations in weight per cent).

of the two polymers (fig. 11c) were $\gamma$-irradiated. The critical concentration amounts to about 0.28 weight percent for polyvinylpyrrolidone and 0.25 weight per cent for polyacrylamide. In all the solutions in fig. 11c, the two polymers were always present at concentrations below their critical concentration. However, the viscosity still increases until a complete network is built up throughout the whole amount of the polymeric material. Apparently, the two polymers are able to substitute each other in their networks which can only be understood if co-crosslinking occurs. Only for one case, where the total polymer concentration was too low (0.20 % PVP plus 0.07 % PAM), there is evidence that microgel formation occurred as can be recognized from the maximum and subsequent decrease of viscosity with dose.

These methods have later been used by other authors [MATSUDA et al., 1961] to study co-crosslinking in aqueous solutions containing various pairs of macromolecular substances. It was found that networks between two different polymer components were built up if both polymers were of the crosslinking type, and, correspondingly, gel formation was retarded if one of the two polymers was of the degradative type.

### 3.3. DEGRADATION

Polymethacrylic acid has been found to degrade in oxygen-free solutions. In the presence of oxygen, the rate of degradation was higher than in deaerated solutions according to one group of authors [ALEXANDER and FOX, 1953, 1954; ALEXANDER and CHARLESBY, 1957]. Other authors [BAXENDALE and THOMAS, 1958] obtained contradictory results. A detailed description of these experiments can be found in CHAPIRO's book [1962]. While polymethacrylic acid is a polymer that does not crosslink at all, a certain amount of degradation could also be evidenced in dissolved polymers that are mainly crosslinked. If polyvinylalcohol is irradiated under an oxygen atmosphere, mainly degradation occurs. When $H_2O_2$ was present in the solution at $10^{-2}$ moles/litre, the yield of degradation increased by a factor of four

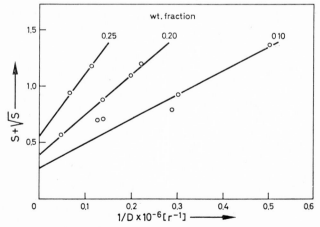

Fig. 12. Plot of $s+s^{\frac{1}{2}}$ *versus* the reciprocal of dose for aqueous solutions of polyvinylalcohol irradiated in air [SAKURADA and IKADA, 1961].

[MATSUMOTO, 1963a]. Crosslinking of this polymer still takes place if the oxygen concentration is not too high. A plot of $s+s^{\frac{1}{2}}$ (see eq. (10)) *versus* the reciprocal of the dose is shown by fig. 12. Values of the ratio $p_0'/q_0'$ between 0.27 and 0.55 depending on polymer concentration are obtained by extrapolation from this plot [SAKURADA and IKADA, 1961]. Similar measurements of the soluble fraction have been reported for the $\gamma$-irradiation of polyvinylpyrrolidone in dilute aqueous solution [SCHNABEL, 1964]. The results are shown by fig. 32. It should be emphasized that oxygen was excluded from the solution in these experiments. In spite of this, a rather large value of the ratio $p_0'/q_0'$ of 0.85 was obtained. It must be concluded from this figure that polyvinylpyrrolidone very probably forms not only microgels when irradiated below the critical concentration, but is also degraded to an appreciable extent. The absence of a maximum in the viscosity-dose curve (fig. 11a) is perhaps due to this simultaneous degradation.

## 3.4. THE EFFECTS OF ADDITIVES

The degradation and the crosslinking in aqueous solution can be influenced by certain additives in small concentration. In one of the first investigations of this kind the retardation of degradation of polymethacrylic acid by protective agents has been studied [ALEXANDER and FOX, 1953]. The substances used in this work, which had been found to decrease the lethal effects of X-rays toward animals, included thiourea, methanol, glucose, various amines and inorganic compounds such as KCN and $NaN_3$. Since the degradation of polymethacrylic acid was assumed to be due to $HO_2$ radicals (in $O_2$-containing solutions) the effect of the protective agents was explained by their efficient competition for this radical. Similarly, OH radicals which may also contribute to the degradation are scavenged by these additives.

The same additives generally retard or inhibit the crosslinking of polymers. Fig. 13 shows the influence of methanol on the rate of crosslinking (or reciprocal gel dose) of polyvinylpyrrolidone in aqueous solution. The decrease in the rate of crosslinking is explained by the scavenging of OH radicals and of H atoms according to $R \cdot + CH_3OH \rightarrow RH + \cdot CH_2OH$. The $\cdot CH_2OH$ radical is much less reactive than the intermediates from the radiolysis of water, and it is not able to abstract an H atom from the dissolved polymer (i.e. the indirect action of radiation becomes less efficient). This effect of methanol will still be amplified by the reaction of the $\cdot$ CH$_2$OH radical with macroradicals formed by either direct action or by the attack of solvent radicals that escape reaction with methanol eq. (19) [HENGLEIN, 1959c].

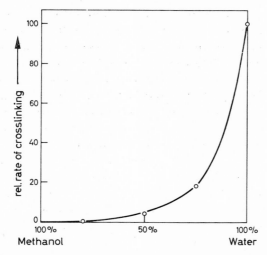

Fig. 13. Relative rate of crosslinking of polyvinylpyrrolidone in mixtures of water and methanol (polymer concentration: 5 weight %) [HENGLEIN, 1959c].

The relationship between the degree of protection (i.e. the relative increase in gel dose) and additive concentration has been studied for a large number of additives in aqueous polyvinylpyrrolidone and polyethyleneoxide solutions [CHARLESBY et al., 1962; CHARLESBY and KOPP, 1962]. The gel dose was generally found to increase with additive concentration. In a few cases, protection occurred up to a limiting concentration and then was unaffected by further increase in concentration. Besides these two cases, one also encountered many reagents which showed no protection at all. Colloidal sulfur at concentration of $10^{-3}$—$10^{-4}$ gram-atom/litre was found to be very effective in retarding crosslinking. A normal radical competition mechanism cannot account for this high efficiency since more free radicals had to be deactivated than there are sulfur atoms present in the solution. However, this conclusion may not be relevant since it is very likely that one sulfur atom reacts with many radicals until it is converted into a stable chemical form. The fate of the sulfur atoms consumed during irradiation needs to be clarified.

The effects of several additives have also been studied in the case of polyvinylalcohol. Thiourea, $Fe^{II}$ and $Cu^{II}$ ions, methylethylketone and ethanol were found to increase the gel dose. $K_2SO_4$ and NaCl were found to be ineffective. The results were in part explained by the scavenging of free radicals from the radiolysis of the solvent as described above. Partly, the effects of the additives were attributed to their reactions with macroradicals [SAKURADA and IKADA, 1963]. Among added acids, $CH_3COOH$, HCl, $HNO_3$, and $H_3BO_3$ completely suppressed gelation in polyvinylalcohol solution (0.2 and 0.4 %). In the case of $HClO_4$, $H_2SO_4$, and $H_3PO_4$, gels were formed at every concentration, even below the critical concentration. The dose for incipient gelation was found to decrease as the concentration of the latter acids increased, but an optimum concentration of the acid seemed to exist. Further, in solutions of NaOH and KOH, gels were not formed, regardless of the concentration of both alkali and polyvinylalcohol. These effects cannot be explained by radical scavenging of the additive, but may be due to configurational changes of the polymer molecules in solution [NARASAKI and FUJIWARA, 1963].

### 3.5. POLYELECTROLYTES

Two cases of polyelectrolytes may be distinguished. a) The polymer contains only a few ionized groups. The Coulomb repulsion between these groups leads to an expansion of the polymer coil. As a consequence of this expansion, the individual coils become more entangled. Intermolecular crosslinking will be favored, i.e. the gel dose and the critical concentration are expected to decrease with increasing degree of ionization. b) The polymer contains a large number of ionized groups. The coils are strongly expanded, but the high density of charged groups along the chains now leads to a repulsion between different macromolecules. This repulsion can be expected to hinder the combination of macroradicals, i.e. the gel dose and critical concentration are expected to increase with increasing degree of ionization. It follows from these considerations that there must exist an optimum degree of ionization of the polyelectrolyte.

Polyvinylalcohol partially acetalized with glyoxylic acid is a typical

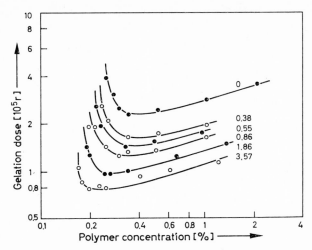

Fig. 14. Gel dose *versus* polymer concentration for polyvinylalcohol of various degrees of acetalization with glyoxylic acid [SAKURADA and IKADA, 1962b] (the mole per cent of glyoxylic acid are given in the figure).

example of case a) [SAKURADA and IKADA, 1962c]. Fig. 14 shows gel dose-concentration plots for various degrees of acetalization. It can be recognized that both the gel dose and the critical concentration decrease as the percentage of carboxyl groups increases. The acceler-

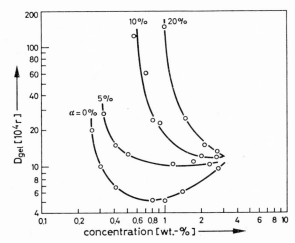

Fig. 15. Gel dose *versus* polymer concentration for polyacrylic acid of various degrees of neutralization [SAKURADA and IKADA, 1963a].

ating effect of the ionized groups in the polymer was found to be compensated by the presence of about 0.2 mole/l sodium chloride during irradiation. NaCl is known to decrease the expansion of the statistical coils of polyelectrolytes.

Polyacrylic acid partially neutralized is an example for case b) mentioned above [SAKURADA and IKADA, 1963a, b]. As can be seen from fig. 15, the gel dose and critical concentration increase with increasing degrees of neutralization. If the ionic strength of the solutions is increased by the addition of about 0.1 mole/l of sodium chloride, the viscosity behaviour of the partially neutralized polyacrylic acid becomes quite similar to that of the uncharged polymer. In such a solution, crosslinking occurs at nearly the same rate as in a solution of pure polyacrylic acid. 100 % neutralized polyacrylic acid is found to crosslink most rapidly at a concentration of 70 weight percent [BASHAW and HARPER, 1962].

# 4. Organic solutions

## 4.1. SIMULTANEOUS CROSSLINKING AND DEGRADATION, BRANCHING OF POLYMERS

The following polymers have been found to crosslink in organic solvents when exposed to $\gamma$-radiation: polyvinylacetate [HENGLEIN, 1959a; SAKURADA and IKADA, 1962a; HENGLEIN et al. 1961; IKADA and SCHNABEL, 1965], polyvinylchloride [WIPPLER and GAUTRON, 1963; WIPPLER, 1958, 1960; DARIMONT, 1960; DIEU and DESREUX, 1963; NAKAMURA, 1960; SCHNABEL, 1965], polyvinylmethylether [SAKURADA and IKADA, 1962a], polyvinylpyrrolidone [HENGLEIN, 1959a; SCHNABEL, 1964; IKADA and SCHNABEL, 1965], polystyrene [IKADA and SCHNABEL, 1965; HENGLEIN and SCHNEIDER, 1958; KOBAYASHI et al., 1963], polybutadiene [GOLUB, 1957, 1958, 1959, 1960; TABATA et al., 1964], and polydimethylsiloxane [SCHNABEL and HENGLEIN, 1961; IKADA and SCHNABEL, 1965; SCHNABEL, 1965]. The dependence of the gel dose upon polymer concentration has often been studied (see, for example, fig. 6). In most cases, the gel dose was higher than in aqueous solutions and the critical concentration was higher than about 10 weight per cent. Only in a few cases, crosslinking could still be observed at concentrations of a few weight per cent.

In the case of polydimethylsiloxane, an oligomer of a degree of polymerization less than 20 has been used as the solvent for two samples of long chain lengths ($\bar{P} = 2560$ and $1550$). As is shown by fig. 16, plotting the reciprocal of the gel dose versus the mole fraction of the polymer yields straight lines. $1/D_{gel}$ becomes infinite at the same

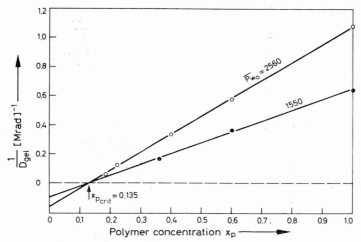

Fig. 16. Reciprocal of gel dose *versus* mole fraction of polydimethylsiloxane irradiated in its own oligomer [SCHNABEL and HENGLEIN, 1961].

critical mole fraction of both polymer samples as is to be expected from eqs. (24) and (25). $x_{\text{pcrit}}$ amounts to 0.135. The ratio of $p_0/q_0$ is therefore equal to 0.27 for polydimethylsiloxane. Absolute values of $q_0$ and $p_0$ could also be calculated from the slopes and the intercepts with the ordinate axis of the two straight lines in fig. 16, eq. (24). $G$-values of crosslink formation and main chain scission of 2.99 and 1.61, respectively, were found this way [SCHNABEL and HENGLEIN, 1961].

According to the theory of simultaneous crosslinking and degradation (section 2.1), the ratio $p_0'/q_0'$ of the dissolved polymer increases in dilute solutions with decreasing polymer concentration. This has been proved experimentally by irradiating polyvinylacetate in methanol solution at concentrations of 10 and 20 weight per cent and plotting the ratio $[\eta]/[\eta]_0$ *versus* $D/D_{gel}$. The results are shown in fig. 17. As has been discussed in section 1.3 (fig. 2), the curves obtained this way can be compared with theoretical curves for various ratios of $p_0'/q_0'$. The experimental data in fig. 17 are consistent with a ratio of $p_0'/q_0'$ near to zero for the polymer irradiated at 20 weight per-cent and of 1.6 for the sample irradiated at the lower concentration [SAKURADA and IKADA, 1962c].

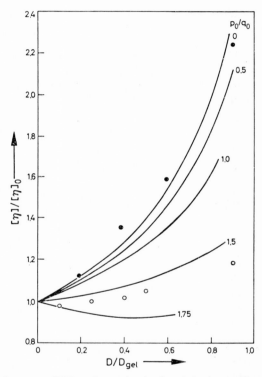

Fig. 17. $[\eta]/[\eta_0]$ versus $D/D_{gel}$ for polyvinylacetate in methanol solution (o: 10 weight per cent. ●: 20 weight per cent. Full lines: theoretical curves for various ratios $p_0'/q_0'$) [SAKURADA and IKADA, 1962c].

In order to test whether the critical concentration in organic solutions is due to a transition from intermolecular crosslinking to degradation (see section 2.1) or to intramolecular crosslinking (section 2.2), light scattering and viscosity measurements were combined. Polyvinylpyrrolidone (in methanol solution), polyvinylacetate (in acetone), polystyrene (in benzene) and polydimethylsiloxane (in benzene) were irradiated at concentrations above and below the critical concentration. In all these cases, both the molecular weight and the viscosity decrease, if the polymer is irradiated below the critical concentration. This shows that degradation of the main chain is the predominant process and no intramolecular crosslinking takes place [IKADA and SCHNABEL, 1965]. Others authors also found a degradation of the main chain of polystyrene irradiated in benzene at a concentration of 2 weight per-cent [PEDEMONTE et al., 1965]. The degradation was found by the decrease in molecular weight determined by light scattering with increasing dose. In this paper, a quantitative relation between yield of degradation and dose rate is also discussed. However, the results in this respect do not appear reliable since the authors seem to have confused the concepts of dose and dose rate.

Not much work has been carried out investigating the changes in the branching of polymers when they are irradiated in solution above and below the critical concentration. Fig. 18 shows results obtained for

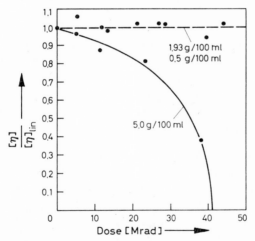

Fig. 18. The ratio $[\eta]/[\eta]_{\text{lin}}$ for polyvinylpyrrolidone in methanol as a function of dose at various polymer concentrations (full line: theoretical curve for $D_{\text{gel}} = 41$ Mrad) [IKADA and SCHNABEL, 1965].

polyvinylpyrrolidone in methanol solutions of various concentrations. The intrinsic viscosity $[\eta]$ and the light scattering molecular weight were determined after irradiation. The relation according to eq. (3) was then used ($k = 2.3 \times 10^{-2}$, $a = 0.65$) to calculate the intrinsic viscosity $[\eta]_{\text{lin}}$ of a polymer of linear structure having the same average molecular weight. The ratio $[\eta]/[\eta]_{\text{lin}}$ is plotted *versus* dose in fig. 18. With increasing degree of branching, this ratio is expected to decrease and to become zero at the gel dose. At the concentration of 5 g/100 ml in fig. 18, gelation occurs at a dose of 41 Mrad. A theoretical curve (solid line in fig. 18) was calculated by inserting this value of the gel dose into the corresponding formulae [KILB, 1959]. The experimental points fit the curve. If the concentration of the polymer was below the critical concentration (0.5 and 1.93 g/100 cc in fig. 18), no change in $[\eta]/[\eta]_{\text{lin}}$ could be observed. The formation of crosslinks apparently occurs with negligible rate when degradation is the principal reaction. In order to obtain more information about the ratio $p_0'/q_0'$ in these dilute solutions, the method described in section 1.3 (fig. 3) has also been applied. Fig. 19 shows the calculated ratio $[\eta]/[\eta]_0$ as function of $D/D^*$ for three values of the ratio $p_0'/q_0'$. $D^*$ is the dose,

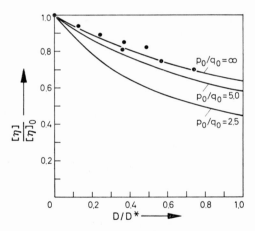

Fig. 19. The ratio $[\eta]/[\eta]_0$ of polyvinylpyrrolidone irradiated in methanol (0.5 and 1.9 g/100 cc) as a function of the ratio $D/D^*$ (full lines: theoretical curves for various ratios of $p_0'/q_0'$) [IKADA and SCHNABEL, 1965].

at which the initial average molecular weight of the polyvinylpyrrolidone (determined by light scattering) had decreased by a factor of two. As can be seen, the experimental points fit the curve for $p_0'/q_0' = \infty$, i.e. there is very little crosslinking in these solutions [IKADA and SCHNABEL, 1965].

The ratio $[\eta]/[\eta]_{\text{lin}}$ has also been determined for polyvinylacetate irradiated in acetone at different concentrations below the critical concentration. The polymer originally had a high degree of branching ($[\eta]_0/[\eta]_{lin} = 0.36$). It is interesting to note that $[\eta]/[\eta]_{lin}$ increased with dose. It seems therefore that radiation induced degradation of a polymer decreases the degree of branching, i.e. produces linear macromolecules of lower molecular weight from initially more branched structures [IKADA and SCHNABEL, 1965].

### 4.2. MICROGEL FORMATION

While the transition from intermolecular crosslinking to degradation at low polymer concentrations has been proved to occur in several organic solutions (section 4.1), not much evidence for intramolecular crosslinking or microgel formation has been obtained. Polyvinylchloride forms a gel in tetrahydrofuran when exposed to $\gamma$-rays at concentrations above 4.5 per cent. At lower concentrations, the light scattering molecular weight was found to increase with dose while the intrinsic viscosity decreased. This was explained by microgel formation (section 2.2) [WIPPLER, 1960]. In a rather dilute solution of polyvinylchloride in tetrahydrofuran (0.5 %), the sedimentation constant did not change during irradiation. However, a broad sedimentation pattern was obtained, which was interpreted as indicating the degradation of the main chain [DARIMONT, 1960]. It should be noted here, that polyvinylchloride is known to aggregate in solution, the degree of aggregation depending on the treatment of the polymer during the process of dissolution [HENGSTENBERG and SCHUCH, 1964].

Solutions of polyvinylmethylether in carbon disulphide became turbid when exposed to $\gamma$-rays at concentrations below the critical concentration [SAKURADA and IKADA, 1962a]. This phenomenon is often observed in the case of dilute aqueous solution where the dissolved polymer forms a microgel.

### 4.3. THE INFLUENCE OF THE SOLVENT ON INTERMOLECULAR CROSS-LINKING

The rate of gel formation strongly depends on the nature of the organic solvent. For example, polyvinylchloride ($\bar{M}_L = 1.5 \times 10^5$) irradiated in solutions of 10 weight per cent requires the following doses for gelation: 2.8 Mrad in dimethylformamide, 9.4 Mrad in tetrahydro-

furan and 103 Mrad in cyclohexanone [SCHNABEL, 1965]. The
critical concentration is also dependent on the solvent. Fig. 20 shows
typical curves of $[\eta]$ versus time of irradiation for polystyrene dissolved

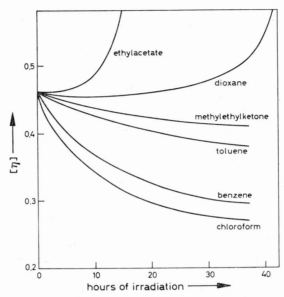

Fig. 20. Intrinsic viscosity *versus* time of irradiation for polystyrene irradiated
in various organic solvents at 5 g/100 cc [HENGLEIN and SCHNEIDER, 1958].

in various liquids at a concentration of 5 g/100 cc. Gelation occurs
only in ethylacetate, dioxane and methylethylketone (after very high
doses) while degradation is predominant in toluene, benzene and
chloroform. It is interesting to note that ethylacetate and dioxane
are poor solvents for polystyrene. These solutions are turbid, which
indicates that certain aggregation of the polymer occurs [HENGLEIN
and SCHNEIDER, 1958; HENGLEIN, 1959a]. Similar experiments on the
influence of the solvent on gelation have been carried out for polyvinylacetate [HENGLEIN, 1959a; SAKURADA and IKADA, 1962c] and
for polyvinylmethylether [SAKURADA and IKADA, 1962a]. The efficiency of the various solvents is quite different for each polymer. The
sole generalization which can be stated is the retarding influence of
chlorohydrocarbon solvents upon crosslinking. For example, 1 %
chloroform in dioxane decreases the rate of crosslinking of dissolved
polystyrene by a factor of two. In a pure solution of polystyrene in

dioxane, energy transfer from solvent to solute probably occurs, thus favouring the formation of macroradicals. Small amounts of chloroform inhibit this energy transfer. Benzene had a similar retarding effect as chloroform [HENGLEIN and SCHNEIDER, 1958].

## 4.4. REACTIONS ACCOMPANYING INTERMOLECULAR CROSSLINKING

When polyvinylchloride is irradiated in morpholine, a substitution reaction occurs besides crosslinking. As can be concluded from the nitrogen content of the polymer after irradiation, molecules of the solvent are incorporated into the polymer with a $G$-value of about 25. A reaction between polyvinylchloride and morpholine also occurs if solutions are heated above 80°C [NAKAMURA, 1960]. An incorporation of solvent molecules has also been reported for the irradiation of polyvinylchloride in tetrahydrofuran [WIPPLER and GAUTRON, 1963]. Similarly, natural rubber [STEFANESCO et al., 1958] and a polystyrene-polybutadiene copolymer [DELMAN et al., 1961] were found to contain chemically bonded chlorine atoms after irradiation in chlorohydrocarbon solvents such as $CCl_4$ or $CHCl_3$.

Cis-trans isomerization occurs in polybutadiene when irradiated in benzene solution. Starting with all-cis or all-trans polybutadiene, the isomerization approaches a stationary equilibrium in which the cis-trans ratio is about 20/80 in contrast to the thermodynamic equilibrium ratio of 8/92. The isomerization in a 1 % solution is about eight times faster than in the pure polymer. The mechanism of the isomerization is believed to involve excitation of the $\pi$-electrons of the polymer double bonds to an antibonding state where free rotation can occur. This excitation is believed to take place via intermolecular energy transfer from excited or ionized solvent molecules to the polymer double bonds. Certain additives such as diphenyldisulphide were found to sensitize the cis → trans conversion. The number of double bonds changed from cis to trans configuration per 100 eV of energy absorbed by the whole solution can exceed 1000. The mechanism is believed to involve geometric interconversion of the transitory isomeric radical adduct formed from polymer double bonds and the thiyl-radicals generated in the radiolysis of the sensitizer [GOLUB, 1957, 1958, 1959, 1960].

## 4.5. DEGRADATION

Polymers may be classified into two groups with respect to their capability of degrading in the main chain when exposed to $\gamma$-rays in solution. 1) Degradation takes place predominantly at all concentrations including the solid state. 2) Degradation is predominant only below the critical concentration while intermolecular crosslinking occurs at higher polymer concentrations. Finally, polymers may undergo a fast oxidative degradation in oxygen containing solutions. Since crosslinking is mostly inhibited, degradation is the predominant process for probably all polymers irradiated in the presence of oxygen.

Among the polymers of the degradative type, polymethylmethacrylate [HENGLEIN and BOYSEN, 1956; SCHNABEL, 1965; HENGLEIN et al., 1957a and 1957b] and polyisobutylene [HENGLEIN and SCHNEIDER, 1959] have thoroughly been investigated. Poly-n-butylmethacrylate has also been shown to degrade in ethylacetate solution [SHULTZ et al., 1963]. Similarly, the copolymer from styrene and $\alpha$-methylstyrene undergoes degradation in toluene solution [PRAVEDNIKOV et al.,

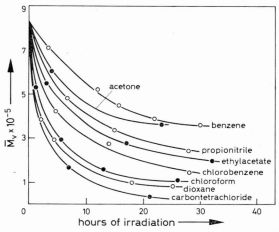

Fig. 21. Average molecular weight *versus* time of irradiation of polymethylmethacrylate in various solvents (Concentration: 0.15 moles/liter) [HENGLEIN et al., 1957].

1962]. Fig. 21 shows the influence of dose on the average molecular weight (determined by viscosity measurements) of polymethylmethacrylate irradiated in various solvents. It is seen that the rate of degradation is very large in carbon tetrachloride, chloroform and dioxane and smallest in benzene solutions. Similar relative efficiencies of the solvents were found in the degradation of this polymer by ultraviolet light [Mönig, 1958]. The radiation chemical yields of degradation are listed in table 2. The $G$-values here give the number of main chain

TABLE 2

Radiation chemical yields for the degradation of polymethylmethacrylate in various solvents (see fig. 21)

| Solvent | $G$ (number of main chain scissions per 100 eV directly absorbed by the polymer) |
|---------|-------------------------------------------------------------------------------------|
| benzene | 0.48 |
| acetone | 0.65 |
| propionitrile | 1.0 |
| ethylacetate | 1.2 |
| chlorobenzene | 1.5 |
| chloroform | 4.0 |
| dioxane | 4.7 |
| carbontetrachloride | 6.4 |

scissions per 100 eV of energy directly absorbed by the dissolved polymer. (This energy was calculated from the electron fraction of the polymer.) Solid polymethylmethacrylate is known to degrade with a yield of 1.64 broken bonds per 100 eV. Smaller $G$-values in table 2 were explained by energy transfer from the polymer to the solvent, while higher yields were regarded an indication for energy transfer from solvent to polymer or for indirect action of radiation via free radicals from the solvent. For example, energy directly absorbed by polymethylmethacrylate is transferred to benzene molecules, while radiation energy dissipated in dioxane is given up to the dissolved polymer. The rapid degradation in the chlorohydrocarbon solvents is explained by the spontaneous decay of polymer radicals, eq. (18), formed via H atom abstraction by Cl-atoms from the radiolysis of the solvent. These mechanisms also explain the phenomena observed in the irradiation of polymethylmethacrylate in mixtures of organic solvents. As can be seen from fig. 22, small amounts of benzene in carbon tetrachloride or chloroform solutions strongly decrease the rate of degradation. At about 20 volume per cent of benzene the rate is even smaller than in pure benzene solution. Benzene scavenges the Cl-atoms from the radiolysis of carbontetrachloride and chloroform, thus protecting the dissolved polymer from the indirect action of radiation. On the

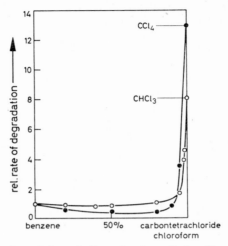

Fig. 22. Relative rates of degradation of polymethylmethacrylate dissolved in mixtures of benzene with chloroform and carbon tetrachloride [HENGLEIN et al., 1957].

other hand, $CCl_4$ and $CHCl_3$ are able to deactivate excited polymer molecules even more efficiently than benzene. This protecting power of the chlorohydrocarbon solvents can only be observed in the presence of small amounts of benzene (or other Cl-atom scavengers) which inhibit the fast degradation by indirect action of radiation in these solvents. The minima in the curves in fig. 22 are explained this way. Similar curves have been observed in the irradiation of chloroform solutions containing various amounts of carbontetrachloride and of dioxane.

The influence of the solvent on the degradation of polyisobutylene is shown by fig. 23. In a number of solvents, the degradation is faster than in the pure polymer which is explained by the higher mobility of the reactive fragments that partly undergo cage recombination in the solid polymer. Since no difference in the efficiencies of the accelerating solvents such as $CCl_4$, $CHCl_3$, $C_7H_{16}$ and $CS_2$ could be observed, the degradation is believed to occur via direct action of radiation on the dissolved polymer. Apparently, no energy transfer occurs in these solutions. However, in cyclohexene, diisobutylene, and in a solution

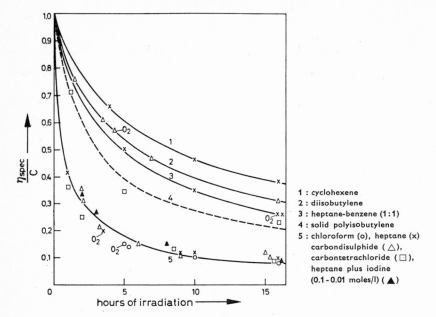

1 : cyclohexene
2 : diisobutylene
3 : heptane-benzene (1:1)
4 : solid polyisobutylene
5 : chloroform (o), heptane (x)
   carbondisulphide ( △ ),
   carbontetrachloride ( □ ),
   heptane plus iodine
   (0.1 - 0.01 moles/l) ( ▲ )

Fig. 23. $\eta_{spec}/c$ of polyisobutylene dissolved in various solvents *versus* time of irradiation (concentration: 10 g/l) [HENGLEIN and SCHNEIDER, 1959].

of benzene in heptane, the rate of degradation is lower than in the solid polymer which indicates transfer of energy in the direction polymer → solvent. Fig. 24 shows that small amounts of diisobutylene

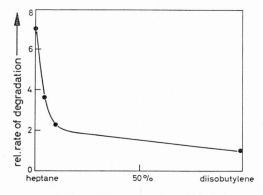

Fig. 24. Relative rates of degradation of polyisobutylene dissolved in various mixtures of n-heptane and diisobutylene (concentration: 10 g/l) [HENGLEIN and SCHNEIDER, 1959].

added to the heptane solution strongly decrease the rate of degradation of dissolved polyisobutylene. This experimental result indicates that energy is rapidly transferred from aliphatic hydrocarbons to olefinic double bonds.

It has already been mentioned in section 4.1 that polystyrene cross-links at high concentrations but is degraded in dilute solutions. The rate of degradation also strongly depends on  the solvent as is shown by fig. 25. The chlorin containing solvents are most efficient as in the

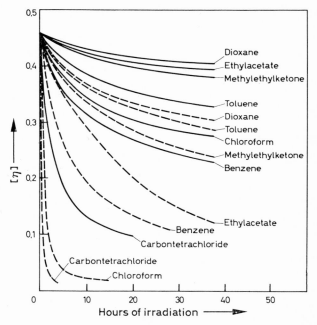

Fig. 25. Influence of dose on the intrinsic viscosity of polystyrene irradiated in 1 % solutions of various solvents [HENGLEIN and SCHNEIDER, 1958] (full lines: oxygen absent; dotted lines: oxygen present in the solutions).

case of polymethylmethacrylate (fig. 21). While benzene was a protecting solvent for the latter, it belongs to the more efficient solvents for the degradation of polystyrene. This indicates that energy is transferred in the opposite direction, i.e. from benzene to polystyrene.

The influence of oxygen on the degradation of dissolved polystyrene can readily be seen from fig. 25. In all solvents, the rate of degradation is increased. Similar experiments have been carried out with polymethylmethacrylate, where the degradation was also found to be accelerated in most solvents. Oxygen had a retarding effect in a few solvents such as in benzene solution. With both polymers, however, the increase in the degradation yield is particularly pronounced in the case of chloroform and carbon tetrachloride. This effect, which is ascribed to an oxidative degradation initiated by free radicals from the solvent, has been studied in detail for polystyrene by other authors [DURUP, 1957a, 1957b, 1958, 1959; DURUP et al., 1958; CHAPIRO et al., 1955; WALL and MAGAT, 1953a and b]. A review of this work can be found in CHAPIRO's book [1962].

## 5. LET effects

### 5.1. THEORETICAL CONSIDERATIONS

LET effects in dissolved polymers have been studied by comparing the yields obtained with $\gamma$-rays and with He and Li-particles from the nuclear reaction $^{10}B(n, \alpha)^7Li$ $\gamma$-rays from $^{60}Co$ have an extremely low LET of 0.2 eV/nm while the heavy particles dissipate 280 eV/nm in a medium of unit density. In order to produce fast He and Li-particles within the irradiated samples, polymer solutions containing trimethyl or triethyl borate or boric acid were irradiated in the thermal neutron facility of a nuclear reactor. The $\gamma$-background was reduced by shielding the samples by at least three centimeters of pure bismuth. Under these conditions, the $\gamma$-background contributed less than 1 per cent to the total absorbed dose. The $\gamma$-irradiated solution contained the same amount of boron compound in order to make sure that the effects were not produced by differences in the chemical composition of the system. All irradiations were carried out at the same total absorbed dose rate by $\gamma$- or He/Li-radiations, respectively, to avoid dose rate effects. Helium ions, deuterons and protons from accelerators have not yet been used in LET studies in polymers, although they would allow one to investigate the effects over a wide range of LET.

LET effects in low molecular weight materials are generally explained by the different geometry of the intermediate reaction products in the spurs or tracks of the ionizing particles. The structure of a track in the gas phase has often been discussed on the basis of photographs obtained in a Wilson chamber. Initial diameters of the tracks of α-particles of the order of $10^{-3}$ cm at 1 atm have been determined this way. In order to calculate initial track diameters in liquids one divided these figures by the density ratio of the two phases. Track diameters of 10.0–20.0 nm are obtained this way. However, it should be noted that these figures mean the diameter of the cylindrical volume, in which negative ions can be found immediately after the passage of the primary high energy particle. As subexcitation electrons travel a rather large distance before they are captured by molecules to form heavy negative ions, the diameter of the cylindrical volume in which the primary and secondary ionizations and excitations take place must be much smaller. It probably amounts to only 2.0 nm in a liquid. This initial diameter of the column of positive ions and excited molecules has not yet been determined experimentally. It would be very desirable to know the initial distribution of ions and excited molecules more exactly in order to explain LET effects in large molecules. The main assumption made in LET studies up to the present time has been that equal numbers of intermediates with the same chemical structures are produced in the tracks of electrons and heavy particles, the only difference being the initial spatial distribution of these intermediates. This concept has been applied in the diffusion kinetics of irradiated water where molecular product yields were successfully calculated by assuming plausible initial distributions in space of H atoms and OH radicals [KUPPERMANN, 1961].

The following consideration shows that the initial concentration of ionized and excited molecules in the track of a fast He or Li-particle must be extremely high. Let $v$ be the volume of a molecule of the medium (molecular weight about 100). The number of ionized and electronically excited molecules per unit track length will on the average be equal to

$$N^* = 2 \left( \frac{-\mathrm{d}E}{\mathrm{d}x} \right) \frac{1}{W}, \tag{32}$$

where $(-\mathrm{d}E/\mathrm{d}x)$ is the specific energy loss in eV/nm and $W$ is the energy required to produce one ion pair. The factor of two appears because it is assumed that one molecule is excited per ion formed. The track volume in which these ionized and excited molecules are initially concentrated amounts to $\frac{1}{4}d^2\pi$, where $d$ is the diameter of the cylindrical track volume in which most of the energy of the fast heavy particle is dissipated. Since this track volume contains $N = \frac{1}{4}d^2\pi(1/v)$ molecules, the fraction of ionized and excited molecules will be equal to

$$\frac{N^*}{N} = \left(\frac{-\mathrm{d}E}{\mathrm{d}x}\right) \frac{8}{W\pi} \frac{v}{d^2}. \tag{33}$$

By inserting a specific energy loss of 280 eV/nm and values of $v$, $d$ and $W$ of 0.2 nm³, 2.0 nm and 34 eV/ion pair, respectively, $N^*/N$ becomes equal to unity, i.e. practically all the molecules within the track are affected. It is quite clear from eq. (33) that the fraction $N^*/N$ will become rapidly smaller if the energy of the primary particle is dissipated by ionizations and excitations within a cylinder of larger diameter $d$. The high concentration of excited molecules has been made responsible for the LET effects observed in the irradiation of liquid benzene [GÄUMANN and SCHULER, 1961; BURNS and REED, 1963]. Changes in the yields of $H_2$ and other products are observed here mainly at the end of the tracks of $\alpha$-particles where the LET is higher than about 100 eV/nm.

Let us assume now that some of the $N$ molecules are connected by chemical bonds and constitute a small part of a long polymer chain. If it is further anticipated that the spatial distribution of ionizations and excitations is the same as before, this part of the polymer (which we will call a "segment") will be ionized or excited in more than one base unit. If the same polymer is exposed to fast electrons, the probability of finding two or even more ionized or excited base units which lie close together in a chain is practically equal to zero. In other words, some of the intermediates directly produced by He- or Li-particles of high LET must be different from those formed in the tracks of electrons. This higher "segment ionization and excitation" by densely ionizing particles is generally expected to result in more efficient fragmentation of the polymer within those segments. If the rate of degradation of the main chain is investigated, the polymers may be classified into two groups according to the difference in their behaviour when exposed to $\gamma$-rays and He- or Li-particles. a) If the polymer is efficiently degraded by low LET radiations, the additional energy dissipation in a segment by fast heavy particles will only slightly enhance the probability of fragmentation of this segment, i.e. part of the transferred particle energy is wasted since it does not produce an additional observable decrease in molecular weight. In the case of radiation sensitive polymers the degradation density $p_0$ is therefore expected to decrease with increasing LET. b) If the polymer is rather stable toward $\gamma$-radiation, i.e. if single ionization or excitation of chains is inefficient in producing main chain scission, the more densely ionizing particles are expected to degrade the polymer with higher yields. $p_0$ would then increase with LET.

LET effects could also arise from the simultaneous ionization or excitation of several segments in the same chain by high LET particles. The diameter of a polymer coil of chain length 1000 in solution is of the order of 10 nm. It generally increases with decreasing polymer concentration since the coils become more expanded by solvent intrusion. These diameters are smaller than the average distance between two adjacent spurs produced in the medium by a fast electron. It will therefore very rarely occur that more than one spur is produced within the volume of a coil. As most of the coil volume is filled with solvent molecules, the ionizations and excitations of the spur will mainly occur on solvent molecules. In other words, in the low LET radiation chemistry of polymers, we are mainly dealing with reactions of singly ionized or excited macromolecules. A He- or Li-particle, however, produces so many ionizations and excitations when traversing a coil that several segments may be affected. These segments generally will be separated by a large number of intact base units. They will probably not strongly interact with each other, i.e. they will fragment independently. If a chain is ionized or excited in several segments at the same time, degradation would lead to a sudden breakdown of a long chain into many small fragments. Because of the increase in the volume of a coil upon dilution, the probability of excitation of several segments by a densely ionizing particle decreases. LET effects that are caused by the simultaneous excitation of several segments are therefore expected to become less pronounced in dilute solutions.

If processes are investigated which are produced by indirect action of radiation such as crosslinking in aqueous solutions, the dependence on LET has to be explained by the difference in the spatial distribution of the free radicals resulting from the decomposition of the solvent. Only about 8 % of the free radicals produced by He- or Li-particles in water escape the tracks while about 77 % of the radicals formed under $\gamma$-irradiation can freely diffuse [HART, 1954]. As the total number of radicals formed in both cases is about the same, nearly ten times less radicals are available in the case of He/Li-particles than in the case of $\gamma$-rays. If these radicals produce macroradicals according to eq. (20), the corresponding gel doses in dilute solutions are expected to differ by a factor of about 10. Nothing can be predicted about the gel doses at higher polymer concentrations since both indirect and direct action will lead to crosslinking in a complex manner.

It also seems difficult to make a prediction for intramolecular crosslinking by He- or Li-particles. As has been pointed out in section 2.2, intramolecular crosslinking by $\gamma$-rays is expected to occur at low polymer concentrations in aqueous solutions where the macromolecules are not entangled, whereas combinations between different macroradicals will be more frequent at higher concentrations. A complete or nearly complete disentanglement is perhaps not necessary in the case of densely ionizing particles. Free solvent radicals are produced here in very high initial concentration along the tracks. As these radicals are very reactive they need not diffuse over a long distance before they abstract an H-atom from the dissolved polymer. A high density of macroradical spots will therefore be produced in a rather narrow cylindrical volume along the track of a fast heavy particle. If the polymer concentration is not too high, these macroradical spots are distributed among a rather small number of entangled macromolecules, so each macromolecule may carry several radical spots. Inter- as well as strong intramolecular combination of these spots could therefore lead to the immediate formation of a microgel along the track. The critical polymer concentration where this happens may therefore be higher than the critical concentration for crosslinking by $\gamma$-rays. If the polymer concentration is rather high, the macroradical spots are distributed among a large number of entangled macromolecules. The coils will now rarely acquire more than one radical spot and therefore undergo mainly intermolecular crosslinking.

## 5.2. ORGANIC SOLUTIONS

In all cases studied to date, He- and Li-particles have been found to be less effective in producing a three-dimensional network in a dissolved polymer than $\gamma$-rays, or have been wholly unable to do so. Typical behaviour is shown in fig. 26 where the intrinsic viscosity of polyvinylacetate irradiated in a methanol-trimethylborate mixture is plotted *versus* the absorbed dose [HENGLEIN et al., 1961]. Curve

No. 1 represents the experimental results obtained with $\gamma$-rays and 120 kV X-rays at different dose rates. Rapid intermolecular cross-linking occurs with these low LET radiations and a gel dose of $2.3 \cdot 10^{20}$ eV/cm³ is found by extrapolation from the steep increase in viscosity.

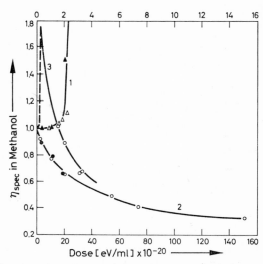

Fig. 26. Specific viscosity of polyvinylacetate as a function of absorbed dose (polymer concentration: 20 weight per cent. Solvent: methanol (24 vol.%)-triethylborate (76 vol.%)) [HENGLEIN et al., 1961].

Curve 1: $\gamma$-rays ($7.08 \cdot 10^{18}$ eV/cc·h): ▲
120 kV X-rays ($1.08 \cdot 10^{20}$ eV/cc·h): △
upper abscissa

Curve 2: He/Li radiation: ○ $2.6 \cdot 10^{20}$ eV/cc·h
● $5.4 \cdot 10^{19}$ eV/cc·h
lower abscissa

Curve 3: dotted: $\gamma$-irradiation
full: He/Li irradiation
lower abscissa

Curve No. 2 shows a steady decrease in viscosity under the influence of He- and Li-particles. Although doses have been applied here which were more than ten times larger than the gel dose for $\gamma$-rays no indication of intermolecular crosslinking could be obtained. The rate of decrease in viscosity was found to be independent of the over all dose rate of the He- and Li-particles, i.e. independent of the neutron flux to which the samples were exposed. Curve No. 3 in fig. 26 describes an experiment in which a sample was irradiated with $\gamma$-rays almost to the gel point (dotted part) and subsequently exposed to neutrons (full part). In other experiments, the samples were $\gamma$-irradiated far beyond the gel point until the solutions became quite stiff. Subsequent irradiation with heavy particles always reliquified the solution. These experiments show that He- and Li-particles are able to destroy the three-dimensional network initially introduced by low LET radiations. In principle, the decrease in viscosity by He and Li-particles may be explained by either a high value of $(p_0'/q_0')$ for the dissolved polymer (this ratio being still smaller than 2.0 in the case of $\gamma$-rays) or by greatly increased intramolecular crosslinking in the case of He- and Li-particles. However, only a large ratio $(p_0'/q_0')$ can explain the destruction of the network in a $\gamma$-irradiated sample by subsequent heavy particle irradiation, since the introduction of intramolecular crosslinks into a three-dimensional network already existing would never destroy the intermolecular links. Furthermore, the polymer concentration in these experiments was so high (20 weight per cent) that intramolecular crosslinking could hardly occur preferentially.

Light scattering and viscosity measurements have been carried out to study the effect of LET on the degradation density $p_0'$ of polymers in dilute solutions. Typical plots of the reciprocal of the light scattering molecular weight *versus* dose are shown by figs. 27 and 28. In the case of fig. 27, polydimethylsiloxane dissolved in a benzene-triethylborate mixture at a concentration of 2 weight per cent was irradiated by $\gamma$-rays and by slow neutrons [SCHNABEL, 1965]. At this concentration, $\gamma$-rays degrade the polymer in the main chain. He- and Li-particles qualitatively have the same effects. The yield of main chain scission, however, is smaller than with $\gamma$-rays as can be recognized from the different slopes of the straight lines in fig. 27. It seems therefore that polydimethylsiloxane belongs to the polymers of group a) mentioned in section 5.1 which are sensitive to $\gamma$-radiation and are less efficiently degraded by high LET radiations. Similar observations have been made on solutions of polymethylmethacrylate [SCHNABEL, 1965]. Fig. 28 shows that the rate of degradation by $\gamma$-rays as well as by He- and Li-particles is dependent on the nature of the solvent. This has been explained by invoking energy transfer (see section 4.5). In all cases, He- and Li-particles are less effective in degrading this polymer than $\gamma$-rays. An increase in the rate of degradation with increasing LET has only been observed for polystyrene [KOBAYASHI et al.,

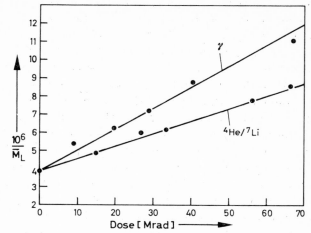

Fig. 27. Reciprocal of molecular weight *versus* dose for polydimethylsiloxane (2 weight per cent) irradiated in benzene (containing 50 % of triethylborate) by $\gamma$-rays and He/Li particles [SCHNABEL, 1965].

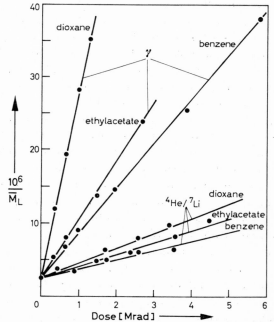

Fig. 28. Reciprocal of molecular weight *versus* dose for polymethylmethacrylate irradiated in various solvents containing 25 % of triethylborate (polymer concentration 1.2 weight per cent) [SCHNABEL, 1965].

1963]. As has already been mentioned in section 4.1, this polymer is degraded by γ-rays in dilute solutions. In fig. 29, the specific viscosity is plotted *versus* dose for several polymer concentrations and for γ as well as He- and Li-particle irradiation. The critical concentration for

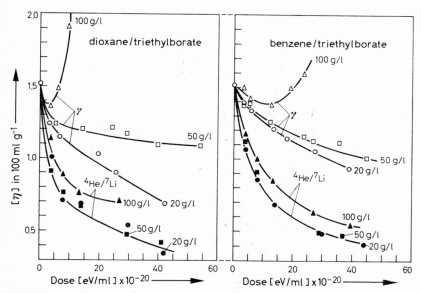

Fig. 29. Intrinsic viscosity *versus* dose for polystyrene irradiated in dioxane-triethylborate and benzene-triethylborate mixtures at various concentrations [KOBAYASHI et al., 1963].

network formation by γ-rays lies between 50 and 100 g/l, since the viscosity continuously decreases at lower concentrations. Fig. 29 shows that He- and Li-particles degrade this polymer at all concentrations, the rate of degradation being higher than in the case of γ-rays. Polystyrene is known to be rather stable toward γ-radiation because of its aromatic groups. Apparently it belongs to the polymers of group b) section (5.1) which are more rapidly degraded by radiations of high LET. The rule which has been derived from the postulate that higher segment ionization and excitation are produced by more densely ionizing particles is therefore well obeyed by the polymers studied in dilute solutions up to this time.

While no network is obtained in the He- and Li-particle irradiation of a concentrated polyvinylacetate solution (fig. 26), crosslinking can be achieved in concentrated solutions of other polymers. For example, polydimethylsiloxane dissolved in benzene-triethylborate at a concentration of 20 weight per cent forms a gel when exposed to slow neutrons [SCHNABEL, 1965]. Fig. 30 shows the observed increase in

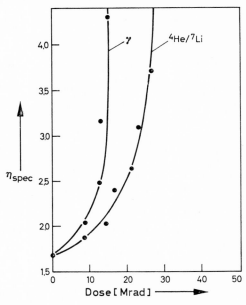

Fig. 30. Specific viscosity *versus* dose of polydimethylsiloxane (20 weight per cent) irradiated in benzene containing 50 % of triethylborate [SCHNABEL, 1965].

viscosity. It can be recognized from this figure that He- and Li-particles are less efficient in producing crosslinks than $\gamma$-rays. Similar observations have been made with polyvinylchloride in concentrated solutions [SCHNABEL, 1965]. If one wants to explain the smaller linking efficiency of He- and Li-particles by postulating a higher value of the ratio $(p_0'/q_0')$ than in the case of $\gamma$-irradiation, one must assume a decrease in $q_0'$ and not an increase in $p_0'$. For $p_0'$ has been shown to be smaller in the case of He- and Li-particles when very dilute solutions of polydimethylsiloxane are irradiated (fig. 27). As has been discussed earlier, the competition of reactions 17 and 19 mainly determines the fate of macroradicals produced by the direct action of radiation in organic solutions. Since both reactions are of second order with respect to radical concentrations, the ratio of the respective rate constants should not be dependent on the dose rate. However, if the radicals are produced so close together that the subsequent combination requires very little diffusion, the initial spatial distribution of the macro- and solvent-radicals will determine the relative probabilities of reactions 17 and 19. It is conceivable that a macroradical produced in the track of a high LET particle is mostly surrounded by solvent-radicals and is very rarely formed next to a macroradical of another chain. This is because of the solvation of the polymer chains which causes them to surround themselves with molecules of the solvent. Immediate de-activation of macroradicals by radicals from the solvent would there-fore occur in the track of a densely ionizing particle. Complications may also ensue in more concentrated solutions because of the simul-taneous ionization and excitation of several segments of the same chain by He- and Li-particles.

All LET effects in dissolved polymers which have been observed to date are compiled in table 3. If He- and Li-particles and $\gamma$-ray qualita-tively produce the same effect, the more efficient reaction is shown *in italics*. The table also contains the experimental results obtained with aqueous solutions of polyvinylpyrrolidone which are more tho-roughly described in the following subsection.

## 5.3. AQUEOUS SOLUTIONS

Extensive studies of LET effects in aqueous solutions have been reported only in the case of polyvinylpyrrolidone [SCHNABEL, 1964]. The dependence of the gel dose on the concentration of this polymer is shown by figs. 31a and 31b. Fig. 31a presents the results obtained with a polymer of low molecular weight ($\bar{M}_w = 3.6 \cdot 10^4$). In order to make a comparison between aqueous and non-aqueous solutions, fig. 31a also shows the results obtained with methanol solutions. In the experiments described by fig. 31b, the molecular weight of the polyvinylpyrrolidone was much higher ($\bar{M}_w = 1.4 \cdot 10^6$).

As has already been discussed in section 3.1, the critical concentra-tion for gel formation by $\gamma$-rays decreases with increasing molecular weight of a polymer dissolved in water. The same effect occurs in the He- and Li-particle irradiation of aqueous solutions of polyvinyl-pyrrolidone. The critical concentrations found were 0.4 and 3 weight per cent, depending on the molecular weight of the polymer (fig. 31a

TABLE 3

Reactions at low and high polymer concentrations induced by γ-rays and He/Li-particles

| Polymer | Solvent | Reactions | | | |
|---|---|---|---|---|---|
| | | low polymer concentration (order of 1 weight per cent) | | high polymer concentration (10-20 weight per cent) | |
| | | γ | He and Li | γ | He and Li |
| Polyvinyl-chloride [a] | dimethylformamide / cyclohexanone } triethylborate | microgel formation | microgel formation | *intermol. crosslinking* | intermol. crosslinking |
| Polyvinyl-pyrrolidone [b] | water-boric acid | microgel formation | microgel formation | *intermol. crosslinking* | intermol. crosslinking |
| Polyvinyl-pyrrolidone [b] | methanol-triethylborate | degradation | degradation | *intermol. crosslinking* | intermol. crosslinking |
| Polyvinyl-acetate [c] | methanol-trimethylborate | | | intermol. crosslinking | degradation |
| Polystyrene [d] | dioxane- / benzene- } triethylborate | *degradation* | *degradation* | intermol. crosslinking | degradation |
| Polydimethyl-siloxane [a] | benzene- / c-hexane- } triethylborate | degradation | degradation | *intermol. crosslinking* | intermol. crosslinking |
| Polymethyl-methacrylate [a] | dioxane- / ethylacetate- / benzene } triethylborate | *degradation* | degradation | *degradation* | degradation |

a) [SCHNABEL, 1965]  b) [SCHNABEL, 1964]  c) [HENGLEIN et al., 1961]  d) [KOBAYASHI et al., 1963]

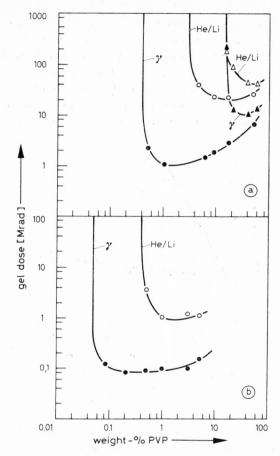

Fig. 31. Gel dose *versus* polyvinylpyrrolidone concentration (concentration of boric acid: 3.7 %). ○ and ●: aqueous solutions; △ and ▲: methanol solutions [SCHNABEL, 1964].

and 31b, respectively). However, the critical concentration for He- and Li-particles is always about 8 times higher than for γ-rays. For non-aqueous solutions, the critical concentration is the same for both types of radiation and much higher than for aqueous solutions.

It has been shown for several polymers in aqueous solution that the critical concentration which is observed in the case of γ-irradiation is caused by the transition from inter- to intramolecular crosslinking (section 3.1). In order to determine whether the higher critical concentration for He- and Li-particles corresponds to a similar transition, two types of experiments have been carried out. 1) The soluble fraction s of polyvinylpyrrolidone irradiated at a concentration of five weight per cent (where both $\gamma$-rays and He- and Li-particles produce a network) was measured as a function of the dose. A plot of $s+s^{\frac{1}{2}}$ *versus* the reciprocal dose is shown by fig. 32. The intercept of the straight lines with the ordinate axis is 0.85 for both types of radiation. Accord-

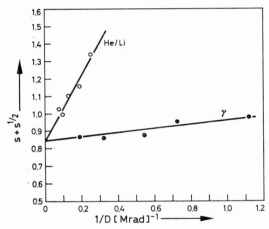

Fig. 32. $s+s^{\frac{1}{2}}$ *versus* reciprocal of dose for polyvinylpyrrolidone irradiated in 5 % aqueous solution (containing 3.7 % of boric acid) by $\gamma$-rays and He/Li particles [SCHNABEL, 1964].

ing to eq. (10), this intercept is equal to the ratio $p_0'/q_0'$ which apparently is independent of LET for the irradiation of polyvinylpyrrolidone in dilute aqueous solution. One must conclude therefore that the high critical concentration for He- and Li-particles cannot be due to a change in this ratio, i.e. this critical concentration is not due to a transition from intermolecular crosslinking to degradation as it is in most organic solutions. 2) In the second type of experiment, the dependences of the specific viscosity, of the light scattering molecular weight, and of the root mean square end to end distance of the statistical coils on the absorbed dose of He- and Li-particle radiation were determined. The concentration of the polyvinylpyrrolidone used was 0.3 weight per cent, i.e. it was below the critical concentration shown in fig. 31. The results are shown by figs. 33a–c. While $\eta_{\text{spec}}$ continuously decreased, $\bar{M}_{\text{w}}$ increased, the end to end distance first rapidly decreased and then remained nearly constant. These findings can only be explained by microgel formation. The higher critical concentration for He- and Li-particles may be explained by the hypothesis presented in section 5.1. It is also of interest to note that a solution of polyvinylpyrrolidone in methanol at a concentration below the critical concentration behaved quite differently when exposed to $\gamma$-rays or to He- and

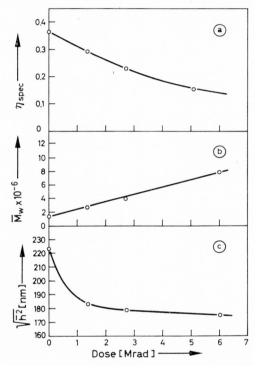

Fig. 33. Intrinsic viscosity (a), light scattering molecular weight (b) and root mean square end to end distance (c) of polyvinylpyrrolidone as function of dose (polymer concentration 0.3 weight per cent). He/Li-particle irradiation [SCHNABEL, 1964].

Li-particles. No indication of intramolecular crosslinking could be found and no change in viscosity was observed, facts which correspond to the case of $p_0'/q_0' = 2.0$ in fig. 1. This again shows that there exist significant differences between non-aqueous and aqueous solutions since the effects are mainly produced by the direct or indirect action of radiation, respectively.

The curves in figs. 31a and 31b can also be used to check the prediction made in section 5.1 with regard to the expected gel doses for $\gamma$- and He- and Li-particle irradiation. If one compares the gel dose for both radiations in the region of the minimum of the curves (where indirect action certainly is predominant and intramolecular crosslinking is not yet significant), a value of about 10 for the ratio $D_{gel_{He, Li}}/D_{gel_{\gamma}}$ is obtained. This agrees with the theoretical expectation that the gel doses should be in the same ratio as the radical yields for the two types of radiation.

## 5.4. CONCLUDING REMARKS

As has been shown in section 5.2, the following LET effects have been observed upon irradiating polymers in organic solvents: In concentrated solution, polyvinylchloride, polyvinylpyrrolidone and polydimethylsiloxane are less efficiently crosslinked by He- and Li-particles than by $\gamma$-rays. In the cases of polystyrene and polyvinylacetate it was found that $\gamma$-irradiation leads to gel formation whereas He- and Li-particles are predominantly degrading these polymers in the main chain. In dilute solution most of the polymers investigated to date are predominantly degraded in the main chain by both types of radiation. However, differences in the efficiency of degradation were observed, e.g. polystyrene is more effectively degraded by He- and Li-particles than by $\gamma$-rays whereas polydimethylsiloxane is degraded more rapidly by $\gamma$-rays. $\gamma$-rays were also found to be more effective than He- and Li-particles in degrading polymethylmethacrylate in both dilute and concentrated solution. Since the radiation effects in polymers dissolved in organic solvents are mainly due to the direct action of radiation, these results thus appear to confirm the postulate (section 5.1) that higher segment ionization and excitation are produced by densely ionizing particles. On the basis of this postulate the classification of the polymers into two groups was derived: a) the degradation density $p_0$ decreases with increasing LET if the polymer is efficiently degraded by low LET radiation, b) the degradation density $p_0$ increases with LET if the polymer is rather stable towards low LET radiations. According to this classification typical examples for the polymers of the groups a) and b) are respectively polymethylmethacrylate and polystyrene.

LET effects in aqueous solution were studied extensively only in the case of polyvinylpyrrolidone (section 5.3): In dilute solution both types of radiation lead to microgel formation. In concentrated solution a threedimensional network is formed. However, He- and Li-particles are less effective. The critical concentration for He- and Li-particles was found to be higher than for $\gamma$-rays. Since in aqueous solutions of low polymer concentration the indirect action of radiation is certainly predominant, the differences in the critical concentration may therefore probably be due to differences in the initial spatial distribution of the radicals from the radiolysis of water. As expected from the considerations in section 5.1, the ratio of the gel doses for $\gamma$- and He- and Li-particle irradiation in the range of low polymer concentrations equals the ratio of the radical yields in water for the two types of radiation.

## References

ALEXANDER, P. and CHARLESBY, A. 1957. J. Polymer Sci. **23** 355.

ALEXANDER, P. and FOX, M. 1953. J. chim. physique **50** 415.

ALEXANDER, P. and FOX, M. 1954. Trans. Farad. Soc. **50** 605.

BASHAW, R. N. and HARPER, B. G. 1962. J. Polymer Sci. **59** 221.

BAXENDALE, J. H. and THOMAS, J. K. 1958. Trans. Farad. Soc. **54** 1515.

BERKOWITSCH, J., CHARLESBY, A. and DESREUX, V. 1957. J. Polymer Sci. **25** 490.

BONI, A. L., 1961. Rad. Res. **14** 374.

BURNS, W. G. and REED, C. R. V. 1963. Trans. Farad. Soc. **59** 101.

CHAPIRO, A. 1962. Radiation Chemistry of Polymeric Systems. (Interscience Publ., New York).

CHAPIRO, A., DURUP, J., FOX, M. and MAGAT, M. 1955. Ricerca Sci. Suppl. A **207**.

CHARLESBY, A. 1960. Atomic Radiation and Polymers (Pergamon Press, Oxford).

CHARLESBY, A. and ALEXANDER, P. 1955. J. chim. physique **52** 699.

CHARLESBY, A., GARRAT, P. G. and KOPP, P. M. 1962. Intern. J. Rad. Biol. **5** 439.

CHARLESBY, A. and KOPP, P. M. 1962. Intern. J. Rad. Biol. **5** 521.

CHARLESBY, A. and LLOYD, D. G. 1960. Proc. Roy. Soc. [London] **A 254** 343.

CHARLESBY, A. and PINNER, E. H. 1959. Proc. Roy. Soc. **A 249** 367.

CROUZET, C. and MARCHAL, J. 1962. J. Polymer Sci. **59** 317.

DANNO, A. 1958. J. phys. Soc. (Japan) **13** 722.

DARIMONT, H. 1960. Mémoire de licences-sciences chimiques (Liège).

DELMAN, A. D., SIMONS, B. B., STANLEY, I. J., RUFF, A. E. and GOLDBERG, E. 1961. J. Appl. Polymer Sci. **17** 501.

DIEU, H. A. 1960. Ind. chim. Belge **25** 785.

DIEU, H. A. and DESREUX, V. 1959. Large Radiation Sources in Industry, Vol. 1. (Confer. Proc. Warsaw) p. 341.

DIEU, H. A. and DESREUX, V. 1963. In: Radiation Effects in Physics, Chemistry and Biology. Eds. Ebert, M. and Howard, A. (North-Holland Publ. Co., Amsterdam) p. 86.

DURUP, J. 1957a. J. chim. physique **54** 739.

DURUP, J. 1957b. J. chim. physique **54** 746.

DURUP, J. 1958. J. Polymer Sci. **30** 533.

DURUP, J. 1959. J. chim. physique **56** 873.

DURUP, M., DURUP, J., KIEFFER, F. and MAGAT, M. 1958. Proc. 2nd. Intern. Conf. Peaceful Uses Atomic Energy, Vol. 29. (Geneva, United Nations) p. 143.

GÄUMANN, T. and SCHULER, R. H. 1961. J. phys. Chem. **65** 703.

GOLUB, M. A., 1957. J. Polymer Sci. **25** 373.

GOLUB, M. A. 1958. J. Am. Chem. Soc. **80** 1794.

GOLUB, M. A. 1959. J. Am. Chem. Soc. **81** 54.

GOLUB, M. A. 1960. J. Am. Chem. Soc. **82** 5093.

HART, E. J. 1954. Rad. Res. **1** 53.

HART, E. J. 1964. Rad. Res. Suppl. **4** 74.

HENGLEIN, A. 1959a. J. phys. Chem. **63** 1852.

HENGLEIN, A. 1959b. In Large Radiation Sources in Industry, Vol. 1. (Confer. Proc. Warsaw) p. 345.

HENGLEIN, A. 1959c. Makromol. Chem. **32** 226.

HENGLEIN, A. and BOYSEN, M. 1956. Makromol. Chem. **20** 83.

HENGLEIN, A., BOYSEN, M. and SCHNABEL, W. 1957. Z. phys. Chem. Neue Folge **10** 137.

HENGLEIN, A., SCHNABEL, W. and HECKEL, E. 1961. Makrom. Chem. **49** 41.

HENGLEIN, A., SCHNABEL, W. and HEINE, K. 1958. Angew. Chemie **70** 461.

HENGLEIN, A. and SCHNEIDER, CH. 1959. Z. phys. Chem. Neue Folge **19** 367.

HENGLEIN, A. and SCHNEIDER, CH. 1958. Z. phys. Chem. Neue Folge **18** 56.

HENGLEIN, A., SCHNEIDER, CH. and SCHNABEL, W. 1957. Z. phys. Chem. Neue Folge **12** 339.

HENGSTENBERG, J. and SCHUCH, E. 1964. Makromol. Chem. **74** 55.

IKADA, Y. and SCHNABEL, W. 1965. Makromol. Chem. **86** 20.

JANSSEN, O., HENGLEIN, A. and PERNER, D. 1964. Z. Naturforschung **19** 1005.

KHENOKH, M. A., KUZICHEVA, E. A., AVERYANOV, S. V. and EVDOKIMOV, V. F. 1960. Zhur. Vsesoyuz. Khim. Obshchestva im D. I. Mendeleeva **5** 105.

KILB, R. W. 1959. J. Phys. Chem. **63** 1838.

KOBAYASHI, Y., SCHNABEL, W. and HENGLEIN, A. 1963. Makrom. Chem. **59** 61.

KUPPERMANN, A. 1961. In Actions chimiques et biologiques des radiations. Haissinsky, M. (Masson et Cie., Paris), p. 87.

MATSUDA, T., LIN, C.-C. and HAYAKAWA, K. 1961. Chem. High Polymers (Japan) **18** 492.

MATSUMOTO, A. 1963a. Chem. High Polymers (Japan) **20** 268.

MATSUMOTO, A. 1963b. Chem. High Polymers (Japan) **20** 275.

MATSUMOTO, A. and DANNO, A. 1959. In Large Radiation Sources in Industry, Vol. 1. (Confer. Proc., Warsaw) p. 331.

MÖNIG, H. 1958. Naturwissensch. **45** 12.

NAKAMURA, Y. 1960. Chem. High Polymers (Japan) **17** 721.

NARASAKI, A. and FUJIWARA, SH. 1963. J. Polymer Sci. **B 1** 153.

OKUMARA, S., MANABE, T., FUTAMI, S., IWASAKI, T., NAKAJIMA, A., ODAN, K., INAGAKI, H. and SAKURADA, I. 1958. Proc. 2nd Intern. Conf. Peaceful Uses Atomic Energy, Vol. 29. (Geneva, United Nations) p. 176.

PEDEMONTE, E., CUNIBERTI, C., ROSSI, C. and BIANCHI, U. 1965. J. Appl. Polymer Sci. **9** 385.

PRAVEDNIKOV, A. N., TELESHOV, W. N., SHEN-KAN, I. and MEDVEDEV, S. S. 1962. J. Polymer Sci. **58** 1039.

RAJU, M. R. and MERRIL, E. W. 1964. J. Polymer Sci. **B 2** 13.

SAITO, O. 1959. J. phys. Soc. (Japan) **14** 792.

SAKURADA, I. and IKADA, Y. 1961. Bull. Inst. Chem. Res. Kyoto University **39** 99.

SAKURADA, I. and IKADA, Y. 1962a. Bull. Inst. Chem. Res. Kyoto University **40** 16.

SAKURADA, I. and IKADA, Y. 1962b. Bull. Inst. Chem. Res. Kyoto University **40** 25.

SAKURADA, I. and IKADA, Y. 1962c. Bull. Inst. Chem. Res. Kyoto University **40** 1.

SAKURADA, I. and IKADA, Y. 1963a. Bull. Inst. Chem. Res. Kyoto University **41** 103.

SAKURADA, I. and IKADA, Y. 1963b. Bull. Inst. Chem. Res. Kyoto University **41** 114.

SAKURADA, I. and IKADA, Y. 1963c. Bull. Inst. Chem. Res. Kyoto University **41** 123.

SAKURADA, I. and IKADA, Y. 1964a. Bull. Inst. Chem. Res. Kyoto University **42** 22.

SAKURADA, I. and IKADA, Y. 1964b. Bull. Inst. Chem. Res. Kyoto University **42** 32.

SAKURADA, I., NAKAJIMA, A. and AOKI, H. 1958. Isotopes and Radiation Tokyo **1** 197.

SCHNABEL, W. 1964. Makromol. Chem. **77** 51.

SCHNABEL, W. 1965. Makromol. Chem. **86** 9.

SCHNABEL, W. and HENGLEIN, A. 1961. Makromol. Chem. **44/46** 611.

SHINOHARA, K., AMEMIGA, A., MATSUMOTO, M., SHINOHARA, Y. and OHNISHI, S. 1958. Proc. 2nd Intern. Conf. Peaceful Uses Atomic Energy. Vol. 29. (Geneva, United Nations) p. 186.

SHULTZ, A. R., ROTH, R. I. and BERGE, J. M. 1963. J. Polymer Sci. **A 1** 1651.

STEFANESCO, D. C., NICOLAU, C. and GARD, E. 1958. Proc. 2nd Intern. Conf. Peaceful Uses Atomic Energy. Vol. 29. (Geneva, United Nations) p. 254.

TABATA, Y., HAMANOUE, K. and SOBUE, H. 1964. J. chem. Soc. Japan, Ind. Chem. Sect. **67** 622.

WALL, L. A., and MAGAT, M. 1953a. Modern Plastics **30/11** 111.

WALL, L. A. and MAGAT, M. 1953b. J. chim. physique **50** 308.

WIPPLER, C. 1958. J. Polymer Sci. **29** 585.

WIPPLER, C. 1960. Nucleonics **18/8** 68.

WIPPLER, C. and GAUTRON, R. 1963. J. Polymer Sci. **A 1** 943.

## II

# SOME CHEMICAL AND BIOLOGICAL EFFECTS OF ELASTIC NUCLEAR COLLISIONS

H. JUNG and K. G. ZIMMER

*Institut für Strahlenbiologie, Kernforschungszentrum Karlsruhe, Germany*

# CONTENTS

# 1. Introduction

It may seem surprising to find a review article written on a topic which does not yet actually exist. There are several reasons, however, which in our view make this undertaking both justifiable and necessary. One may enquire how the concept of "Current Topic" should be interpreted. One can regard it as a line of work which is being actively pursued by many experimentors at the present time, or, on the other hand, as a topic which may not be widely known at present, but which is likely to be important for the further development of radiobiological research. If we may emphasize the latter interpretation, then we believe that a treatment of the chemical and biological effectiveness of elastic nuclear collisions may justifiably be considered as a "Current Topic" in radiation research.

The interest of this theme for radiation biology is confirmed by the fact that numerous authors in the course of the last 15 years have repeatedly pointed out that elastic nuclear collisions may be an important primary mechanism in radiation biology. Consequently, radiobiological experiments in which the radiation energy is *not* transferred by excitation and ionization, are therefore highly desirable. They might also open up a new possibility of studying more closely the initial processes of radiation action. It is precisely these physical events which occur very rapidly (within times of the order of $10^{-13}$ to $10^{-10}$ sec) which it has hitherto been impossible to study by means of biological systems, and it has therefore become necessary to apply the mechanisms studied by physicists, for the most part in very simple chemical systems, to the complex systems encountered in biology, and to do this without experimental verification. Since the manner in which radiation energy is transferred to molecules by elastic nuclear collisions is *totally* different from that which it has been customary to envisage in radiation chemistry and radiation biology, the physical processes in question may well have some importance in the future in illuminating fundamental aspects of the action of radiation on biological materials.

In this chapter we intend to make clear the importance of the elementary processes involved in elastic nuclear collisions for radiation chemistry and, especially, for radiation biology. In doing this we shall first show at what point in the long and complex chain of events between radiation absorption and the biological effect finally observed, this mechanism is effective. After a short description of the physical aspects, including only a brief reference to the relevant theoretical investigations, we shall draw together the numerous but widely distributed references in the literature to the possible importance of elastic nuclear collisions in radiation biology. A description of the problems involved in such experiments and of their importance for different branches of radiation research then follows. Finally, in sections 8 and 9, we describe experiments which we have recently conducted in this field and by means of which we have been able to demonstrate the biological effectiveness of elastic collisions. An analysis of our results by target theory has compelled us to re-think the hypotheses of target theory anew, in order to explain the discrepancies found by us, and by numerous other experimentors, between the molecular weights determined by target theory and by the methods of colloid chemistry. This discussion is given as an appendix to our treatment of elastic nuclear collisions.

The bibliography at the end of the paper makes no claim to completeness; we hope, however, that it does justice to the publications which have appeared on this topic.

## 2. Mechanisms of energy transfer in the absorption of radiation

Between the absorption of ionizing radiation and the biological effect finally observed there lies a complex sequence of events which include physical, physico-chemical, chemical and biological processes. For the discussion of fundamental radiation chemical and radiation biological problems it has proved fruitful to divide the chain of events into separate characteristic temporal stages [PLATZMAN, 1958, 1962a; HART and PLATZMAN, 1961].

In the first or "physical stage" of the radiation action, there is produced, either by the incident primary radiation itself or by the secondary particles liberated, acting through a variety of different processes, a large number of activated molecules. Depending upon the mechanism of energy transfer, these primary products may have very different forms. It is characteristic, however, that they all are exceedingly reactive. In the "physico-chemical stage" these primary products undergo secondary reactions; when the system has attained thermal equilibrium, these reactions continue during the "chemical stage" until a stable state is finally attained. In the "biological stage" which follows, the damage to biological macromolecules leads in the end through a succession of different levels of organisation to the biological effect which is finally observed (cf. "Amplification Theory of Organisms" by JORDAN, 1948).

First we shall set out the different primary processes which are effective during the physical stage.

### 2.1. EXCITATION AND IONIZATION

During the absorption of high energy quantum or corpuscular radiation the energy of the incident radiation is transferred to the irradiated material in a large number of separate elementary events. A fast-moving charged particle exerts an electrostatic force for a brief interval on the electrons belonging to molecules lying close to the particle's track. Quantum transitions are thus induced in many of these molecules and as a result excited and ionized molecules are the most frequent primary products formed during the physical stage. Details of the physical processes involved are comparatively well understood and are described in various review articles [FANO, 1952; MORRISON, 1952; FANO, 1954; PLATZMAN, 1958; HART and PLATZMAN, 1961, HUTCHINSON and POLLARD, 1961a; BOAG, 1963; FANO, 1963; NORTHCLIFFE, 1963]. It is one of the important aims of radiation chemistry and radiation biology to study the final chemical and biological changes resulting from the chain of reactions occurring between primary products and to elucidate the separate steps in this chain of events.

### 2.2. OTHER PRIMARY MECHANISMS

Besides the two dominant primary processes, excitation and ionization, there are other ways in which energy can be transferred. The two most important of these are nuclear collisions and the Auger effect. The first of these is the direct removal of an atom from its original position in a molecule by means of an elastic collision with a fast charged particle. The second, the Auger effect, consists in the removal of an electron from an inner shell followed by an Auger cascade, leading to the decomposition of this molecule. In addition, part of the energy of positive ions can be dissipated by charge exchange processes in which an incident particle captures an electron and then gives it up again in a subsequent interaction. In addition, direct multiple excitations and multiple ionizations are possible. By multiple excitations (or ionizations) we mean the simultaneous promotion of several electrons in a single atom or molecule to higher levels by the passage of the same charged particle; such processes, however, are much less frequent than are ordinary excitations and ionizations [smaller by a factor of about 1000; PLATZMAN, 1952] and therefore they are unlikely to be of special importance in radiation chemistry and radiation biology. Further details can be found in the papers by PLATZMAN [1952] and by HART and PLATZMAN [1961].

## 3. Physical properties of elastic nuclear collisions

Soon after the discovery of uranium fission, CORSON and THORNTON [1939] and JOLIOT [1939] were able to show by cloud chamber pictures that the tracks due to fission were characterised by an extremely high ion density and by frequent branching. The branching of the tracks was ascribed to elastic collisions between the fast moving charged fission fragments and the atoms of the gas in the expansion chamber. BROSTRØM, BØGGILD and LAURITSEN [1940] studied the frequency distribution of the angular deflection of the particle as a function of the distance along its path measured from the point of collision to the end of its range—that is to say, as a function of the residual energy of the particle at the instant of collision. On the basis of these measurements BOHR [1940, 1941] worked out the theoretical principles governing the contribution which elastic collisions make to the energy dissipated by fast charged particles in matter. These ideas, which were further developed by BOHR [1948], have recently been extended and improved by Lindhard, Scharff and their colleagues [NIELSEN, 1956; LINDHARD and SCHARFF, 1961; LINDHARD, NIELSEN, SCHARFF and THOMSEN, 1963; LINDHARD, SCHARFF and SCHIØT 1963]. The latter authors [LINDHARD, SCHARFF and SCHIØTT, 1963] derived a general formula for the nuclear stopping power, in which they made use of a Thomas-Fermi model in order to determine the effects of screening.

In elastic collisions between atoms the interaction occurs between the (partially screened) Coulomb field of the incident particle and the (partially screened) Coulomb field of the nucleus of the atom struck. For this reason the process in question is generally referred to as a "nuclear collision". Sometimes the term "nuclear collision" is used to denote the initiation of a nuclear transformation under bombardment by fast particles [FANO, 1954]. Since "nuclear collisions" and "nuclear reactions" are totally different processes, however, it seems desirable to distinguish between them in the terminology used. Nuclear collisions are frequently called "elastic collisions". They are elastic in the sense that the total kinetic energy of the incident and of the struck atom is conserved, but this does not mean that the incident atom is scattered without loss of energy. In contrast with this process there are "inelastic collisions" in which the incident particle interacts with the electron shell of the struck atom. This process only appears as inelastic when one considers the collision as occurring between the incident particle and the whole of the atom struck; the collision of the particle with the electron, on the other hand, must be regarded as elastic.

At high velocities $v \gg v_0$ (Bohr velocity $v_0 = c/137 = e^2/\hbar = 2.183 \times 10^8$ cm/sec = the velocity of an electron in the lowest orbit of the hydrogen atom) a heavy charged particle in traversing material loses only very little energy by elastic atomic collisions. This is no longer true when the particle is moving so slowly $(v \sim v_0)$ that its mean charge approaches zero. In this energy range the electronic stopping power decreases as the velocity of the ion diminishes, since the collisions with the atomic electrons become more and more adiabatic. In contrast with this the energy loss per unit path length due to elastic collisions increases rapidly; approximately as $\beta^{-2} (\beta = v/c)$. At low ion velocities there is, therefore, a critical velocity below which more energy is dissipated by elastic collisions than by interaction between the incident ion and the atomic electrons of the irradiated material.

Not only heavy ions, but also electrons may lose energy through elastic collisions. However, collisions in which sufficient momentum is transferred to release an atom from its molecular bond are extremely rare. This remains true even when the energy of the electrons is so large that their mass greatly exceeds the rest mass. For electrons with energies below 100 keV, molecular damage through nuclear collision is impossible on grounds of insufficient energy. For neutrons, elastic collisions with the atomic nuclei of the irradiated material are the most important primary process in energy transfer, but interaction occurs here not by means of Coulomb forces but through nuclear forces. For this reason the efficiency of neutrons to produce displacements in solids is high.

## 4. Nuclear stopping power for water and tissue

In recent years, papers have been published from which one can obtain the cross section for nuclear interaction and for electronic interaction for biologically important substances and for different particle energies. Moreover, there have been some estimates of the energy limit below which more energy is transferred to the irradiated material by nuclear collisions than by interaction with electrons.

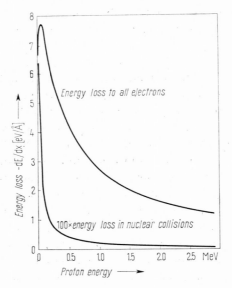

Fig. 1. Electronic stopping power and nuclear stopping power calculated for protons in water [PLATZMAN, 1952].

PLATZMAN [1952] calculated the various kinds of energy loss for protons in water of unit density (fig. 1). For convenience in applying the data to radiation chemistry and radiation biology the energy loss is given in electron volts per 0.1 nm. (Here one might mention that the mean spacing of neighbouring water molecules is about 0.3 nm.) The calculations are based on the assumption that the stopping power of water is equal to the sum of the stopping powers of its constituent atoms, that the Born approximation holds, and that the Bethe theory is therefore valid. The values for the mean excitation potentials of hydrogen and of oxygen were determined from experimental data on the stopping power of the elements and some of their compounds. Since there was no reliable theory for energies below 300 keV, Platzman estimated the stopping power as accurately as possible by using the experimental data of CRENSHAW [1942] on water vapour. The cross sections for nuclear collisions were determined according to BOHR [1948].

The great difficulty, which exists even today, in calculating accurately the energy losses due to electronic interaction in the low energy region can be seen from two papers by SNYDER and NEUFELD [1957]. These authors calculated the cross sections for energy loss by nuclear collisions and by electronic interaction for a number of different heavy ions in tissue. They assumed that tissue could be considered as a homogeneous mixture of hydrogen, carbon, nitrogen and oxygen in the proportions given in table 1. The amount of energy which is trans-

TABLE 1

Atomic composition of tissue normalized to density 1.0 g/cm³ [EVANS, 1949]

|  | H | C | N | O |
|---|---|---|---|---|
| Per cent by weight | 10.1 | 12.1 | 4.0 | 73.6 |
| $10^{22}$ atoms/cm³ | 6.02 | 0.603 | 0.171 | 2.74 |

ferred in elastic collisions with atomic nuclei was calculated from the charge, mass and velocity of the incident and of the ejected particles, in accordance with the theory of BOHR [1941]. The energy losses due to interaction with the atomic electrons were determined according to KNIPP and TELLER [1941] and to NEUFELD [1953]. To determine the shape of the curve in the low energy region, the experimental data of HALL [1950] were used. When more exact measurements of the energy losses of slow ions in matter later became available, the cross sections for stopping by electronic interaction were re-determined

[NEUFELD and SNYDER, 1961] and considerable divergences were found from the calculations based on the older data. The cross sections for energy loss by nuclear collisions and by electron interaction taken from this paper are shown in fig. 2 for protons with tissue as the stopping medium. The velocity of the protons is given in multiples of the Bohr velocity, $v_0$ ($= e^2/\hbar$). For convenience, the proton energy is given on the upper scale. The figure shows that protons in tissue have a maximum probability of producing ionization at energies between 60 keV and 100 keV. This probability decreases rapidly for decreasing proton energy, while the cross section for nuclear collisions simultaneously increases greatly. The energy at which the energy losses by the two different mechanisms are equal, lies for protons at 1.5 keV.

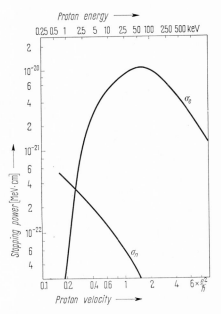

Fig. 2. Electronic stopping power ($\sigma_e$) and nuclear stopping power ($\sigma_n$) for protons in tissue [NEUFELD and SNYDER, 1961].

For heavier ions this energy level is displaced towards higher energies as shown in table 2. DIENES and VINEYARD [1957] estimated the boundary energy separating nuclear collisions from ionizations according to a formula given by SEITZ [1949] and by KINCHIN and PEASE [1955]. They state as a rule of thumb that ionization can be

TABLE 2

Critical energy dividing the regions in which electronic and nuclear collision energy loss predominate, for various ions in tissue [SNYDER and NEUFELD, 1957; DIENES and VINEYARD, 1957].

| Z of incident particle | Critical energy region (keV) | |
|---|---|---|
| | SNYDER and NEUFELD [1957] | DIENES and VINEYARD [1957] |
| 1 | 1.5 | 1 |
| 2 | 13 | 4 |
| 6 | 94 | 12 |
| 7 | 130 | 14 |
| 8 | 180 | 16 |

disregarded whenever the energy of the moving particle (in keV) is less than its atomic weight.

As separate estimates for metals and insulators have shown, this value is largely independent of the nature of the irradiated material. The accuracy of this estimate is said to be within a factor of 2. It should be noted that the energy limits (table 2) derived from the approximation used here [DIENES and VINEYARD, 1957] are considerably smaller than those determined by SNYDER and NEUFELD [1957]. If one takes account of more recent experimental data when determining the electron stopping power [NEUFELD and SNYDER, 1961], it seems possible that appreciably lower values would be obtained for the energy limits shown in table 2 [based on SNYDER and NEUFELD, 1957].

## 5. The possible significance of elastic nuclear collisions for radiation chemistry and radiation biology

### 5.1. THEORETICAL CONSIDERATIONS

An atom which experiences an elastic collision may be ejected from its original position in a molecule. If it receives enough kinetic energy, it may give up a part of this in excitations and ionizations; the remainder will be used up in subsequent nuclear collisions. A large part of the energy which is transferred by the latter mechanism appears as molecular vibrations, and is ultimately degraded to heat; another part of the energy transferred is preserved as increased potential energy of the medium due to the changed arrangement of the atoms. This rearrangement of atoms represents a chemical change, which in biological structures may cause permanent damage.

As early as 1950 Platzman expressly drew attention to the fact that in addition to the two predominant primary processes of excitation and ionization, there are other mechanisms of energy transfer and that it is therefore imprudent to maintain that chemical and biological effects are produced solely by excitation and ionization. In the paper quoted above he discussed the extent to which nuclear collisions, multiple ionizations, charge transfer from positive ions, and the Auger effect might be of significance in radiation chemistry and radiation biology. He came to the conclusion that charge-transfer, as well as direct multiple ionization or multiple excitations, are probably unimportant as far as their chemical and biological effects are concerned, but that in certain cases nuclear collisions and the Auger-effect may play a significant role. However, no one had succeeded in demonstrating convincingly the effectiveness of either of these two mechanisms in radiation chemistry or radiation biology. This is a remarkable fact: for the significance of elastic nuclear collisions in the production of radiation effects in solids, for instance, has been recognized for many years. The failure to establish a similar proof for radiation-chemical and radiation-biological systems is due chiefly to the fact that such systems, in contrast to solids, are extremely sensitive to ionization. Moreover, for the types of radiation usually employed, the number of ionizations is several orders of magnitude greater than the number of nuclear collisions it makes. According to PLATZMAN [1952], a 10 MeV alpha particle passing through air will transfer an energy of about 8 keV in elastic collisions, and of this about 1 keV will occur at the very end of its range. In about two thirds of all the nuclear collisions which take place in a low-atomic number material, enough energy will be transferred to break an intra-molecular bond. From this it is possible to estimate the total number of atoms removed from their parent molecules by a 10 MeV alpha particle; it amounts to about 100, including the atoms released in secondary collisions.

Since a 10 MeV alpha particle excites or ionizes approximately one million atoms and these are for the most part chemically effective, it can be seen that, in the case of ordinary ionizing radiations, the effect of nuclear collisions will be vanishingly small compared with the effect of the ionizations, and consequently it is impossible to distinguish between the two effects. Moreover, there is no system known in which excitation and ionization are so ineffective in the production of chemical and biological change that nuclear collisions attain special importance. Nevertheless, PLATZMAN [1952] does not dismiss out of hand the possibility that nuclear collisions may have a greater significance in the inactivation by radiation of very large and stable molecules; for the removal of one atom (particularly if this sets free other atoms from the same molecule) may seriously damage the molecular structure. Moreover, it seems much less likely that a molecule can "recover" from the loss of an atom than from the loss of an electron.

In addition to Platzman, who has worked out the essential theoretical aspects of the possible significance of nuclear collisions in radiation chemistry and radiation biology [PLATZMAN, 1952, 1958; FRANCK and PLATZMAN, 1954; HART and PLATZMAN, 1961], other workers [FANO, 1954; ZIMMER, 1956; RIEHL, 1956] have also put forward the view that nuclear collisions might prove to be extremely effective in producing biological changes. ZIMMER [1956] discussed at length the exceptional importance of this primary process for the dosimetry of epithermal neutrons, and hence for the establishment of tolerance doses for epithermal neutrons. All these authors pointed out the need to carry out experiments to clarify the radiation biological effects of nuclear collisions.

## 5.2. EXPERIMENTAL ATTEMPTS

In spite of the numerous comments quoted above on the need for and on the interest of an experimental proof of the chemical and biological effects of elastic nuclear collisions, very few investigators have yet attacked this problem. Some authors (AHNSTRÖM, EHRENBERG and ZIMMER, 1960; AHNSTRÖM and EHRENBERG, 1961] tried to demonstrate the effect of elastic nuclear collisions on plexiglass, in order to use this substance for measuring the dose of mixed reactor radiation consisting of fast and epithermal neutrons and gamma rays. In these experiments plexiglas 1 mm thick was irradiated with deuterons of energies between 5 and 100 keV, and the change in optical absorption at 295 nm was studied. The change in extinction per unit dose proved to be largely ($\pm 10$ %) independent of the energy of the incident deuterons, but from this it is not possible to decide whether nuclear collisions have the same effect per unit dose on the optical absorption of plexiglas as do, for example, ionizations. KÜHN [1960a] investigated the variation in the cross section for inactivation of lactic acid dehydrogenase by means of slow protons as a function of the energy of the incident protons. In these experiments the thickness of the irradiated enzyme layer was always twice as great as the range of the incident protons, and therefore the cross sections obtained are to be regarded as average values integrated over the energy spectrum between zero and the energy of the incident protons. It was not possible to establish any energy dependence of the inactivation cross section for protons in the energy range studied, i.e., between 18.5 keV and 79 keV. The mean inactivation cross section [corrected according to KÜHN, 1960b] for this energy range was found to be $7 \times 10^{-13}$ cm².

## 5.3. SUITABLE METHODS OF RESEARCH

As the foregoing sections show, the problem of elastic nuclear collisions in radiation chemistry and radiation biology has not yet been successfully investigated; the reason for this is to be found in the experimental difficulties it presents. When using fast charged particles, excited and ionized molecules are much more numerous than nuclear collisions (section 5.1) and there is no known chemical or biological system which does not respond, or even which responds only weakly, to ionizations. Another possibility would be to use neutrons which transfer practically all their kinetic energy to the medium by elastic collisions with atomic nuclei. However, if fast neutrons are used the biological effects of the nuclear collisions will be swamped by the effect of the ionizations produced by the recoil protons, and thus proof of their effect will again be unobtainable; on the other hand, radiation-biological experiments with epithermal neutrons, which might partly avoid this difficulty, have not as yet been published. Moreover, when slow neutrons are used for irradiation, nuclear reactions occur, and in such experiments the effects observed are always the sum of the effects produced by the recoil protons and by the radiation arising from the nuclear reactions induced. In principle one could also use for such experiments systems in which spontaneous or artificially produced nuclear transformations occur. When an electron, proton or $\alpha$-particle is emitted in such a transformation, then the principle of conservation of momentum requires that the emergent nucleus shall have the same momentum as the emitted particle. The kinetic energy of this recoil nucleus is, of course, on account of its greater mass, considerably smaller than that of the emitted particle. The kinetic energy of the recoil nucleus amounts in the case of alpha decay to some 100 keV, and in the case of beta decay to some 10 to 100 eV. The recoil nuclei lose their kinetic energy along a very short path, and because of their small velocity almost entirely through elastic collisions. Details of this process in relation to its effect on solids have been discussed more fully by RIEHL [1956] and in relation to its effect on chemical systems by HART and PLATZMAN [1961]. Here we need only mention that it should be possible in principle to demonstrate the radiation biological effectiveness of elastic collisions by means of recoil nuclei; however, here too it is difficult to distinguish the effects of the recoiling nuclei from those of the ionization produced by the emitted particles.

The best of the possible ways of investigating the effect of nuclear collisions independently of other mechanisms of energy transfer appears, then, to be by the use of low energy charged particles. The lower the velocity of the incident particle, the smaller is the ionization probability, and the greater is the cross section for nuclear collisions. These facts underline the main experimental difficulty of such an investigation, i.e. the choice of the system to be irradiated. The slow particles suitable for such experiments have a range of only some tens of nanometers and the chemical or biological indicator system must therefore be of extreme sensitivity if it is to provide quantitative proof of the changes arising from nuclear collisions.

## 6. Importance of experiments on the biological effectiveness of elastic nuclear collisions

In spite of all the experimental difficulties it seems urgently necessary to carry out experiments of this kind for, as already indicated, on both theoretical and practical grounds, there is an incentive to understand the chemical and biological effects of nuclear collisions. We emphasise especially the following reasons.

### 6.1. IMPORTANCE FOR RADIATION BIOLOGY

From the point of view of radiation biology the types of radiation ordinarily employed are all very similar as regards their mode of action. All these radiations, excepting only ultraviolet light (in the domain of photobiology) possess quantum energies greatly exceeding the energies of chemical bonds. They are able to eject from widely different atoms electrons, all of which dissipate their energy in similar fashion. In this way the energy of the incident particle is gradually broken up into smaller and smaller 'packets'. Packets of 1 to 10 eV are large enough to initiate chemical changes. This subdivision of the energy of ionizing radiation is a complicated but comparatively well-understood process; it is known that the various types of radiation produce their effects by the same mechanism, so that "all ionizing radiations—on the whole—produce remarkably similar effects" [FANO, 1954]. It is clear from this fact that the exclusive use of ionizing radiation for the elucidation of fundamental radiobiological mechanisms represents, *a priori*, a severe limitation of the possible lines of research. In most experiments of this kind one induces some change in a biological system as a result of the absorption of radiation energy, and one analyses the reaction of the system to this disturbance. The various types of ionizing radiation always produce in the irradiated system the same primary products, viz. excited and ionized molecules, and in the main it is only the spatial distribution of these primary products which varies according to the type of radiation used. It would, therefore, seem very advantageous to elucidate not only the changes produced by excitation and ionization, but also those due to reactions induced by nuclear collisions. In this way one should attain a deeper understanding of the processes which occur during the "inactivation" of a biological system.

### 6.2. IMPORTANCE FOR THE DOSIMETRY OF EPITHERMAL NEUTRONS

The difficulties encountered in the dosimetry of epithermal neutrons are the second important point which calls for an elucidation of the biological effect of slow particles. In setting up a permissible dose level for epithermal neutrons one has more or less assumed that this must lie between the permissible levels for thermal and for fast neutrons. If one compares the different ways in which thermal, epithermal, and fast neutrons interact with matter, however, this assumption seems to be an extrapolation for which there is little justification [ZIMMER, 1956]. Calculations of the dose due to thermal neutrons are based on the known capture cross sections for neutrons. In biological tissue two reactions are important: neutron capture by hydrogen and an (n, p) process in nitrogen. These two reactions yield respectively 2.2 MeV gamma radiation and 660 keV protons. From the ionization produced by these radiations, the absorbed dose in tissue due to neutron capture may be calculated. Fast neutrons lose their energy chiefly by elastic collisions with nuclei, and in biological material some 85 % to 95 % of such collisions produce recoil protons. In somewhat extended absorbers the dose due to fast neutrons is taken to be the sum of the dose due to the ionizing power of these recoil protons and the dose due to the nuclear reactions arising from capture of the neutrons after they have been slowed down to thermal energies.

The dose delivered by epithermal neutrons has generally been calculated in the same way. The recoil protons emerging from elastic collisions have a small ionization efficiency; moreover, the ionization due to charge-exchange processes has not, as a rule, been allowed for. If the dose is calculated solely on a basis of the ionization produced, then, in an extended medium of 30 cm thickness, the contribution due to recoil protons is only about one tenth of the total dose. The major contribution comes from the nuclear reactions initiated by thermalized neutrons [SNYDER, 1957]. The small contribution which recoil protons make to the total dose is surprising. A slow neutron of say 1 keV energy traversing hydrogenous material can knock several hydrogen atoms out of their parent molecules by elastic collisions, continuing to do so until its energy is so low that the process is no longer energetically possible. The slow recoil protons thus produced can liberate further protons by elastic collisions, and the total number of hydrogen atoms set free is considerably increased by these secondary recoil protons. It is not, however, possible to determine exactly the number of recoil protons produced in this way. For this it would be necessary to know what fraction of the energy of the recoil protons is utilised in exciting rotational and vibrational states of molecules and in charge-exchange processes. Besides, it is possible that the recoil protons may react with further hydrogen atoms after they have lost their kinetic energy. In this way the number of hydrogen atoms removed from molecules could be doubled once again without the occurrence of ionization. Energy is transferred to the material by the removal of a hydrogen atom from a molecule and not solely by the ejection of an electron, and one may therefore ask why the absorbed dose takes account only of the energy absorbed in electronic processes and not that which is transferred in elastic collisions. One ground for this probably lies in the fact that it has not yet been shown experimentally to what extent nuclear collisions may have a significant biological effect.

Ninety per cent of the neutrons which escape from the shielding around reactors consist of epithermal neutrons. An under-estimate of the biological effectiveness of such neutrons could therefore lead to the exposure of the operating staff of reactors to a radiation dose exceeding the permissible limit. This possibility makes it urgent to take account, in dosage calculations, of the fraction of the total dose due to elastic collisions, but this is only possible once the biological effectiveness of this primary process is understood.

### 6.3. IMPORTANCE FOR NEUTRON CAPTURE THERAPY

A third consideration which makes it seem necessary and desirable to investigate the biological effectiveness of nuclear collisions consists in the possibility of therapeutic applications of epithermal neutrons. One important difficulty in radiation therapy is the fact that, when irradiating a tumour, a large number of healthy cells are damaged in addition to the tumour cells. For this reason new methods have long been sought, e.g. the application of thermal neutrons. A comprehensive presentation of the development of neutron therapy with extensive references to the literature has been given by FOWLER [1964]. Fowler comes to the conclusion that neutron capture therapy is unlikely ever to be successful if only thermal neutrons are used. As an alternative he points out the fact that FRIGERIO [1962], using epithermal neutrons, obtained considerably better values of depth dose *. This also empha-

---

* See also this Volume, Chapter VII.

sises the need for an experimental study of the biological effect of nuclear collisions (epithermal neutrons lose their energy almost exclusively by this mechanism), a field which has hitherto been almost neglected.

## 7. Own investigations: General considerations and instrumentation

The grounds set forth in section 5.3 convinced us that the use of slow charged particles would be the most convenient method of distinguishing the effect of nuclear collisions as clearly as possible from the effects of the other possible primary mechanisms. This argument is based principally upon the fact that for heavy ions below a certain energy, both the ionization probability and the cross section for nuclear collisions are strongly energy-dependent (compare fig. 2). At low enough energies it is to be expected that only a small fraction of the observed radiation effect will be produced *via* excitation and ionization, and thus the effect of nuclear collisions can, to a large extent, be isolated. The experiments therefore aim at studying a chemical or biological effect as a function of the energy of the incident ions, and at deducing from the shape of the curve representing effective cross-section for damage *versus* energy any effect ascribable to nuclear collisions.

Two possibilities present themselves: (1) The integral effect for ions of different initial energy may be measured. In this case the irradiated object must be thicker than the range of the incident particles so that the latter may be completely stopped within the material. In this way one observes the sum of the effects of ions having an energy spectrum extending from zero up to the incident energy. This method also requires that the changes produced in layers of material only a few tens of nanometers thick should be accessible to quantitative measurements. Of course, in this method, even when the differential cross section for damage varies strongly with the energy of the incident particle, one can expect only a weak energy-dependence of the overall effect, so that such experiments are hardly likely to lead to quantitative estimates of the effectiveness of elastic nuclear collisions. It is thus not surprising that in the experiments undertaken hitherto, all of which studied the integral effect of slow ions on different systems (compare section 5.2), no energy dependence of the observed radiation effect could be established.

(2) It should, therefore, be much more interesting to determine the differential cross-section for the effect as accurately as possible as a function of the energy of the ions used. The difficulty in doing this lies in the fact that the range of penetration of ions suitable for such experiments amounts to only a few tens of nanometers. The irradiated object must, therefore, be less than 10 nm thick, corresponding to an energy deposition of about 1 keV. Moreover, the changes produced by radiation in this thin system must be capable of exact quantitative measurement. In our experiments we aimed at determining the effect of slow ions in two different systems in order to come to conclusions which would be as general as possible. It seemed possible to attempt method (1) using plastic foils and looking for a chemical change brought about by elastic nuclear collisions. On the other hand, to measure the differential biological effectiveness of slow ions in accordance with method (2), it seemed that thin layers of enzyme or bacteriophage would be particularly suitable. The thickness of the layer of irradiated biological material as stated above, must not exceed a few tens of nanometers in order to permit a good energy resolution. Moreover, the condition must be satisfied that an ion, in passing through one of the irradiated biological units, must have little chance of inducing more than one inactivating event. If this condition is not fulfilled one cannot anticipate any energy dependence of the inactivation cross section. For protons the electronic stopping power amounts to about $10^{-20}$ MeV cm$^2$/atom (fig. 2). If one assumes a mean energy loss of 60 eV per primary ionization (compare section 11.1) then one can calculate that in protein the mean spacing between the separate primary ionizations is about 0.5 to 0.6 nm. The ionizations are therefore so close together that the only suitable experimental material is an enzyme with as small a molecular weight as possible, and one for which an extremely sensitive detecting method is available. The same considerations also indicate that the charged particles used should have as small an ion density as possible. Protons are therefore greatly preferable to alpha particles or other heavier ions. Protons have also the great advantage that the shape of the ionization probability curve is known fairly accurately down to very low energies, while for heavier ions this quantity is very imprecise [NEUFELD and SNYDER, 1961].

For our experiments an accelerator was constructed giving protons up to a maximum energy of 60 keV [JUNG, 1964b, 1965a]. The accelerating voltage was taken from a commercial high voltage circuit (Nucletron type $2 \times$ NU-1250) for the range 500 to 5000 volts. For higher voltages a Greinacher circuit (AEG-Zeiss, type HA 60) was available. The protons were produced in a Penning ion source as described by KELLER [1949]. The accelerating gaps consisted of three cylindrical brass tubes maintained at different potentials. They were designed to spread the proton beam in order to obtain a homogeneous radiation intensity over the whole surface of the irradiated sample. The unwanted components in the beam, such as $H_2^+$ and $H_3^+$ ions, were separated from the protons in a homogeneous magnetic field. Immediately in front of the irradiation chamber there was a sliding valve of diameter 50 mm (Vacuum Research Company type 2 TN 8). This permitted the irradiation chamber, to which it was attached, to be closed off from the rest of the vacuum system before air was admitted to it. The construction of the irradiation chamber can be seen from fig. 3. In front of the chamber there is a plate pierced by a 15 mm hole.

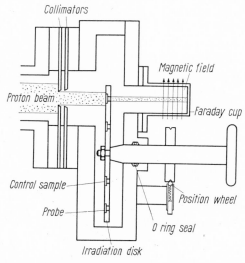

Fig. 3. Irradiation chamber (schematic).

This plate is maintained at a negative potential of 300 V in order to prevent secondary electrons liberated by the protons from leaving the irradiation chamber.

A second plate, having an opening of 16 mm diameter and maintained at 50 V positive with respect to the first one, is intended to capture the secondary electrons originating from the edge of the first plate [KEENE, 1949]. The irradiation chamber is supported on insulators so that the radiation intensity can be determined by measuring the current with a nanoammeter (Knick type H 21) or with a current integrator (Elcor type A 309B). The back wall of the chamber carries a sealing gland through which passes a rotating shaft carrying a steel disc of 150 mm diameter on which the samples to be irradiated are mounted. In this disc there are twelve depressions around a circle of 60 mm radius into which the samples fit. Nearer the axis there are eight corresponding depressions for the un-irradiated control samples. When large surfaces are to be irradiated homogeneously the particle flux density in the proton beam must be constant over the whole irradiated area. By introducing stops of different diameter into the path of the beam, separate parts of the proton beam can be examined. The beam passing through the stop is then trapped in a Faraday cup mounted on the back wall of the chamber and is measured with a nanoammeter. As can be seen from fig. 4, even at very low

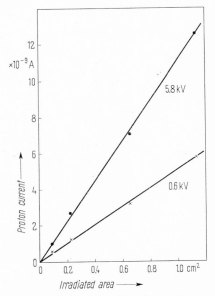

Fig. 4. Proton current incident on irradiated area at accelerating voltage of 0.6 and 5.8 kV, respectively.

accelerating voltages the proton current is directly proportional to the area of the stop used. The complete apparatus can be maintained at a pressure below $10^{-5}$ Torr by a set of vacuum pumps (Leybold P15). By using mercury pumps one avoids the possibility that oil molecules might be broken up in the ion beam and that the organic radicals so formed might react with the macromolecules to be studied and modify the direct radiation effect.

## 8. Experiments on the chemical effectiveness of elastic nuclear collisions with polyethyleneterephthalate

The use of plastic foils seemed appropriate for these experiments since much work has recently been done on changes in the properties of a great variety of plastics, and it was therefore possible, by examining this extensive material, to find a system possessing the necessary sensitivity for our experiments. Besides, information on the behaviour of plastics is not without interest for radiation-biological research; however, one must always be careful in transferring results from one field into another.

The effect of ionizing radiation on polymers can manifest itself in many ways. For instance, in the case of transparent plastic materials, the optical absorption properties are often altered by irradiation. Since this phenomenon was first observed in coloured perspex by DAY and STEIN [1951] the influence of ionizing radiation on the optical absorption properties of many substances has been studied. Since most workers attempted to develop a simple and cheap method of dosimetry for gamma rays and electrons, purely descriptive publications are numerous and in the case of most materials it is not known what the reactions are which follow radiation absorption and what chemical changes are responsible for the observed colouration. It seems possible that particular reactions should lead, at any rate in certain cases, to quite specific changes in absorption. If, in the absorption of slow protons, the energy is dissipated by two different mechanisms which perhaps lead to two different chemical reactions, then one might expect that this would reveal itself by the occurrence of two different absorption spectra [JUNG, 1965b].

## 8.1. MEASURING METHODS

For the experiments foils of polyethyleneterephthalate were used, these foils being commercially available as Hostaphan, Melinex or Mylar. The manufacturer stated that they were completely free from plasticizer and polymerizer, which are usually found to a greater or lesser extent in most other plastic materials. This fact is very important, for in experiments with particles which penetrate only 10 nm any nonuniformity in the distribution of additive molecules could easily lead to considerable experimental errors. The foils used must also be as thin as possible in order to achieve a favourable ratio of irradiated material (within range of the particles) to unirradiated material. This requirement too is better satisfied by Hostaphan than by other polymers since Hostaphan foils are manufactured in thicknesses down to a few microns. These positive advantages of Hostaphan are, however, offset by the fact that only a few workers have as yet studied the effect of ionizing radiation on this substance [LITTLE, 1952, 1954; TODD, 1954; BOPP and SISMAN, 1955; TESZLER and RUTHERFORD, 1956; BOAG, DOLPHIN and ROTBLAT, 1958; RITZ, 1961]. This point is not of great importance from the point of view of our own experiments, however. Hostaphan foils are transparent to visible light, but the absorption rises suddenly below 315 nanometers. In order to be able to measure small changes in transmission in the UV part of the spectrum, each foil was compared with a control foil before and after irradiation using a spectrophotometer (Zeiss PMQ II). The cross section of the light beam was 1.5 mm × 8 mm so the measurement represents a mean value over this surface. The difference between the two measured values gave the change in absorption due to radiation.

## 8.2. RESULTS

The absorption spectra found in Hostaphan after irradiation with slow protons of various energies are shown in fig. 5. For all proton energies the dose amounted to $5 \times 10^{14}$ protons per square centimeter. There is a sharp absorption maximum at 308 nm, whose height increases with the energy of the protons. At 250 nm there is in addition a broad absorption peak. Its height, in relation to the absorption at 300 nm (the reason for taking this as standard will be given later) is the same for all proton energies. One can deduce from this that the broad maximum is produced by a mechanism which only becomes effective to a significant extent below proton energies of 2 keV. To confirm this deduction Hostaphan foils were irradiated *in vacuo* with 2 MeV protons from a Van de Graaff accelerator. Further comparative experiments were made in helium at atmospheric pressure with 3.4 MeV alpha particles from a polonium source, and with $^{60}$Co gamma radiation. These fast protons and the alpha particles have enough energy to pass right through the foils. The energy loss amounts to 150 keV and 1100

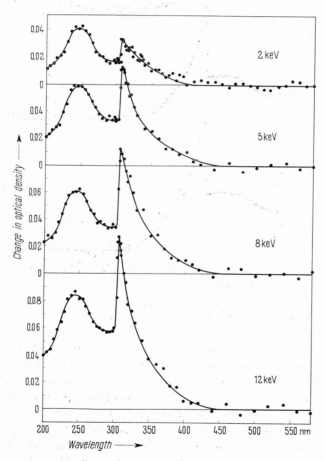

Fig. 5. Absorption spectra produced in Hostaphan by irradiation with slow protons of different energies, the doses being about $5 \times 10^{14}$ protons/cm².

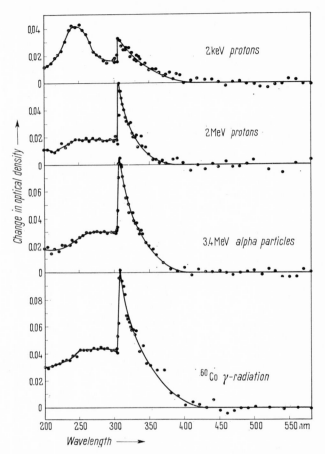

Fig. 6. Absorption spectra produced in Hostaphan by irradiation with 2 keV protons, 2 MeV protons, 3.4 MeV alpha particles, and $^{60}$Co gamma radiation.

keV in the two cases. For these reasons specific mechanisms which occur only at the end of the particle tracks can make no contribution to the spectra observed in these cases. The spectra observed are given in fig. 6. They show only the sharp absorption peak at 308 nm and not the broad maximum at 250 nm. This result proves that the absorption maximum at 308 nm can be produced by very varied types of ionizing radiation, while the broad maximum at 250 nm is due to some mechanism which is not observed after irradiation with fast ionizing particles.

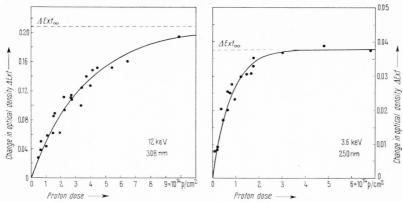

Fig. 7. Left: Change in optical density at 308 nm produced in Hostaphan by irradiation with 12 keV protons at different doses.

Right:  Change in optical density at 250 nm produced in Hostaphan by irradiation with 3.6 keV protons at different doses.

Under irradiation by slow protons, the absorption peaks at 308 and 250 nm increase with increasing dose, and at very high doses reach a saturation level (fig. 7). This behaviour can be explained by supposing that saturation is reached when all possible changes in the material which can occur within the region where the particular mode of energy transfer operates have already occurred, so that further irradiation

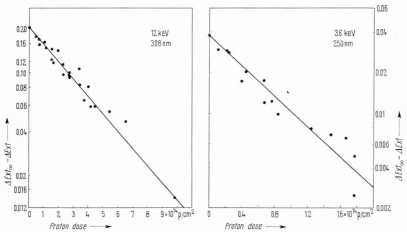

Fig. 8. Difference between saturation value ($\Delta_{\mathrm{Ext}\infty}$) and change in optical density ($\Delta_{\mathrm{Ext}}$) at 308 nm (left) and at 250 nm (right) at different proton doses.

cannot produce an enhanced effect. Other explanations are, however, possible. If one plots the difference between the observed change in extinction ($\Delta_{\mathrm{Ext}}$) and its saturation value ($\Delta_{\mathrm{Ext\infty}}$) against the proton dose, the curve obtained is a straight line in a semilogarithmic plot (fig. 8). That is to say, the growth of the extinction follows the equation

$$\Delta_{\mathrm{Ext}} = \Delta_{\mathrm{Ext\infty}}(1 - e^{-D/D_{63}})$$

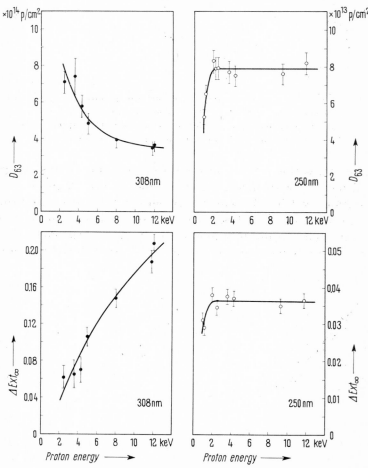

Fig. 9. Top: $D_{63}$ for the production of the absorption maxima at 308 nm and 250 nm, respectively, in dependence of proton energy (N.B. the ordinate scales differ by a factor of 10).
Bottom: Saturation value ($\Delta_{\mathrm{Ext\infty}}$) at 308 nm and 250 nm found after irradiation with protons of different energies.

in which $\Delta_{\text{Ext}}$ is the observed change in extinction at dose $D$, $\Delta_{\text{Ext}\infty}$ is the saturation value, and $D_{63}$ is the dose at which the change in extinction has reached 63 % of its saturation value. This relation between dose and effect holds for both the peak at 308 nm and the broad maximum at 250 nm, but the values of $D_{63}$ and of $\Delta_{\text{Ext}\infty}$ depend upon which mechanism is involved and upon the proton energy. It is seen from fig. 9 that the 63 % dose corresponding to the 308 nm peak decreases as the proton energy is increased, that is to say, the effectiveness of protons in producing this peak increases with proton energy

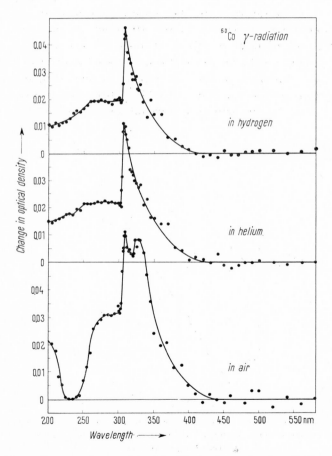

Fig. 10. Absorption spectra produced in Hostaphan after irradiation with $^{60}$Co gamma radiation in hydrogen, helium, and air, the doses being 43 Mrad.

in the range 2 to 12 keV. In contrast with this, the $D_{63}$ value for the broad absorption peak at 250 nm is largely independent of the energy of the incident protons. The energy has to be reduced below 2 keV before any appreciable decrease in effect can be detected: the effectiveness of the radiation thus increases as the proton energy is reduced. The limiting value of $\Delta_{Ext\infty}$ for the peak at 308 nm increases with increasing proton energy, while the corresponding limiting value of the 250 nm peak is only slightly affected.

To obtain further information on the nature of the different absorption spectra, Hostaphan foils were irradiated by [60]Co gamma radiation at a dose rate of 130 rad/min. The spectra obtained after irradiation in different gases are shown in fig. 10. Each of the three samples received a dose of 43 Mrad. In an atmosphere of hydrogen or helium the spectra obtained had the same form as that found after irradiation with fast protons *in vacuo*, or with alpha particles in helium (fig. 6). Irradiation in the presence of air yields a different spectrum (fig. 10 below): besides the maximum at 308 nm one observes a well-defined

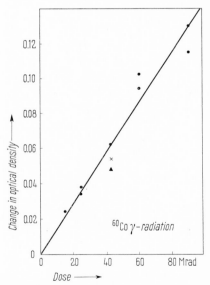

Fig. 11. Change in optical density at 308 nm produced in Hostaphan by irradiation with different doses of [60]Co gamma radiation

● Irradiation in air
× Irradiation in helium
▲ Irradiation in hydrogen

minimum at 240 nm and an additional peak at about 325 nm. The change in extinction at 308 nm increases linearly with dose up to a dose of 90 Mrads (fig. 11). It is noteworthy that the extinction changes at this wavelength produced in the presence of hydrogen or helium agree fairly well with those found in air. Although the different gas atmospheres affect the form of the spectra, the height of the peak at 308 nm is largely independent of the conditions during irradiation. If one compares the shapes of the spectra given in figs. 5, 6 and 10, three types can be recognized:

(1) the spectra due to irradiation by slow protons show the sharp peak at 308 nm and the broad maximum at 250 nm.

(2) after irradiation by 2 MeV protons, 3.4 MeV alpha particles, or $^{60}$Co gamma radiation in the absence of oxygen, spectra are obtained which include the sharp peak at 308 nm but which decline monotonically between 300 and 200 nm.

(3) the third type of spectrum results from irradiation by $^{60}$Co gamma radiation in the presence of air. Here, too, one finds the maximum at 308 nm. In addition there is a further maximum at 325 nm and a pronounced minimum at 240 nm.

Three spectra, one of each of the above types, are superimposed in fig. 12. By appropriate transformation of the ordinate scales the height of the peak at 308 nm has been made the same for all three curves. Spectrum II, found for various types of irradiation in the absence of oxygen, serves as the standard of reference. The difference between spectra I and II shows the extent to which the absorption spectrum produced by irradiation with slow protons differs from that due to fast protons. This part of the change in extinction (fig. 12, Curve I–II) is therefore due to some mechanism which occurs preferentially at the end of the range of the slow particles. The effect produced is a broad symmetrical absorption 'line', whose peak lies at 245 nm and whose half-width is about 40 nm. Since this spectrum is superimposed on spectrum II, the height of the broad maximum ($\Delta_{Ext}$) is always given in comparison to the absorption at 300 nm.

The difference between spectra III and II shows how the effect of gamma irradiation is modified by the presence of oxygen (fig. 12, Curve III–II). The difference consists of a broad symmetrical absorption peak and  a similar absorption minimum. The minimum occurs between 240 and 245 nm and has a half-width of 40 nm. This comparison shows that the line width and the position of this minimum are the

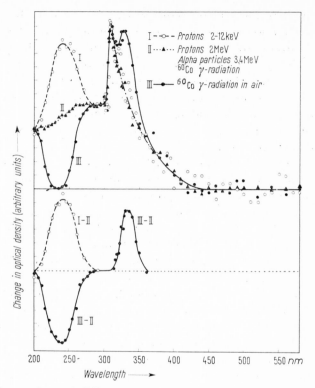

Fig. 12. Comparison of different types of absorption spectra (further details may be found in the text).

same as for the maximum in the difference curve I–II. The effect of oxygen is thus to extinguish optical absorbing centres in the same spectral region as that in which absorbing centres are formed (surplus to spectrum II) by slow protons at the end of their range. Besides this minimum the difference curve III–II shows a symmetrical maximum at 335 nm whose half width is 25 nm. The variation in height of this peak with the radiation dose given was not studied in detail.

## 8.3. DISCUSSION

Our comparative experiments with different types of radiation have shown that the absorption maximum at 308 nm occurs after irradiation with slow and fast protons, alpha particles and gamma rays. The broad maximum at 250 nm, on the other hand, only appears after irradiation with slow protons. It must, therefore, be caused by a process which occurs to only a slight extent or not at all for the other "ionizing" kinds of irradiation. Since intense UV irradiation cannot produce either of these maxima to a measurable extent, it would seem that excitation cannot play any important part in causing the absorption spectrum. It is, therefore, a plausible assumption that the changes in Hostaphan to which the maximum at 308 nm is due are related to ionization. This is also supported by the fact that the $D_{63}$ for the formation of this maximum decreases with increasing proton energy (fig. 9), since this means that the probability of the particular mode of action inceases. In the energy range considered, the overall ionizing probability of the protons also increases, confirming the hypothesis that the maximum at 308 nm is caused by ionization.

The broad absorption maximum at 250 nm is formed by a process which occurs with significant frequency only at very low particle velocities (see fig. 6); moreover, the total cross-section for this process increases as the proton energy decreases (as can be seen from fig. 9 the corresponding $D_{63}$ declines in the same energy range). These findings indicate that the primary process involved is elastic collisions between the incident slow particles and the atoms of the irradiated material, and that this process causes specific changes which lead to the formation of the absorption maximum at 250 nm.

If Hostaphan foils are irradiated in the presence of oxygen, the resulting change in extinction at 250 nm is considerably smaller than that found under anaerobic conditions, while the absorption at 335 nm is increased (fig. 12 Curve III–II). It has not yet been possible to establish whether the optical centres formed under anaerobic conditions, which absorb at 250 nm, are changed by the action of oxygen into a different type, absorbing at 335 nm, or whether the two maxima are independent of one another. The occurrence of the broad absorption maximum at 325 nm (only after forming the difference with spectrum II is the maximum absorption III–II displaced to 335 nm; compare fig. 12) is in agreement with the findings of BOAG, DOLPHIN, and ROTBLAT [1958] who irradiated polyethyleneterephthalate foils in air with 1.8 MeV electrons and found a broad absorption centred at 325 nm.

The experiments described above do not permit any conclusions to be drawn about the nature of the chemical changes responsible for the various components in the spectra observed. Obviously the changes in extinction are all related to relatively stable optical centres. Allowing the foil to stand in air at room temperature for 8 weeks, or heating to 100°C for 1 hour, did not affect any of the components in the various spectra observed. This agrees with the data of RITZ [1961], who irradiated Mylar foils $6.2\mu$ thick and detected no change in absorption at 325 nm with time after the end of the irradiation.

## 9. Experiments on the biological effectiveness of elastic nuclear collisions in ribonuclease

In order to measure as accurately as possible the differential effect of slow protons as a function of their energy, it seemed that the enzyme ribonuclease (RNase) was specially suitable. Its molecular weight of 13 680 [HIRS, MOORE and STEIN, 1956, 1960] is comparatively low, thus satisfying of the conditions of section 7.1. A layer of enzyme 10 nm thick and 1 cm in diameter contains about $10^{-6}$ g. It proved to be possible to detect a few times $10^{-8}$ g of enzyme with adequate accuracy, and this material therefore possesses the high detection-sensitivity necessary in such experiments.

### 9.1. MEASURING TECHNIQUES

Commercial ribonuclease (RNase) made by the Sigma Chemical Co., St. Louis, U.S.A., was used in the experiments, without further purification. This RNase was extracted from calf pancreas, had been recrystallized five times and was free from salts and protease. Its enzymatic activity was determined by a modification of the method of KALNITSKY et al. [1959]. The sample to be tested was dissolved in 1 ml of acetate buffer ($p$H 5.0, 0.1 Molar) and the reaction between enzyme and substrate was started by adding 1 ml of RNA substrate solution, whose preparation will be described. The reaction mixture was maintained at a constant temperature of 30.0°C in a water bath. After an incubation time of 30 minutes, the remaining RNA was precipitated by adding 1 ml of 0.75 per cent solution of uranyl acetate in 25 per cent perchloric acid, the mixture being cooled immediately to 0°C in an ice bath, and after a further 20 minutes the precipitate was centrifuged down at 6000 rpm. 1 ml of the supernatant liquid was diluted 1 to 3 with distilled water, and the absorption of this solution at 260 nm was measured against that of a control containing no enzyme. Commercial RNA usually contains a high proportion of oligonucleotides, which reveal themselves by a strong absorption at 260 nm. In order to permit the determination of activity of very small amounts of RNase, 100 ml of a 1 per cent solution of commercial RNA from yeast (Merck, Darmstadt) was dialized in a 0.1 Molar acetate buffer ($p$H 5.0) against 1 litre 0.01 Molar acetate buffer ($p$H 5.0) at about 5°C for 5 to 7 days. The addition of a little thymol prevented the destruction of the RNA by bacteria.

In order to calibrate the assay method, mixtures of 1 $\mu$g RNase and 1 ml of substrate were allowed to react for times varying between 5 and 30 minutes. Within these limits the extinction at 260 nm increased linearly with the incubation time (fig. 13). In a corresponding experiment using an incubation time of 30 minutes, the quantity of RNase was varied between 0.2 and 1.0 $\mu$g. As fig. 13 indicates, the change in extinction measured at 260 nm is proportional

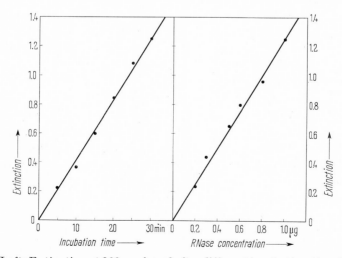

Fig. 13. Left: Extinction at 260 nm found after different incubation time between 1 $\mu$g ribonuclease and 1 ml RNA substrate solution.
Right: Extinction at 260 nm found with different RNase concentrations, the incubation time being 30 minutes.

to the quantity of enzyme used. These calibration experiments were conducted with special care. Ribonuclease becomes adsorbed very readily on glass [SHAPIRA, 1959; DEERING, 1960] and considerable errors can arise through the use of pipettes and of glass vessels for diluting the enzyme solution to the desired concentration. This is especially so when working with low enzyme concentrations.

For irradiation experiments with slow protons the samples must satisfy the following requirements:

(1) The RNase must be in a layer whose thickness is small compared with the range of protons.

(2) The backing which supports the enzyme must be of metal in order to prevent electrostatic charging during irradiation.

(3) The backing must be as smooth as possible to prevent any enzyme molecules getting into cracks or pores on the surface.

(4) The material of the backing should not have any strong chemical affinity for oxygen, to exclude the possibility of oxygen modifying the radiation damage to the enzyme.

On the above grounds, discs of polished rolled gold sheet (10 mm in diameter and 1.5 mm thick) where used for these experiments. The gold plates were cleaned by immersion for one hour in a cleaning solution consisting of 120 g NaOH, 120 ml water and 760 ml ethanol. After this they were immersed for several hours in running tap water and thereafter rinsed, first with distilled water and finally with double distilled water from a quartz still. RNase is adsorbed on glass in a monomolecular layer [DEERING, 1960] but is not adsorbed on gold. The RNase was, therefore, dissolved in double distilled water from the quartz still in concentrations of 0.05, 0.10 and 0.40 mg per ml. For each experiment 0.01 ml of the appropriate solution was pipetted onto a gold plate and distributed uniformly over its surface. A special device using a 0.1 ml pipette allowed this to be done with $\pm 4.5 \%$ accuracy. The gold plate was then placed on a brass block which had previously been cooled to $-78°C$ by a mixture of carbon dioxide snow and acetone. This sudden freezing of the solution, followed by freeze-drying, gave much more uniform enzyme layers than the method of evaporation in a dessicator, as could be demonstrated by the slow proton irradiations.

For each irradiation with slow protons, 11 samples were attached around the outer circle on the irradiation plate, while three samples acting as controls were on the inner circle. Each experiment consisted of two series of irradiations, so that the determination of a complete dose-effect curve involved 22 irradiated samples, 6 unirradiated controls and 4 'blank' controls (without enzyme). After irradiation the ribonuclease was dissolved off each gold plate by immersion in 1 ml acetate buffer (*p*H 5.0, 0.1 molar) in a centrifuge tube. The efficiency of removal was not determined, since the gold discs remained in the tubes throughout the enzymatic reaction and were only removed immediately before centrifuging out the precipitated RNA. In this way the fraction of the RNase which had not been completely removed from the discs or which had been adsorbed onto the glass tubes could also take part in the reaction.

## 9.2. RESULTS

The inactivation of enzymes by means of ionizing radiations is usually an exponential function of the applied dose and can be expressed by the formula $N/N_0 = \exp(-DS)$. $N/N_0$ is the fraction of the enzyme molecules which is still active after irradiation to a dose $D$; $S$ is the inactivation cross section. The latter varies according to the characteristics of the irradiated enzyme molecule and the type of radiation used. When ionizing particles are used as the source of radiation, it is better to quote the dose $D$ in particles per square centimeter. If $N/N_0 = 0.37 = e^{-1}$ then the inactivation cross-section ($S$) is obtained directly in square centimetres from the 37 % dose, $S = 1/D_{37}$. In order to determine the variation of the cross section for the inactivation of RNase by protons of different energies, the 37 % dose was first determined for various particle energies. In the experiments described here, the minimum proton energy used was 0.8 keV. For this energy fig. 14 shows the reduction in enzymatic activity as a function of the proton dose. The enzymatic activity approaches a constant value as the dose increases, indicating that the thickness of the irradiated ribonuclease layer must exceed the range of the protons in some places. After subtracting this constant value, the RNase activity decreases with dose, in correspondence to a single-hit curve (fig. 14 above). From this the $D_{37}$ for the inactivation of RNase by protons of energies between 0 and 0.8 keV can be read off. It amounts to $(8.2 \pm 1.7) \cdot 10^{12}$ $p$/cm². However, the ratio between total initial activity and the constant 'indestructible' fraction of the

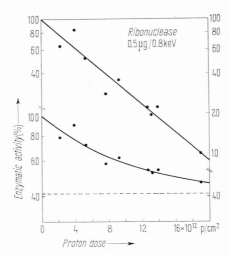

Fig. 14. Curve below: Inactivation of 0.5 μg ribonuclease with 0.8 keV protons. Top curve: Inactivation curve after subtraction of a constant "undestructible" component.

RNase does not permit us to draw any conclusions about the range of the 0.8 keV protons. For this, the thickness of the layer would have to be greater than the proton range at all points of the irradiated surface. This condition is not satisfied when the range of the protons is comparable with the molecular diameter and when such very small quantities of enzyme are used. Irradiation with 1 keV protons of a layer 1.3 μg/cm² thick and with 1.2 keV protons of a layer 5 μg/cm² thick showed similar results. In both these cases the thickness of the enzyme layer exceeded the range of the protons. After subtracting the constant "indestructible" fraction in these experiments, the 37 % values found were $(7.8\pm1.3)\times10^{12}$ protons/cm² and $(1.8\pm0.3)\times10^{13}$ protons/cm² in the two cases, and these may be regarded as average values for the ranges 0 to 1 keV or 0 to 1.2 keV, respectively.

When 1.2 keV protons are used to irradiate 1μg samples of RNase no "indestructible" fraction remains after high doses (fig. 15). This shows that 1.2 keV protons can penetrate right through a RNase layer of 1.3μg/cm². Since the value for the $D_{37}$, i.e. $(1.9\pm0.15)\times10^{13}$ p/cm², agrees within experimental error with that obtained when using a very thick layer, the layer corresponding to 1μg does not seem to be significantly smaller than the range of the 1.2 keV protons. The $D_{37}$ obtained as above, may, therefore, be regarded for practical

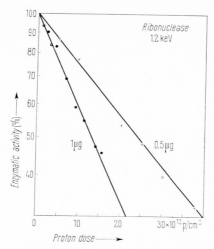

Fig. 15. Inactivation of ribonuclease with 1.2 keV protons using 0.5 and 1 $\mu$g RNase, respectively (corresponding to layers of 0.65 and 1.3 $\mu$g/cm$^2$, respectively).

purposes as an integral value for the energy interval between 0 and 1.2 keV. When an amount of 0.5 $\mu$g RNase per gold plate is used, the thickness of the layer is approximately only half as great as the range of the 1.2 keV protons. The $D_{37}$ value taken from fig. 15 $(3.4\pm0.3)\times 10^{13}$ p/cm$^2$ is considerably higher than the average value for the total interval between 0 and 1.2 keV; this demonstrates clearly that the $D_{37}$ value is strongly dependent on energy, in this particular range of energies. If the proton energy is increased to 1.4 keV, the inactivation curve measured for 0.5 $\mu$g RNase will show a further rise of the $D_{37}$ to $(4.25\pm0.4)\times 10^{13}$ p/cm$^2$ (fig. 16.).

In the manner described above, protons of various energies were used to irradiate thin layers of ribonuclease and the $D_{37}$ values were determined graphically from the inactivation curves. Quantities of 0.5 or 1.0 $\mu$g of RNase were used on each gold plate, and the maximum proton energy used was 60 keV. As an example of the inactivation at these higher proton energies, fig. 16 shows the dose-effect curve obtained with 50 keV protons and 0.5 $\mu$g of RNase. The dependence of $D_{37}$ on proton energy is shown in fig. 17. The limits of error drawn in correspond to one standard error in $D_{37}$, and, respectively, to the energy loss of the protons in the enzyme layer. In estimating the energy deposited by the protons in the layer of RNase, an energy loss of 1 keV/10

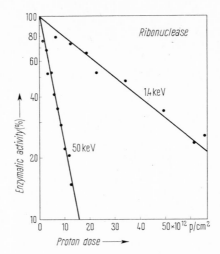

Fig. 16. Inactivation of 0.5 $\mu$g ribonuclease with slow protons at energies of 1.4 and 50 keV, the thickness of the enzyme layer being 0.65 $\mu$g/cm². 

nm was assumed. This was based on the mean of the range-energy curve for slow protons in protein [PERSON, 1956; PERSON, HUTCHINSON and MARVIN, 1963]. The uncertainty in determining the proton energy is negligible, for small proton energies, compared with the energy loss in

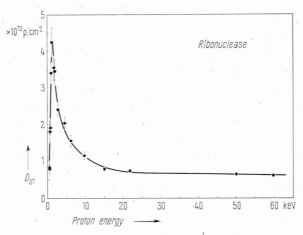

Fig. 17. 37 per cent dose $(D_{37})$ for the inactivation of ribonuclease with protons of different energies.

the RNase layer. At higher energies $D_{37}$ is insensitive to proton energy, and so any small errors in determining the energy are unimportant and have been neglected. Fig. 17 shows that, at higher proton energies, $D_{37}$ varies little with proton energy. Towards lower energies $D_{37}$ rises steadily and reaches a pronounced maximum at about 1.2 keV. Attention is drawn to the fact that below 1.2 keV the value of $D_{37}$ falls steeply, which simply means that the effectiveness of the protons in inactivating ribonuclease increases rapidly with decreasing proton energy. This fact is even clearer from fig. 18, in which the inactivation cross section for protons on ribonuclease is presented as a function of the proton energy. The inactivation cross section was obtained by taking the reciprocal of the 37 % dose. To present the data in the low energy region more clearly, the proton energy scale is a logarithmic one.

The errors indicated represent one standard error in the determination of inactivation cross section, or the energy loss of the protons in the enzyme layer. Below 0.9 keV these energy losses are comparable

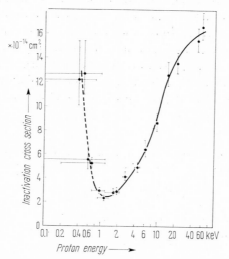

Fig. 18. Cross section for the inactivation of ribonuclease with protons of different energies.

with the incident energy; in this range of energies it is, therefore, difficult to assign the appropriate proton energy to the measured cross sections (broken curve in fig. 18). However, the diagram clearly indicates that below 1.3 keV the inactivation probability rises steeply with decreasing proton energy. At the higher proton energies the inactivation cross section also rises, and at about 50 to 60 keV it appears to approach a saturation value.


9.3. DISCUSSION

The variation in the inactivation cross section in fig. 18 in the region of higher proton energies can be easily explained by the fact that the probability of proton ionization below 60 keV decreases with decreasing proton energy and, therefore, the probability of inactivation decreases correspondingly. The sharp increase at energies below 1 keV shows that at low proton energies a mechanism of energy transfer comes into play which increases greatly in efficiency as the proton energy decreases. In this energy range the only mechanism of inactivation which need be considered is the damaging of the RNase molecule by elastic collisions between the slow protons and the atoms forming the RNase molecule. The cross sections calculated by NEUFELD and SNYDER [1961] for energy losses by nuclear collisions and electronic interaction for protons in tissue (fig. 2) make possible a quantitative comparison. It must first be investigated how the cross sections are modified when the calculations are made on a basis of the atomic composition of RNase (table 3) instead of tissue (table 1).

TABLE 3

Atomic composition of ribonuclease normalized to density 1.0 g/cm³ [HIRS, MOORE and STEIN, 1956, 1960; SCHERAGA and RUPLEY, 1962]

|                        | H    | C    | N    | O    | S    |
|------------------------|------|------|------|------|------|
| Per cent by weight     | 6.6  | 50.5 | 17.5 | 22.6 | 2.8  |
| $10^{22}$ atoms/cm³    | 3.97 | 2.53 | 0.75 | 0.77 | 0.05 |

The values shown in table 3 were calculated according to HIRS, MOORE and STEIN [1956, 1960] with modifications introduced by SCHERAGA and RUPLEY [1962]. It proved that, in spite of the different composition of the two materials, the stopping cross sections worked out for RNase agreed with those for tissue within the limits of accuracy of the calculations [SNYDER and NEUFELD, 1957]. The curves calculated by NEUFELD and SNYDER [1961] for tissue (fig. 2) can thus be used directly for a comparison with the inactivation cross sections found experimentally for RNase. To this end, the cross sections for energy losses by nuclear collisions (curve $\sigma_n$, right hand ordinate scale) and for energy losses by electronic interaction (curve $\sigma_e$, right hand ordinate scale) are therefore shown in fig. 19; in addition, the experimentally determined cross sections for inactivation are also shown (open circles, broken curve $S$, left hand ordinate scale). In order to make the figure as clear as possible the limits of error are not drawn in: however, these can be seen in fig. 18. Within this energy range between 0 and 60 keV, the primary mechanisms of energy transfer which have to be considered are excitations, ionizations and nuclear collisions. Since excitations are known to be relatively ineffective for inactivating biological macromolecules [McLAREN, 1949; HUTCHINSON, 1954, 1960; SETLOW, 1957, 1960], these will not be further discussed here. The curve $S$ determined experimentally should therefore be regarded as the sum of the biological effects of ionizations and nuclear collisions ($S = S_e + S_n$). At a proton energy of 60 keV the cross section for nuclear collisions $\sigma_n$ is smaller by a factor of about 500 than the energy loss due to interaction with the atomic electrons $\sigma_e$. It may, therefore, be assumed that at this proton energy the mechanism of nuclear collisions can be ignored in comparison with the much more numerous ionizations (60 keV: $S_n \approx 0$, $S \approx S_e$). In fig. 19, therefore, the two different scales for the inactivation cross section $S$ and the stopping cross section $\sigma$ have been so arranged that at 60 keV, where only electronic interaction is important, the curves $S$ and $\sigma_e$ coincide. If no inactivation of RNase due to nuclear collisions occurs anywhere in the range of energies studied ($S_n = 0$) then one would expect that, with decreasing proton energy, the inactivation cross section should decline in the same way as the ionization probability $\sigma_e$. This presupposes that it is relatively rare for several inactivating events to occur in a RNase molecule as a result of the passage of a single proton through it. The difficulties of carrying out this analysis by target theory are set out in detail in the appendix (section 11). As can be seen from fig. 19, $S$ and $S_e$ do not coincide, and $S_n$ therefore differs from zero. In order to distinguish between the effect of nuclear collisions and that of ionizations, the difference between the experimental values and the curve $S_e$ are shown in fig. 19 (curve $S_n$). If the same energy is necessary for the inactivation of an RNase molecule by means

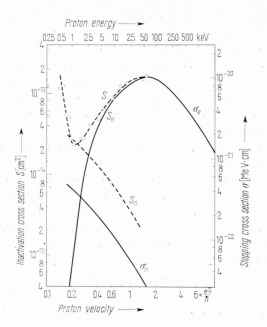

Fig. 19. Experimentally determined inactivation cross sections (o) compared with the electronic stopping power ($\sigma_e$) and the nuclear stopping power ($\sigma_n$) as calculated by NEUFELD and SNYDER [1961]. The difference betweens the experimental results (o) and curve $S_e$ is represented by curve $S_n$. This curve $S_n$ describes the cross section for the inactivation of ribonuclease by elastic nuclear collisions as a function of energy of the incident protons.

of nuclear collisions as for inactivation by means of ionizations, the curves $S_n$ and $\sigma_n$ should coincide. But the curve $S_n$ lies above the curve $\sigma_n$ by a factor of about 4. It can, therefore, be concluded that the amount of energy required for the inactivation of a RNase molecule by nuclear collisions is approximately 25 % of the energy which must be expended for inactivation through ionization. Whether this factor of 4 is to be explained by a lower average energy expenditure for inactivation by a nuclear collision than for inactivation by a primary ionization, or whether a nuclear collision is more likely than a primary ionization to inactivate a RNase molecule, cannot be deduced from the above experiments.

## 10. Comparison of the biological effectiveness of the various primary mechanisms

In the last section experimental proof was adduced that elastic collisions between slow charged particles and atomic nuclei are capable of destroying the enzymatic activity of RNase very effectively. As this enzyme enjoys no unique position, we may expect that the primary mechanism of nuclear collisions, now under investigation, can also cause changes with considerable efficiency in other chemical and biological systems. It seems useful at this point to compare the various primary mechanisms whose biological effectiveness has been investigated experimentally. It will be particularly illuminating to quote the work of R. B. SETLOW [1960] and HUTCHINSON [1954, 1960].

Setlow irradiated ribonuclease with ultraviolet light of wave length between 100 and 320 nm and determined the fraction of the absorbed quanta which caused the inactivation of a RNase molecule (quantum yield). This quantum yield is plotted in fig. 20 (above) against the energy of the UV quanta. HUTCHINSON [1954, 1960] irradiated bovine serum albumin (BSA) with electrons in the energy range between 1 and 250 eV and calculated the inactivation cross section for loss of the ability to bind specific antibodies. This inactivation cross section is plotted in fig. 20 (centre) against the energy of the incident electrons. For comparison, the variation of the cross section for inactivation of ribonuclease by slow protons, as determined by us, is shown in fig. 20 (below).

From these three curves the following deductions may be made. With decreasing energy the probability of ionization by all three types of radiation also decreases, and the inactivation cross sections decrease in a corresponding way. When UV light is used, the falling off in effectiveness of the radiation occurs within a range of a few electron volts (since UV quanta transfer their whole energy in a single process), whereas the variation in the inactivation cross section, when slow electrons or protons are used, extends over a wider range of energies. In the two papers of Setlow and Hutchinson it was shown experimentally that ionizations are capable of inactivating biological macromolecules with high yield whereas excitations are far less effective. As can be seen from the steep rise in the inactivation cross section for low proton energies (fig. 20 below), we have proved conclusively

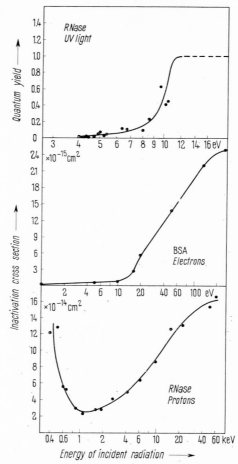

Fig. 20. Comparison of experiments demonstrating the biological effectiveness of different kinds of radiations.

Top: Quantum yield for the inactivation of ribonuclease by ultraviolet light as a function of quantum energy [SETLOW, 1960].

Middle: Cross section for inactivation of bovine serum albumin (BSA) by slow electrons as a function of electron energy [HUTCHINSON, 1954, 1960].

Bottom: Cross section for inactivation of ribonuclease by slow protons as a function of proton energy (this paper).

that not only ionizations but also nuclear collisions are capable of inactivating biologically important macromolecules.

We have thus worked out the conditions which should permit further investigations of this kind. Moreover, we consider the problem we have attacked so interesting that further experiments are fully justified; for the use of very slow charged particles or monoenergetic epithermal neutrons opens up the possibility of investigating more closely the factors which operate during the physical stage of radiation action on chemical and biological systems. For example, experiments carried out at different temperatures might provide information on whether the resistance to radiation conferred by low temperatures, which has been observed in numerous systems, should be ascribed to a modification of the phenomena occurring in the physico-chemical or in the chemical stage of radiation action. Similarly, one could also study the action of radiation-protective substances in experiments where the damage is produced by nuclear collisions. By comparing the protective factors derived from such experiments with the corresponding values for ionizing radiations, valuable pointers might emerge to the fundamental physical and chemical mechanisms underlying the protective effect.

It can also be deduced from our experiments that a considerable number of the changes produced by slow protons are referable to the effect of nuclear collisions; for example, protons of 1 keV energy produce more than 99 % of the observed effect *via* the mechanism of nuclear collisions, and only 1 % is due to the ionizing effect of such protons. On account of this finding, it must be expressly pointed out that in making dose calculations for epithermal neutrons, the energy absorbed by a medium must be taken to include not only the ionization due to recoil protons arising from neutron collisions, and that due to the radiations emitted in nuclear reactions produced by the capture of thermalized neutrons, as has hitherto been usual, but also the energy transferred in elastic nuclear collisions. The latter must be allowed for in a manner appropriate to the biological effectiveness of this primary process.

# 11. Appendix: On the significance of the "impact parameter" in target theory analysis

## 11.1. TARGET THEORY ANALYSIS OF OUR OWN RESULTS

In agreement with the assumption (cf. LEA [1946]) that one ionization is necessary for the inactivation of a macromolecule, FANO [1938], ZIMMER [1943a, 1943b] and TIMOFÉEF-RESSOVSKY and ZIMMER [1947] have used the equation

$$S = S_0(i - e^{-it})$$

to describe the variation of the inactivation cross section $S$ as a function of the ion density of ionization produced by the incident particles. $S_0$ is the geometrical cross section of the irradiated molecule, $i$ the mean number of primary ionizations per centimetre and $t$ the mean thickness of the irradiated molecule. The above equation shows how the inactivation cross section $S$ approaches the geometrical cross section of the irradiated molecule as the ion density of the radiation used is increased; for whenever a particle of very high ion density traverses a molecule, so many ionizations are produced within it that the irradiated molecule is inactivated. If one defines a 'hit' as simply the passage of a densely ionizing particle through the molecule, one avoids the difficult question as to the effectiveness of the different primary processes which occur in the absorption of radiation [cf. ZIMMER, 1961]. However, the magnitude of the inactivation cross section $S$ also depends on a variety of additional factors, which have to be taken into consideration in target theory analysis of experimental data. Physical factors such as temperature and state of aggregation or intra- and intermolecular energy transfer may also be important, and also environmental factors such as the gaseous atmosphere in which the irradiation takes place, or added substances which may confer protection against or sensitization to radiation. If the irradiation is carried out with the substance in solution, the 'direct effect' of the radiation may be enhanced by the action of the reactive species formed in the solvent. In experiments with fast charged particles it is not only the structures actually traversed by a particle which are damaged; in addition, the $\delta$-rays liberated by the incident ion along its path may produce further effects. Consequently, the molecular cross sections and molecular weights worked out by means of target theory are occasionally greater than the dimensions of the irradiated macromolecule.

The influence of the various factors mentioned above on the inactivation curve can be largely eliminated by conducting the experiments *in vacuo* using dry samples free from impurities. Since delta rays cannot be prevented, however, methods have been devised for correcting the experimental data to allow for the delta rays [LEA, 1946; POLLARD and BARRETT, 1957; FLUKE, BRUSTAD and BIRGE, 1960]. Lea's method may overestimate the effect of $\delta$-rays by a factor of 2 [POLLARD, et al., 1955]; moreover there are some doubts about the validity of the assumptions made in this method [BRUSTAD, 1961]. In this situation the use of slow particles with high ion density should be a good way of avoiding these difficulties, for then no delta ray correction is needed. For example, the mean energy of the secondary electrons released by 10 keV protons lies in the region of 10 eV, while their maximum energy amounts to about 20 eV. Even at the highest proton energies used in our experiments, only a small proportion of secondary electrons with energies over 100 eV are released, which could be classified as delta rays according to LEA [1946]. For this reason it is to be expected that the inactivation cross section determined by irradiating ribonuclease with slow protons can be used without further correction or modification for target theory calculations.

In this analysis we take as basis the known dimensions of the RNase molecule and the most reliable of the available data on the ionizing probability of slow protons [NEUFELD and SNYDER, 1961] and attempt to calculate the expected variation of the inactivation cross section $S$ in order to compare the result with the experimental values. First of all the geometrical cross section of the RNase molecule ($S_0$) must be determined. Studies by HARKER [1960] on the crystal structure of ribonuclease seem to suggest that the molecule is an ellipsoid of dimensions $3 \times 3 \times 3.8$ nm³. This gives a volume of 17.9 nm³. If one determines the average cross section (mean value of all projections of such a molecule) according to CAUCHY [1832, 1841] then one arrives at a surface area of 8 nm² for the geometrical cross section of the RNase molecule. According to HARRINGTON and SCHELLMAN [1956] the RNase molecule seems to be approximately spherical in shape; measurement of the hydrodynamic parameter [SCHERAGA, 1961] in dilute solution showed that the ratio of the axes of the molecule scarcely differs from 1. From the molecular weight of 13 683 [HIRS, MOORE and STEIN, 1956, 1960] and the density of protein, 1.3 g/cm³, the volume of a RNase molecule can be estimated to be 17.5 nm³. For a spherical molecule this gives a geometrical cross section of 8.2 nm². Both estimates lead therefore to concordant results.

In order to determine the mean number of primary ionizations produced by a particle in traversing a RNase molecule, the mean thickness of the RNase molecule ($t$) and the mean energy expenditure per ion cluster must be known. The former value, calculated for a spherical RNase molecule, is 2.2 nm, while the latter figure is not so easily determined. In the older literature a figure of 115 [POLLARD and FORRO, 1951], or 110 eV [POLLARD et al., 1955] is given for the mean energy expenditure per primary ionization. This value was obtained from cloud chamber data with various gases and it was assumed that it would also be valid for biological material. SOMMERMEYER and PHILIPP [1959] claimed that this figure was probably 30 to 40% too high. In 1962 direct measurement of the energy loss of fast electrons in plastic and metal foils of varying thicknesses gave a mean energy per primary event of 60 eV [RAUTH and HUTCHINSON, 1962]. Making use of a recently published paper by ORE and LARSEN [1964] on the frequency distribution of the number of ion pairs contained in a cluster, and assuming a $W$-value of 33 eV (energy expenditure per ion pair), one arrives at a mean energy per ion cluster of 54 eV. This value seems to confirm the results of the measurements by Rauth and Hutchinson. Taking a value of 60 eV per primary ionization, the expected variation of the inactivation cross section as a function of the proton energy has been calculated, and in fig. 21 this is compared with the values

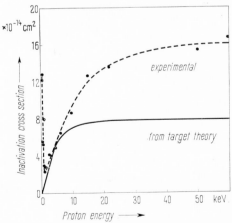

Fig. 21. Comparison of experimental results and values determined from target theory.

determined experimentally. The calculated curve shows marked differences from the experimental curve both in its shape and in the magnitude of the absolute cross section. Particularly notable is the fact that the inactivation cross section of 16.65 nm$^2$ obtained when using protons of 60 keV energy is more than twice as large as the geometrical cross section of the RNase molecule. It is also surprising that even in the low energy region, in which the mechanism of nuclear collisions predominates, the inactivation cross sections derived from the experiments are larger than the molecular dimensions.

There are numerous examples which show that "target molecular weights" derived from target theory analysis are appreciably larger than the values determined by the methods of colloid chemistry, although, according to Pollard and his co-workers [POLLARD et al., 1955; HUTCHINSON,1960, 1961, 1963; HUTCHINSON and POLLARD, 1961b] there is approximate agreement in the molecular weights derived by the two methods for a large number of macromolecules, whose weights range over several orders of magnitude. Nevertheless, the discrepancies under discussion are so great that they cannot be explained as merely experimental errors. From the experimental data it appears that the discrepancies (after correcting for delta rays) become greater, the higher the probability of ionization by the radiation used in the experiment. Very careful experiments on the inactivation of dry RNase by means of $^{60}$Co $\gamma$-radiation [GÜNTHER, 1965] showed a 37 % dose of 43 Mrad. Assuming an energy expenditure of 60 eV per primary ionization we arrive at a molecular weight of 13 450, in excellent agreement with the well-known value of 13 000 [ROTHEN, 1940] or 13 700 [HIRS, MOORE and STEIN, 1956, 1960]. This finding is confirmed by HUNT, TILL and WILLIAMS [1962] who found a $D_{37}$ of 48 Mrad for RNase irradiated with cobalt gamma irradiation, and this corresponds to a molecular weight of 12 000. The experiments of DEERING [1956] on RNase using deuterons and alpha particles, which are quoted in reviews [HUTCHINSON and POLLARD, 1961b; DESSAUER and SOMMERMEYER, 1964] as proof of the relevance of target theory in the determination of molecular weights, gave a molecular weight of 27 000 which is greater than the known weight of RNase by a factor of 2. By using even heavier ions one would expect, according to target theory, that with increasing linear energy transfer the experimentally determined inactivation cross sections would approach a limit (the molecular cross section). Very extensive and careful experiments by BRUSTAD [1960, 1961, 1962] on lysozyme, trypsin and deoxyribonuclease with energetic nuclei of hydrogen, carbon, oxygen and neon showed, nevertheless, that as the LET of the radiation increases, the size of the inactivation cross section also steadily increases right up to the maximum LET values used. When neon nuclei are used for irradiation the experimental cross sections are about 15 times as large as the known molecular cross sections. In order to bring this experimental data into agreement with the molecular dimensions through a simple 'one-hit' analysis, it would, for example, be necessary to assume that, in the case of the highest LET values used, 93 % of the damage observed is due to delta-rays. The use of heavy ions does not, therefore, seem to be an appropriate experimental method for testing critically the applicability of target theory.

In order to explain the large inactivation cross section which occurs at high LET values, BRUSTAD [1961] assumes that an enzyme molecule hit by a heavy ion does not "retain" the total energy transferred, but that part of this energy is passed on by a process of 'energy transfer' to neighbouring molecules which thereby become inactivated. DESSAUER and SOMMERMEYER [1964] believe that when particles of high LET are used, more than 90 % of the observed effects are due to delta rays, while NORMAN and SPIEGLER [1962] suggest that with high LET values enzyme molecules close to the path of the particles may be inactivated by thermal effects. There is no possibility of explaining the discrepancies between our estimated curve (fig. 21) and the experimental values by either of the above two hypotheses. At the proton energies we used, there is really no question of delta rays; besides the probability of the protons producing ionization is so small that in traversing a RNase molecule it is very rare for the proton to leave more than one primary ionization behind. This excludes the possibility that part of the observed inactivation is due to heating. Moreover, the amounts of energy transferred per molecule are so small that in our view the inactivation of several molecules by means of 'energy transfer' was extremely unlikely in our experiments. The experimentally determined inactivation cross sections seem to be influenced by other factors which are not sufficiently taken into consideration in "classical" target theory. We will now study these more closely in the following section.

## 11.2. SIGNIFICANCE OF THE IMPACT PARAMETER

It seems probable that target theory is based on a somewhat too mechanistic view of the primary processes operating in radiation absorption. The premise that a charged particle can produce an effect only in a biological structure which it directly traverses is based on the admittedly attractive, but physically not quite accurate picture, than an ionization is a more or less direct knocking out of an electron from a molecule. This mechanistic viewpoint does not correspond with physical reality. From what we know today (and have known for some time) about the physical events in the production of excitations and ionizations, it is well established that a charged particle can produce ionizations at surprisingly great distances from its path. It seems, therefore, useful to summarize briefly the separate processes occurring at an ionization and to investigate their significance for target theory.

When a fast charged particle traverses matter it exerts a force on the separate electrically-charged parts of the molecules lying close to its path. This force increases as the particle approaches the molecule and decreases as it moves away. The electrical field acts for only a brief interval and is, therefore, called an "impulsive" field. The collisions of the primary particle may be divided into two classes according to the energy distribution of the secondary electrons released through the operation of such an impulsive field; these classes are "knock-on" and "glancing" collisions.

"Knock-on" collisions occur when the velocity of the colliding particle is many times higher than the velocity of the atomic electrons and when it passes sufficiently close to an electron. The interaction period is so brief that the slow atomic electrons have no chance to "follow" the changing electric field; they may, therefore, be considered to remain at rest during the collision. "Knock-on" collisions may be studied theoretically with great accuracy on the basis of classical electrodynamics. As long as the energy transferred during the collision is large in comparison with the energy binding the electrons to their atom or molecule, the effect of these binding forces can be neglected. The electrons are ejected in accordance with Rutherford's law of scattering, i.e. the energy distribution of these "secondary electrons" decreases as $1/E^2$. The probability of "knock-on" collisions depends only on the electron density and not on the chemical composition of the irradiated material.

Besides this kind of interaction there are other very important collisions, the so called "glancing" collisions. In this case it is not necessary for the colliding particle to approach close to the electron; for the particle can exert electrostatic forces on the atomic electron even when it passes at some distance away. The distance of closest approach is called the "impact parameter". The magnitude of the impact parameter (or "radius of action") may amount to 100 nm for such "glancing" collisions [FANO, 1954]. It is characteristic of this process that the energy transferred is comparable with the binding energy of the electrons and that the incident particle is only slightly diverted from its path. The effect of such "glancing" collisions shows great similarities with that of electromagnetic radiation; for in both cases a rapidly changing force is acting on the atom (or molecule) and this force is uniform over the whole atom at any given instant. This kind of collision can no longer be described in terms of simple mechanics of electrostatic forces. The movement of the atomic electrons, during these relatively slow and weak collisions, must be taken into account. Moreover it is not only the incident particle and the atom it strikes which have to be considered. Because of its charge, the incident particle may polarize the surrounding region, and the resulting change in charge distribution can affect the forces acting on the atomic electrons. Consequently the rate of energy loss depends not only on the electron density but also (though only slightly) on the chemical composition of the irradiated materials. "Glancing collisions" are, in typical cases, about 8 to 10 times more frequent than "knock-on" collisions [FANO, 1952], since in the latter case the colliding particle must pass in immediate proximity to the ejected electron, and this occurs more rarely.

It seems possible that the description of "glancing" collisions will have to be modified in the near future. As PLATZMAN [1962a, 1962b] has shown on a basis of theoretical considerations, it seems probable that in this type of collision the interaction does not take place directly between the colliding particle and a single atomic electron, resulting in the latter being ejected from the atomic bond; but rather, that the energy is transferred in the first place to the molecule as a whole, which is thus raised to a "super-excited state". Such states can then lead either to the dissociation of the molecule or to an ordinary ionization. There is some experimental evidence indicating the existence of such super-excited states. If a fixed amount of energy is delivered by two quite different processes, on the one hand by collisions of the second kind with excited noble gas atoms (Penning-Effect) and on the other hand by absorption of a light quantum of corresponding energy, and if the ionization yield in both experiments is then compared, surprisingly good agreement between the two values is found [PLATZMAN, 1960, 1962a]. It has also been shown experimentally that molecules containing different isotopes such as $C_2H_4$ and $C_2D_4$ have different ionization probabilities [JESSE and PLATZMAN, 1962]. Both findings seem to suggest that a large part of the ionizations are not produced by direct interaction between the colliding particle and a single atomic electron, but that they arise from super-excited states of the molecule and occur in competition with dissociation. The super-excited molecular states may be included in the description of "glancing" collisions merely by modifying the latter to include transfer of energy to the whole molecule instead of to a single electron. However, this does not affect the statement that "glancing" collisions can produce ionizations at relatively great distances from the track.

The distance over which ionization can be produced by "glancing" collisions depends essentially on the charge and velocity of the incident particle. The maximum impact parameter, which is generally known as the "adiabatic limit", increases as the charge of the primary particle increases and as its velocity decreases (so long as the velocity does not fall below a certain threshold). In this way a qualitative explanation is possible for the fact that the inactivation cross sections determined with $\gamma$-rays (cf section 11.1) agree better with the molecular weights determined by colloid chemistry than do the values obtained by heavy ion irradiation, and that the discrepancies between "target theory" molecular weights and the molecular dimensions become greater for the heavier (i.e. slower) incident particles and for those with multiple charges. The cross sections determined in our experiments with slow protons (cf fig. 21) may easily be brought into agreement with the known cross section of the RNase molecule by introducing an impact parameter of 1 to 2 nm into the target theory analysis. Even the molecular weights obtained with heavy ions can be interpreted by using an impact parameter of less than 5 nm. Ionizations may, however, be produced at much greater distances in "glancing" collisions, as has already been shown.

Beyond the "adiabatic limit" the force acting on an atom increases and decreases so slowly that the atomic electrons have time to follow the changing field. In this case one speaks of "adiabatic" collisions; for the reversibility implies that no energy is transferred in these collisions. The electric field at the position of a particular atom can then be considered to be a slowly-approaching perturbation, if the velocity of the passing particle is extremely small. A fast particle which passes the atom at a considerable distance (beyond the adiabatic limit) has the same effect. Since 1962 it has been known that ionizations can be produced even beyond the adiabatic limit [NEUFELD, 1962] through the mechanism of "distant ionizations". In this process the approaching ion lowers the Coulomb barrier of the orbital electrons in the atoms (or molecules) of the irradiated material. Electrons may thus escape leaving the atom behind in an ionized state. These "distant ionizations" represent a further possible mechanism by which a charged particle traversing material can produce ionizations at a surprisingly great distance from its path.

It is not the purpose of this section to make any definitive statement on the quantitative effect which the impact parameter may have on the molecular weights and cross sections determined in radiation experiments. We only wish to point out that charged particles can produce ionization at considerable distances from their path and that the influence of the impact parameter in target theory analysis needs to be carefully studied. It seems, however, that further experiments with slow ions will enable us to obtain the data needed for assessing the importance of the impact parameter quantitatively.

# References

AHNSTRÖM, G. and EHRENBERG, L. 1961. In: Selected Topics in Radiation Dosimetry. (Internat. Atomic Energy Agency. Vienna) p. 603.

AHNSTRÖM, G., EHRENBERG, L. and ZIMMER, K. G. 1960. Report to Statens råd för atomforskning. (Stockholm).

BOAG, J. W. 1963. Am. J. Roentgenology **90** 896.

BOAG, J. W., DOLPHIN, G. W. and ROTBLAT, J. 1958. Rad. Res. **9** 589.

BOHR, N. 1940. Phys. Rev. **58** 654.

BOHR, N. 1941. Phys. Rev. **59** 271.

BOHR, N. 1948. Mat. Fys. Medd. Dan. Vid. Selsk. **18** No. 8.

BOPP, C. D. and SISMAN, O. 1955. Nucleonics **13** No. 7, 28.

BROSTRØM, K. J., BØGGILD, J. K. and LAURITSEN, T. 1940. Phys. Rev. **58** 651.

BRUSTAD, T. 1960. Rad. Res. Suppl. **2** 65.

BRUSTAD, T. 1961. Rad. Res. **15** 139.

BRUSTAD, T. 1962. Adv. Biol. Med. Phys. **8** 161.

CAUCHY, A. 1832. Mémoire sur la rectification des courbes et la quadrature de surfaces courbes (Paris).

CAUCHY, A. 1841. Hebd. Séances Acad. Sci. **13** 1060.

CORSON, D. R. and THORNTON, R. L. 1939. Phys. Rev. **55** 509.

CRENSHAW, C. M. 1942. Phys. Rev. **62** 54.

DAY, M. J. and STEIN, G. 1951. Nature **168** 644.

DEERING, R. A. 1956. Rad. Res. **5** 238.

DEERING, R. A. 1960. Archiv Mat. Nat. (Oslo) **55** No. 6.

DESSAUER, F. and SOMMERMEYER, K. 1964. Quantenbiologie (Springer-Verlag, Berlin).

DIENES, G. J. and VINEYARD, G. H. 1957. Radiation Effects in Solids (Interscience, New York).

EVANS, R. D. 1949. In: Science and Engineering of Nuclear Power, Vol. II (Addison-Wesley Press, Reading, Mass.) p. 252.

FANO, U. 1938. Unpublished manuscript.

FANO, U. 1952. In: Symposium on Radiobiology. Ed. Nickson, J. J. (John Wiley and Sons, New York) p. 13.

FANO, U. 1954. In: Radiation Biology, Vol. I, 1. Ed. Hollaender, A. (McGraw-Hill, New York) p. 1.

FANO, U. 1963. Ann. Rev. Nucl. Science **13** 1.

FLUKE, D. J., BRUSTAD, T. and BIRGE, A. 1960. Rad. Res. **13** 788.

FOWLER, J. F. 1964. In: Biological Effects of Neutron and Proton Irradiations, Vol. II (Internat. Atomic Energy Agency, Vienna) p. 185.

FRANCK, J. and PLATZMAN, R. L. 1954. In: Radiation Biology, Vol. I, 1. Ed. Hollaender, A. (McGraw-Hill. New York) p. 191.

FRIGERIO, N. A. 1962. Phys. Med. Biol. **6** 541.

GÜNTHER, W. 1965. Private communication.

HALL, T. 1950. Phys. Rev. **79** 504.

HARKER, D. 1960. Brookhaven Symposia in Biol. **13** 86.

HARRINGTON, W. F. and SCHELLMAN, J. A. 1956. Compt. rend. Lab. Carlsberg, Sér. chim. **30** 21.

HART, E. J. and PLATZMAN, R. L. 1961. In: Mechanisms in Radiobiology, Vol. I. Eds. ERRERA, M. and FORSSBERG, A. (Academic Press, New York) p. 93.

HIRS, C. H. W., MOORE, S. and STEIN, W. H. 1956. J. Biol. Chem. **219** 623.

HIRS, C. H. W., MOORE, S. and STEIN, W. H. 1960. J. Biol. Chem. **235** 633.

HUNT, J. W., TILL, J. E. and WILLIAMS, J. F. 1962. Rad. Res. **17** 703.

HUTCHINSON, F. 1954. Rad. Res. **1** 43.

HUTCHINSON, F. 1960. Rad. Res. Suppl. **2** 49.

HUTCHINSON, F. 1961. Science **134** 533.

HUTCHINSON, F. 1963. Ann. Rev. Nucl. Sci. **13** 535.

HUTCHINSON, F. and POLLARD, E. 1961a. In: Mechanisms in Radiobiology, Vol. I. Eds. Errera, M. and Forssberg, A. (Academic Press, New York) p. 1.

HUTCHINSON, F. and POLLARD, E. 1961b. In: Mechanisms in Radiobiology, Vol. I. Eds. Errera, M. and Forssberg, A. (Academic Press, New York) p. 71.

JESSE, W. P. and PLATZMAN, R. L. 1962. Nature **195** 790.

JOLIOT, F. 1939. Comptes rendus **208** 647.

JORDAN, P. 1948. Das Bild der modernen Physik (Stromverlag, Hamburg).

JUNG, H. 1964a. In: Biological Effects of Neutron and Proton Irradiations, Vol. I (Internat. Atomic Energy Agency, Vienna) p. 43.

JUNG, H. 1964b. Thesis. University of Heidelberg.
JUNG, H. 1965a. Z. Naturforschg. **20b** 764.
JUNG, H. 1965b. Makromolekulare Chem. In press.
KALNITZKY, G., HUMMEL, J. P., RESNICK, H., CARTER, J. R., BARNETT, L. B. and DIERKS, C. 1959. Annals N.Y. Acad. Sci. **81** 542.
KEENE, J. P. 1949. Phil. Mag. **40** 369.
KELLER, R. 1949. Helv. Phys. Acta **22** 78.
KINCHIN, G. H. and PEASE, R. S. 1955. Repts. Progr. Phys. **18** 1.
KNIPP, J. and TELLER, E. 1941. Phys. Rev. **59** 661.
KÜHN, H. 1960a. Z. Naturforschg. **15b** 277.
KÜHN, H. 1960b. Z. Naturforschg. **15b** 626.
LEA, D. E. 1946. Actions of Radiations on Living Cells. 1st. ed. (University Press, Cambridge).
LINDHARD, J. and SCHARFF, M. 1961. Phys. Rev. **124** 128.
LINDHARD, J. NIELSEN, V., SCHARFF, M. and THOMSEN, P. V. 1963. Mat. Fys. Medd. Dan. Vid. Selsk **33** No. 10.
LINDHARD, J., SCHARFF, M. and SCHIØTT, H. E. 1963. Mat. Fys. Medd. Dan. Vid. Selsk. **33** No. 14.
LITTLE, K. 1952. Nature **170** 1075.
LITTLE, K. 1954. Nature **173** 680.
McLAREN, A. D. 1949. Adv. in Enzymology **9** 76.
MORRISON, P. 1952. In: Symposium on Radiobiology. Ed. Nickson, J. J. (John Wiley and Sons, New York) p. 1.
NEUFELD, J. 1953. Proc. Phys. Soc. **66** 590.
NEUFELD, J. 1962. In: Second International Congress of Radiation Research. Abstracts of Papers (Harrogate, England) p. 127.
NEUFELD, J. and SNYDER, W. S. 1961. In: Selected Topics in Radiation Dosimetry (Internat. Atomic Energy Agency, Vienna) p. 35.
NIELSEN, K. O. 1956. In: Electromagnetically Enriched Isotopes and Mass Spectrometry (Academic Press, New York) p. 272.
NORTHCLIFFE, L. C. 1963. Ann. Rev. Nucl. Sci. **13** 67.
NORMAN, A. and SPIEGLER, P. 1962. Rad. Res. **16** 599.
ORE, A. and LARSEN, A. 1964. Rad. Res. **21** 331.
PERSON, S. 1956. Thesis. Yale University.
PERSON, S., HUTCHINSON, F. and MARVIN, D. 1963. Rad. Res. **18** 397.
PLATZMAN, R. L. 1952. In: Symposium on Radiobiology. Ed. Nickson, J. J. (John Wiley and Sons, New York) p. 97.
PLATZMAN, R. L. 1958. In: Radiation Biology and Medicine. Ed. Claus, W. D. (Addison-Wesley Press, Reading, Mass.) p. 15.
PLATZMAN, R. L. 1960. J. Physique et le Radium **21** 853.
PLATZMAN, R. L. 1962a. Vortex **23** 372.
PLATZMAN, R. L. 1962b. Rad. Res. **17** 419.
POLLARD, E. and BARRETT, N. 1959. Rad. Res. **11** 781.
POLLARD, E. C. and FORRO. F. 1951. Arch. Biochem. Biophys. **32** 256.
POLLARD, E. C., GUILD, W. R., HUTCHINSON, F. and SETLOW, R. B. 1955. Progr. in Biophys. and Biophys. Chem. **5** 72.
RAUTH, A. M. and HUTCHINSON, F. 1962. In: Biological Effects of Ionizing

Radiation at the Molecular Level (Internat. Atomic Energy Agency, Vienna) p. 25.

RIEHL, N. 1956. Atomkernenergie **1** 297.

RITZ, V. H. 1961. Rad. Res. **15** 460.

ROTHEN, A. 1940. J. Gen. Physiol. **24** 203.

SCHERAGA, H. A. 1961. Protein Structure (Academic Press, New York).

SCHERAGA, H. A. and RUPLEY, J. A. 1962. Adv. in Enzymology **24** 161.

SEITZ, F. 1949. Disc. Farad. Soc. **5** 271.

SETLOW, R. B. 1957. Adv. Biol. Med. Phys. **5** 37.

SETLOW, R. B. 1960. Rad. Res. Suppl. **2** 276.

SHAPIRA, R. 1959. Biochem. Biophys. Res. Comm. **1** 236.

SNYDER, W. S. 1957. In: Protection against Neutron Radiation up to 30 Million Electron Volts (Handbook 63, National Bureau of Standards, Washington).

SNYDER, W. S. and NEUFELD, J. 1957. Rad. Res. **6** 67.

SOMMERMEYER, K. and PHILIPP, K. 1959. Z. Naturforschg. **14b** 33.

TESZLER, O. and RUTHERFORD, H. A. 1956. Textile Res. J. **26** 796.

TIMOFÉEFF-RESSOVSKY, N. W. and ZIMMER, K. G. 1947. Biophysik I. Das Trefferprinzip in der Biologie (S. Hirzel, Leipzig).

TODD, A. 1954. Nature **174** 613.

ZIMMER, K. G. 1943a. Biol. Zbl. **63** 72.

ZIMMER, K. G. 1943b. Physikal. Z. **44** 233.

ZIMMER, K. G. 1956. Strahlenther. **101** 143.

ZIMMER, K. G., 1961. Studies on Quantitative Radiation Biology (Oliver and Boyd, Edinburgh and London).

# III

# ENERGY TRANSPORT IN CARBOHYDRATES

## GLYN O. PHILLIPS

*Department of Chemistry, University College, Cathays Park, Cardiff, Wales, U.K.*

# CONTENTS

# 1. Introduction

The term 'energy transfer' has been used to cover a multitude of observations associated with the chemical and biological effects of radiations and certain spectral phenomena. Three aspects of these interconnected fields will be distinguished so that the scope of the present review can be defined:

## 1.1. ENERGY UTILISATION IN BIOLOGICAL SYSTEMS OR BIOENERGETICS

Normal metabolic processes, such as, for example, oxidative phosphorylation involve electron and energy transfer steps, which in purely physical terms are ill-defined. The energy packets here are small ($\not< 10$ kcals) and thus cannot involve even the first electronic excitation levels of the participating molecules. Thus semiconduction and resonance transfer phenomena cannot play a significant rôle in these processes, and hence the present considerable interest in the possible participation of charge transfer complexes in biological processes. (See Symposium on Bioenergetics, Rad. Res. Suppl. 2, 1960.)

## 1.2. PROCESSES INITIATED BY ULTRAVIOLET AND VISIBLE LIGHT

In photosynthesis, biological oxidative processes and photobiology generally, certain molecules, even when present in least preponderance can act in a central rôle by first absorbing the light, and subsequently participating in energy transfer processes. Generally, as, for example, in the porphyrins, aromatic compounds play a vital part in the energetics of the living cell. For such compounds with well defined absorbing groups, and generally recognisable low lying excited states, the primary processes initiated by the light can be visualised [RABINOVITCH, 1964].

## 1.3. EFFECTS OF HIGH-ENERGY RADIATIONS OR RADIOBIOLOGY

Here the energy packets involved are considerably in excess of those utilised in normal biological processes. Little is known about the nature of the excited states produced, and there is little unequivocal evidence concerning energy transfer in radiobiological systems. When dealing with high energy radiations, the energy is absorbed approximately in the proportion to which the material is present. In radiobiology, therefore, the selectively absorbing compounds would not be expected to occupy the dominant rôle which they have in light induced biological processes.

Considerable attention has been given to the energy transfer properties of proteins [STRYER, 1960]. Low energy pathways (aspect 1) which are applicable to ordinary biological phenomena have been suggested which might involve charge-transfer complexes [HARBURY and FOLEY, 1958; ISENBERG and SZENT-GYORGI, 1958] or electron transport via oriented water molecules on the surface of the protein molecule [KLOTZ, 1958; BALAZS et al., 1959]. Using ultraviolet and visible light (aspect 2) energy transfer has been demonstrated in proteins by sensitized fluorescence [BANNISTER, 1954; SHORE and PARDEE, 1956], fluorescence quenching [WEBER and TEALE, 1959a], photodissociation of carbon monoxide and complexes with the haem proteins, and fluorescence depolarization [ORE, 1959; WEBER and TEALE 1959b]. Semiconductivity measurements indicate an energy gap of about 2–3 eV [ELEY et al 1953; ELEY and CARDEW 1959] and there is some theoretical support that such a band structure could be present as a result of $\pi$-electron delocalisation through the hydrogen-bond framework of a polypeptide chain. On balance, however, it would seem that resonance transfer more readily accounts for the observed energy transfer in proteins than a mechanism based on conduction-band transfer. Exciton theory has been applied to interpret the absorption spectra of helical proteins, and it is clear that irregularities and aperiodicity will determine to a great measure the exact forms of the exciton states produced by interaction with electromagnetic radiation [AVERY and MASON 1965; MASON, 1965]. However, there is little or no information about the nature of the excited states produced by high energy radiation (aspect 3), although some progress has been made recently in applying exciton theory to the radiation inactivation of enzymes [AUGENSTEIN et al., 1964].

The energy transfer characteristics of nucleic acids and other biological molecules have also been examined in some detail, and in common with the proteins least is known about the excited states and energy transfer processes following exposure to high energy radiation.

The available information is even less for carbohydrates for their energy transfer properties have not been examined according to any one of the three aspects outlined above, despite the extensive occurrence and important rôle which these compounds play in biological processes. The object of this review will be to summarise recent information obtained about the energy transfer properties of carbohydrates as indicated by the chemical effects of $\gamma$-irradiation on the solid state [PHILLIPS, 1965]. These compounds permit an unequivocal demonstration of electronic energy transfer and provide information about the nature of excited states formed by the ionizing radiations. First, however, to set the study into proper perspective, experimental demonstrations and possible mechanisms of electronic energy transfer will be considered. Here, the most reliable information has been obtained from photochemical studies (sections 3 and 4). Generally, it has proved difficult, if not impossible, to identify the excited states formed by ionising radiations. This situation has led to an indiscriminate postulation of their participation under the general, but seldom well-defined expression energy transfer. Before considering energy transfer evidence in carbohydrates, therefore, attention will be given to the areas where it seems that most reliable information about this phenomenon in high energy radiation processes is given (section 5).

## 2. Transfers of energy from high energy radiations

Energy transfer in its broadest sense embraces the complete sequence of processes following the interaction of radiation with the medium through which it passes. For ionizing radiation, energy is first transferred from the charged particle to the electronic system of the molecules of the medium, and for condensed systems it is probable that energy deposition first extends over a domain. Ionization and excitation will occur during this primary physical act. The collective excitation (ionization processes are included here in the word excitation) produced at this stage involves the electrons of a considerable volume of the medium, possibly 100 cu Å or more and lasts in its initial form for an extremely short period of time ($\sim 10^{-15}$ sec) [FANO, 1960]. There is subsequently localisation of the energy, by way of series of further energy transfer processes to the individual molecules undergoing chemical change.

Consider first the highly excited states initially produced. Little is known about their nature although photochemical and spectroscopic evidence provides some indication of their subsequent fate [DAINTON, 1965]. Excited states may also be formed by energy transfer from the first electrons (kinetic energy *ca.* 10 eV) formed during the primary act. These can lose their energy by the formation of relatively low-lying excited states of molecules in their path. Such excitations are not limited by the restrictions of optical transitions and may involve optically allowed transitions or produce triplet states by optically forbidden transitions. The excited states are in this way formed some distance from the track of the primary electron. In polar media, particularly, the electrons may be trapped in potential wells, when the polarized aggregate has well defined quantized energy levels. Such solvated electrons have now been detected in liquids and glasses by a variety of techniques. [CZAPSKI and SCHWARZ, 1962; COLLINSON et al., 1962; HART and BOAG, 1963; KEENE, 1963]. Alternatively, the electrons during their diffusion through the matrix may become attached to individual molecules [HAMMILL, 1963]. For example, with naphthalene, tetracyanoethylene or other appropriate solutes, characteristic anion spectra have been observed in irradiated glasses. An example of dissociative attachment is found with halogen containing molecules which react:

$$RX + e^- \rightarrow R \cdot + X^-.$$

Such processes are well known in mass spectrometry [HICKAM and BERG, 1958]. A further possibility is that the electrons may recombine with positive holes after encounter with some $10^3$ molecules, and so produce highly excited molecules by yet another energy transfer process.

In contrast to liquids and glasses, crystals of non-polar molecules, particularly where imperfections are absent, contain relatively few trapping sites for electrons. Thus, although electrons may possess considerable mobility in such media, the chemical changes will in large measure depend on the charge neutralisation processes, which lead either to free radicals or excited states. The nett effect here again is to form excited states at a considerable distance from the primary ionization. The subsequent migration of energy from the excited states, however they are formed, has a considerable bearing on the chemical effects of radiation, and has been shown to be considerably influenced by the state of aggregation in the condensed phase [COLLINSON et al., 1963a].

Following the primary act a range of processes can thus lead to molecular dissociation, *viz.* electron capture, charge neutralisation, excitation, and inter- and intra-molecular energy transfer. While it is not possible to draw strict lines of demarcation between these inter-dependent processes, our main concern here will be with the behaviour of excited molecules produced in condensed phases. This review will mainly consider examples of the reactivity of these excited states during encounter with molecules of the same or different chemical species.

First, however, it is necessary to consider the experimental evidence which demonstrates that intra- and inter-molecular transfer of electronic energy is possible. Although states of energy higher than the first excited levels are undoubtedly populated by the primary action of ionising radiations, it is unlikely that these play any significant rôle in the final inter- and intra-molecular energy transfer processes. As a result of the relatively high density of the higher excited states, much intersystem crossing can occur and internal conversion [KASHA, 1950] of the higher to the lowest excited states will be rapid ($10^{-13}-10^{-12}$ sec). Thus fluorescence yields are almost always independent of exciting wave-length. An exception is azulene which because of special symmetry properties fluoresces from the second excited level. Information about energy transfer processes derived from photochemistry can, therefore, be of value in radiation chemistry, despite the difference in the origin and selectivity of the excitation processes. Throughout this discussion energy transfer will not be used in connection with any process which involves the transfer of excitation by exchange of atoms or nett electrical charge.

## 3. Experimental evidence for electronic energy transfer
[BOWEN, 1965]

### 3.1. INTERMOLECULAR TRANSFER

The first observation of electronic energy transfer was made by CARIO and FRANCK [1923] in their classical experiments on sensitized fluorescence of atoms in the vapour phase. A mixture of mercury and thallium vapour, when irradiated with light of the mercury line at 253.7 nm, showed the emission spectra of thallium in addition to mercury. Since thallium atoms cannot absorb the light directly, excitation must occur indirectly by transfer from mercury atoms. Similarly, the mercury-sensitized fluorescence of sodium was possible, and here the transfer occurs over distances very much larger than those in normal collisional separations. Thus transfer of energy by collision with an electronically excited species could be excluded. The excitation energy of $(6^3P_0)Hg$ is within 0.03 eV of that of $(7^2S_{\frac{1}{2}})Na$, and the exchange

$$(6^3P_0)Hg + (3^2S_{\frac{1}{2}})Na \rightarrow (6^1S_0)Hg + (7^2S_{\frac{1}{2}})Na$$

should, therefore, occur efficiently.

In addition to the transfer of excitation between atoms described, it has been demonstrated that transfer of electronic energy from an atom to a diatomic molecule may occur also, as observed during the Xe-sensitized dissociation of $H_2$. The excitation energy corresponding to the first resonance line of $Xe(\lambda\ 147.0\ nm)$ is approximately 8.4 eV. There is a repulsive state of the $H_2$ molecule $(^3\Sigma_u^+)$ 8–10 eV above the ground state $(^1\Sigma_g^+)$ and the allowed transition:

$$Xe^* + (^1\Sigma_g^+)H_2 \rightarrow Xe + (^3\Sigma_u^+)H_2$$

can occur. Within the time of a single vibration, the $(^3\Sigma_u^+)H_2$ will break up into two ground-state hydrogen atoms with a very high kinetic energy.

Much of the information about energy transfer processes has been obtained from experiments on sensitized fluorescence. A good example is the sensitized fluorescence which can be observed with molecular crystals such as anthracene or naphthalene [BOWEN, 1938, 1944, 1945, 1947]. One-tenth of a per cent of naphthacene in anthracene is sufficient to quench the blue violet fluorescence of anthracene almost completely and replace it with a yellow-green fluorescence which is characteristic of naphthacene. Similarly crystals containing as little as $10^{-4}\%$ of tetracene fluoresce green, even when the exciting light is entirely absorbed by the anthracene, which when pure emits blue [BOWEN et al., 1949]. FÖRSTER [1949] made the first quantitative experimental study of sensitized fluorescence in a fluid solution when he measured the quenching of the fluorescence of tryptaflavin by rhodamine B. By these experiments, Förster was able to demonstrate that non-radiative transfer of excitation can occur over distances as great as 7 nm.

The possibility that the transfer was due to 'trivial process', whereby the fluorescence of the donor is absorbed by the acceptor, followed by further fluorescence was eliminated by BOWEN, BROCKLEHURST and LIVINGSTON [1953, 1954, 1955] using the system 1-chloroanthracene and perylene dissolved in benzene. The chloroanthracene was excited by 365 nm. Since chloroanthracene has a very low fluorescence yield, if it had to emit and the fluorescence re-absorbed by the perylene (a highly fluorescent material), the total yield could not exceed that of chloroanthracene. In fact, it proved much larger, showing that efficient resonance transfer from anthracene to perylene occurred in a time shorter than the internal degradation of energy within the anthracene molecule (singlet → triplet).

It has also been observed that the fluorescence emitted by polyatomic molecules in viscous solution is partially polarized. This behaviour, referred to as concentration depolarisation, is the result of the transfer of excitation energy between differently oriented molecules [PERRIN, 1925].

## 3.2. INTRAMOLECULAR ENERGY TRANSFER

An example of intra-molecular energy transfer was found by WEBER and TEALE [1958] using 1-dimethyl aminonaphthalene 5-(N benzyl) sulphonamide (I) and

and 1-dimethyl aminonaphthalene 5-(N phenyl) sulphonamide (II). Both substances have two independent systems of conjugated double bonds. Absorption in the ultraviolet (benzene band) leads to fluorescence similar in character to that of 1-dimethylamino 5-sulphonamide, which consists of a single symmetric, unresolved band with a maximum in ethanol solution, at 530 nm for I and 540 nm for II. Neither substance was found to emit fluorescence between 250 and 370 nm where the benzene nucleus would be expected to emit fluorescence. The resonance transfer of electronic energy between the two non-conjugated systems must complete with the radiative as well as radiationless transitions from the benzene ring. In II it was seen that the radiationless deactivation of the benzene ring competes favourably with the transfer to the naphthalene ring, while in I the opposite seems to be the case.

Transfer of excitation energy in crystals takes place over considerably greater distances than those found for sensitized fluorescence in solution. SIMPSON [1956] observed the transfer of excitation across a thin crystalline anthracene specimen, and observed a diffusion length of 46.0 nm, which in an isotopic medium would correspond to a root-mean-square displacement of 112.0 nm between the point of origin and decay of the excitation.

## 3.3. ENERGY TRANSFER IN BIOLOGICAL SYSTEMS

Resonance energy transfer can also be demonstrated in the biological field, as for example in the pigments present in photosynthetising plants [RABINOVITCH, 1957]. The experimental evidence for energy transfer in such systems is of two general types, and examples only of each type will be given here. There is first the photochemical type experiment, as for example, the investigation of BUCHLER and KASPERS [1947] on the photochemical decomposition of carbon monoxide-myoglobin. It was found that the decomposition occurs with the same high quantum yield, whether the active light is absorbed in the porphyrin component or in one of the aromatic amino acids of the protein. The reaction occurs in the porphyrin component, indicating that there must be efficient energy transfer from the aromatic amino acids to the porphyrin. Other chromoproteins have been studied in a similar manner by Lautsch and co-workers [LAUTSCH et al., 1957; LAUTSCH and BROSER, 1958]. It is typical of all such investigations that only electronic excitation energy is given to the molecules, and is less than the ionization energies of the molecules and the band dissociation energies. It is unlikely, therefore, that charged species or radicals are the mobile entities in the energy transfer processes.

The second type of observation associated with energy transfer in biological systems comes from fluorescence experiments. The chromoprotein phytocyanin, contrary to carbon monoxide-myoglobin, does not dissociate photochemically but does fluoresce [BANNISTER, 1954]. Such fluorescence can be observed either when the light is absorbed by the amino acids or by the chromophoric group responsible for the fluorescence. Again the quantum yield of fluorescence is similar under direct and indirect excitation. Thus electronic energy is transferred from the oscillator originally excited to the haem. It should be noted that the fluorescence emission from the amino acids is well covered by the absorption band of the haem and the average distance among random points in the protein molecule is of the order at which transfer may be expected to occur (1–3 nm). [TEALE and WEBER, 1957]. Electronic energy transfer to the haem can also be studied in the fluorescent naphthylamido conjugates of the haem proteins [WEBER, 1952]. Experiments on photosynthetic systems yield similar results when fluorescence of chlorophyll is sensitized by absorption in the accompanying pigments [DUTTON et al., 1943; LINSCHITZ, 1960; LIVINGSTON, 1960]. Flash methods have indicated here that triplet states take part in the transfer processes.

## 3.4. TRIPLET STATE PARTICIPATION

TERENIN and ERMOLAEV [1956] first observed that energy transfer can occur via triplet states as well as through singlet states. Experiments based on the observation of long-lived phosphorescence were carried out with frozen binary solutions of organic compounds, for here transfer could not occur over ca. 5 nm as for singlet transfer, and indeed the molecules need to be in contact. A good example is the system benzophenone and napthalene dissolved together in a low-temperature glass. When a solution of naphthalene (A) in ethanol at −195°C is excited by 366 nm radiation, no luminescence is observed since the absorption spectrum of naphthalene lies at 327 nm. However, when benzophenone (D) is added to the solution a bright phosphorescent emission of the triplet spectrum of naphthalene in

the visible appears. After first producing excited singlet benzophenone
molecules (D*) these do not fluoresce in the glass at −195°C but
rapidly convert to the triplet level (D$^T$) from which they can phos-
phoresce (reaction 1). When naphthalene is present, triplet energy
is transferred and only the naphthalene phosphoresces (reaction 2).

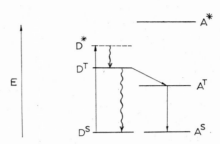

Fig. 1. Electronic levels of energy donor and acceptor during sensitized phosphorescence in benzophenone and naphthalene glasses.

The sequence of events shown on the energy diagram in fig. 1 may
thus be represented:

$$h\nu_D+D \rightarrow D^* \underset{\searrow D^T}{\overset{\nearrow D}{\phantom{x}}} \nearrow \underset{+A \rightarrow D+A^T}{\overset{D+h\nu_D^1(1)}{\phantom{x}}} \underset{\searrow A+h\nu_A(2)}{\overset{\nearrow A}{\phantom{x}}}$$

The rates for the triplet-triplet transfer process were estimated
(table 1).

Triplet-triplet transfers have also been demonstrated in organic
crystals over distances of *ca.* 1 nm [AVAKIAN and MERRIFIELD,

TABLE 1

Triplet-triplet energy transfer in organic glasses at −195°C.

| System | $k_t\,(\text{sec}^{-1})$ |
|---|---|
| benzophenone*+naphthalene | $1.6 \times 10^2$ |
| benzophenone*+α-methyl naphthalene | $1.65 \times 10^2$ |
| benzaldehyde*+naphthalene | $4.8 \times 10^2$ |
| carbazole*+naphthalene | $3.8 \times 10^{-1}$ |
| diphenylamine*+naphthalene | $5.4 \times 10^{-1}$ |

* initial light acceptor

1964; HOCHSTRASSER 1964] using host crystals containing guest molecules has demonstrated that in these crystals triplet energy migration is more efficient than singlet energy migration. The advent of triplet states heralded many diverse and complex mechanisms of energy transfer. An example is the investigation of HAMMOND, STOUT and LAMOLA [1964] on the photodimerisation of coumarin. In non-polar solvents such as benzene, dimerization does not occur during interaction of excited state coumarin with ground state coumarin; only self-quenching occurs. In polar solvents such as ethanol, interaction of the excited singlet with ground state coumarin leads to self-quenching, but a small amount of *cis*-head-to-head dimer (III) is formed.

In the presence of triplet sentitizers, however, such as benzophenone, the *trans*-head to head dimer (IV) is formed in both polar and non-polar solvents. The sequence of energy transfer process postulated is as follows. First, light is absorbed by the coumarin and the singlet coumarin transfers its energy to singlet benzophenone, where intersystem crossing takes place and the triplet formed. The triplet excitation is then transferred back from benzophenone to the coumarin. Interaction of excited triplet coumarin with ground state coumarin is then able to produce the dimer with relatively high quantum yield.

$$C \xrightarrow{h\nu} C^{*1}$$
$$C^{*1} + B \rightarrow C + B^{*1}$$
$$B^{*1} \rightarrow B^{*3}$$
$$B^{*3} + C \rightarrow B + C^{*3}$$
$$C^{*3} + C \rightarrow IV + IV$$

Attention has been directed recently to processes of the type [PARKER and HATCHARD, 1963; CUNDALL and GRIFFITHS, 1963a]:

triplet A+singlet B → singlet A+triplet B

which occurs readily if $E_{A^T} > E_{B^T}$. In such processes, the total spin momentum of the whole system has to be preserved [WIGNER, 1927]. In the absence of degradation possibilities, triplet energy migration can re-populate the singlet level. Thus even singlet energy migration may in certain circumstances be dependent on triplet energy migration.

Observation on the normal and delayed fluorescence of pyrene in ethanol have been interpreted on this basis [PARKER and HATCHARD, 1963]. Both series of spectra show bands due to singlet excited monomer and excited dimer. The sequence of reactions giving rise to singlet excited monomer and excited dimer as observed by *normal* fluorescence are as follows

$$S \xrightarrow{h\nu} S^* \xrightarrow{+S} S_2^{**}$$

When the light is shut off both excited states decay rapidly to much lower concentrations which are maintained by triplet-triplet quenching.

$$T+T \rightarrow S_2^* \rightarrow S^*+S$$

Thus in normal fluorescence it is the excited monomer which is first formed, while in delayed fluorescence it is the excited dimer which is first formed.

## 4. Mechanisms of energy transfer*

The experiments which have been described demonstrate conclusively that transfer of excitation energy intermolecularly and intramolecularly can occur over considerable distances. The fluorescence which indicated intermolecular transfer, we have seen, cannot be explained purely on the basis of a radiative mechanism, where the emission of one quantum

* [VAVILOV, 1943; FÖRSTER, 1946, 1948, 1959, 1960; DEXTER, 1953; SIMPSON and PETERSON, 1957; FOX and SCHNAPP, 1955; McCLURE, 1959; WOLF, 1959; KASHA, 1963; DAVYDOV, 1962; FRENKEL, 1931, 1936; CUNDALL, 1964; WANNIER, 1937].

of fluorescence from the initially absorbing molecule was reabsorbed by the acceptor which then produces the secondary fluorescence (the so-called 'trivial process'). Intramolecular transfer also occurs between separate $\pi$-electron systems not connected by conjugated systems. The groups containing $\sigma$-electrons which link up the two active centres would effectively act as insulators for transfer of $\pi$-electron excitation and so exclude the possibility of transfer mechanisms based on electron transfer or electron exchange.

To explain the non-radiative transfer of excitation energy theories have been developed along two independent approaches, although it is now becoming clear that there is considerable overlap between the concepts as defined. There are first the excitation transfer mechanisms which have been concerned mainly with fluorescence effects. Basic to these mechanisms is the concept of resonance transfer or transfer by inductive resonance. The second group of mechanisms have been applied particularly to excitation transfer in molecular aggregates, or in molecular crystals and the band splitting effects which have been observed in such systems. The theoretical problem of the energy levels of molecular crystals was studied by DAVYDOV [1962], and the theory is an application to molecular crystals of FRENKEL'S exciton theory [1931, 1936].

## 4.1. RESONANCE TRANSFER

The principles of excitation transfer by resonance were interpreted by classical physics first by PERRIN [1925]. The approximation used is that the electronic system of a molecule be represented by one single electron, bound to the assembly by a quasielastic force such that it might vibrate with frequency $\nu_0$. If this electronic oscillator is excited, its vibration will be damped by the emission of electromagnetic radiation. However, the oscillator of one molecule will interact with oscillators of other ones, the interaction energy decreasing like that of two dipoles, proportional to the inverse third power of the distance between them ($R$). If a second dipole is not too far away from the first excited one, and if the frequencies of both electronic oscillators are nearly the same, the energy will be transferred to the second molecule before it can be emitted as radiation. From this simple model, for conditions of exact resonance, the critical distance is $\lambda_0/2\pi$ where $\lambda_0$ is the wave length of the oscillator. Transfer distances of $\sim 100$ nm are thus possible. The same conclusion can also be arrived at using a quantum mechanical approach.

Three cases must be distinguished according to the amount of coupling between the two molecules, which will be dependent on molecular vibrations and relaxations. These may be illustrated by reference to a simplified model of a molecule with an electronic ground state, and only one excited state on which are superimposed the vibrational levels with single frequency $\nu_s = 1/2\pi T$, where $T$ the vibrational time constant is $\sim 10^{-14}$ sec. The molecule may be excited to a higher vibrational level, but by the process of thermal relaxation (time constant $T^1 \sim 10^{-12}$ sec) it will drop to lower vibrational levels, where it will remain until it becomes deactivated at the end of its lifetime $\tau$. Transfer may be (a) rapid and occurring during the time interval $T$, (b) less rapid during relaxation time $T^1$ or (c) slow and occurring during the remainder of the lifetime $\tau$. Only in case (a) will it be possible to recognise a change in absorption and fluorescence spectra for the aggregate compared with the single molecule. Since the rapid transfer is faster than molecular vibration, the spectra would be modified and the excitation cannot be considered to be associated with a single molecule, but distributed over the aggregate. Here one is clearly dealing with excitons as these have been defined. Nevertheless, during a classification of excitation processes FÖRSTER [1946, 1948, 1959, 1960] sub-divides resonance transfer into types, a, b and c, which are described as strong, medium and weak interaction. KASHA [1963], on the other hand, makes a distinction between the vibrational relaxation resonance transfer (type c, slow) and the remainder, and in company with other workers extends the term, exciton, to energy transfer effects in weakly bound crystals such as anthracene, where the vapour and crystal spectra resemble each other quite closely. It has been suggested that this is perhaps an unwarranted extension of the term exciton [BOWEN, 1965]. However, the distinction may eventually resolve itself into one of the semantics, despite Kasha's categorical view that the Förster mechanism differs fundamentally from the exciton model mechanisms.

In any event, the most practical distinction between the individual cases is based on the strength of the intermolecular electronic interaction between excited states relative to the strength of intramolecular vibrational-electronic coupling. If $\varDelta\varepsilon$ is the Franck-Condon energy which results from the difference between nuclear equilibrium configurations of ground and excited states, and $\Delta\varepsilon^1$ the width of a single vibrational level, then the three different cases are

(a) interaction energy $\gg \Delta\varepsilon \gg \Delta\varepsilon^1$      strong
(b) $\Delta\varepsilon \gg$ interaction energy $\gg \Delta\varepsilon^1$      medium
(c) $\Delta\varepsilon \gg \Delta\varepsilon^1 \gg$ interaction energy      weak

Case (a) on each of the methods of approach is concerned with production of exciton states, according to the development of the Davydov theory. Case (b) was included by SIMPSON and PETERSON [1957] in the exciton model. KASHA [1963] further extends the exciton model to include case (c) also although on practical grounds it would be impossible to distinguish this from the Förster Slow Transfer Mechanism with which a considerable overlap in transfer rates might be anticipated.

## 4.2. FÖRSTER SLOW TRANSFER MECHANISM

Here the interaction energy is less than vibrational band width and only small regions of corresponding bands are in resonance. With the broad spectra of polyatomic molecules, there is always sufficient coincidence between the transitions in two unlike molecules if the absorption spectrum of one overlaps the fluorescence spectrum of the other. Interaction is strongest if both corresponding transitions are allowed and as for dipole-dipole interactions, the interaction energy ($u$) can be expressed as follows:

$$u = \frac{k|m|^2}{n^2 R^3}$$

where $m$ is the transition moment between ground and excited state, $k$ is a factor dependent on the mutual orientation of both molecules, and $n$ the refractive index of the surrounding medium. Since the transfer rate is proportional to $u^2$ it falls off as $1/R^6$. FÖRSTER [1946, 1948, 1959] has developed PERRIN'S [1925] simple theory to allow for imperfect resonance between molecules and derived the following expression for critical transfer distance ($R_0$)

$$R_0 = \frac{\lambda}{2\pi n} \sqrt[6]{\frac{3\eta^2}{8\tau\Delta\nu}}$$

where $n$ = refractive index of medium

$\eta$ = the fluorescence quantum yield

$1/\Delta\nu$ represents the overlap integral of the absorption and fluorescence spectra.

If thermal equilibrium of the excited state has occurred then the transfer frequency is given by

$$\frac{9000 \, \ln_{10} k^2}{128\pi^6 n^4 N \tau_s R^6} \int_0^\infty f_s(\nu) \varepsilon_A(\nu) \frac{d\nu}{\nu^4}$$

where $\nu$ is the wave number, $\varepsilon_A(\nu)$ the molar decadic extinction of the acceptor, $f_s(\nu)$ the spectral distribution of the fluorescence of the sensitizer, $N$ Avogadro's number, $n$ refractive index of the solvent, $R$ the distance between sensitizer and acceptor molecules, $\tau_s$ the intrinsic or radiative lifetime of the sensitizer, and $k$ the orientation factor.

The resonance theory of Förster, which involves only allowed transitions was extended by DEXTER [1953] to include transfer also by means of forbidden transitions. The transfer mechanisms of importance, in order of decreasing strength are (i) the overlapping of the electrical dipole fields of the sensitizer and activator; (ii) the overlapping of electrical dipole fields of the quadrupole field of the activator and (iii) exchange effects. Dexter concluded that these were in the ratio of $10^{3-4}$, $10^2$ and 30 for singlet states.

In addition to spin conservation a further condition for energy exchange is $M_s^* = M_A^*$ and $M_A = M_s$, where $M_s^*$ and $M_A^*$ are the multiplicity of the sensitizer and acceptor in their excited states and $M_s$ and $M_A$ the multiplicity in the ground states. The probability of energy exchange between two molecules under these specified conditions is

$$\frac{4\pi^2}{h} Z^2 \int f_s(\varepsilon) F_A(\varepsilon) d\varepsilon$$

where the integral is the overlap integral between the emission spectrum of the sensitizer and absorption spectrum of the acceptor. $Z^2$ is a complex parameter with the dimensions of energy. The probability of energy exchange decreases rapidly with distance: an increase of about a molecular diameter leads to a hundred-fold decrease in probability. However, since it will be demonstrated that in the carbohydrates triplet energy transfer does not occur, the detailed characteristics of this mechanism will not be considered here. A full account of the role of triplet energy transfer in radiation processes has been given by CUNDALL and GRIFFITHS [1964, 1965].

## 4.3. EXCITON MECHANISMS

The exciton model has been defined as the treatment of the resonance interaction between excited states of weakly coupled aggregate systems. Here transfer of excitation energy occurs through the static coupling of molecules. Following the interaction of electromagnetic radiation with a molecular crystal, the excitation energy belongs to the system as a whole or a large domain of it rather than a stationary state where the excitation is localised on one molecule.

Excitation of a non-metallic crystal in its fundamental absorption band often does not promote conduction, since in such crystals the lowest excited states are not those in which charge carriers are freed [SIMPSON, 1956]. Non-conducting excited states (or exciton states) can arise in strongly bound or covalent crystals, where the constituents have lost their individuality. Here allowed excited electronic states of identical molecules in the aggregate interact. The electron may be removed from one atom, but remains bound within the field of the residual positive hole. As noted previously the term exciton has also been extended to cover weakly bound solids such as anthracene. Here the exciton bands correspond closely to the lowest excited states of the individual molecules which compose the aggregate in the free state, and where no spectral shifts occur.

FRENKEL [1931] in his original contribution to the subject demonstrated that each eigen function is characterised by a wave-number vector **K** and that the energy values split into bands. The wave function represents a region of excitation being propagated through the crystal with wave vector **K**. The mobile excitation represents the exciton, and in the weakly bound solid the exciton is simply an excited molecule which immediately hands on its energy to its neighbour. Transfer rates will depend on the strength of intermolecular coupling.

WANNIER [1937] extended this idea for the strongly-bound solids where in this case the exciton may be regarded as a hole and electron pair, bound in their mutual Coulomb field travelling through the crystal. Thus collective excitation of the individual units of the aggregate occurs in the strongly bound solids, and the transfer rate is faster than the rate of displacement of molecules from their equilibrium position. Spectral changes are thus apparent, in the aggregate. The Wannier exciton is particularly suitable also for discussions of migration of energy in atomic or ionic crystals. The Frenkel exciton is more suitable for the more weakly bound molecular crystals.

The exciton model has been particularly successful in discussions of the change in absorption properties of weakly-coupled units in intensity and/or position compared with those of the monomer. The ground state wave function of the dimer is the product of the wave functions $\psi_1$ and $\psi_2$ for the two monomers

$$\Psi_G = \psi_1\psi_2 \tag{1}$$

For identical monomers, the two wave functions are equally correct in describing the excited state of the dimer

$$\Phi_1 = \psi_1^*\psi_2 \quad and \quad \Phi_2 = \psi_1\psi_2^* \tag{2}$$

according to whether the excitation is considered to be located on molecule 1 or 2. The correct wave functions for describing the excited state is a linear combination of eq. (2)

$$\Psi_1 = \frac{1}{\sqrt{2}} (\Phi_1 + \Phi_2) = \frac{1}{\sqrt{2}} (\psi_1\psi_2^* + \psi_1^*\psi_2)$$

and

$$\Psi_2 = \frac{1}{\sqrt{2}} (\Phi_1 - \Phi_2) = \frac{1}{\sqrt{2}} (\psi_1\psi_2^* - \psi_1^*\psi_2)$$

$\Psi_1$ and $\Psi_2$ are the stationary exciton waves of the system and express the physical situation that the excitation is located on both molecules.

In the simplest case of two molecules held together by weak interactions, the exciton model can profitably be compared with the formation of a hydrogen molecule from two hydrogen atoms. The individual electrons (1s) of each individual atom go into a bonding molecular orbital where the electrons are paired. The antibonding molecular orbital, into which the electrons may be excited is unfilled. The individual electrons are no longer associated with a particular atom and thus electron exchange is possible in the hydrogen molecule. A similar situation can be envisaged for the exciton, but the electrons in the weakly-bonded dimer remain localised at the individual molecules. Only the excitation is delocalised. Thus the ground state is not split into separate energy levels, whereas following excitation delocalisation the excited state is split. The energy separation of the exciton states, or exciton band width is given by

$$\Delta E = \frac{2M_1^2}{R^3}$$

where $M_1$ is the transition moment integral for the absorption in the monomer and $R$ is the intermolecular separation. Selection rules do not allow two electronic transitions from the ground state to both excited states, and which of the transitions is allowed will depend on the type of stacking in the dimer. For parallel stacking there is a blue-shift in the absorption spectrum and for hydrogen bonded head-to-tail packing there is a red-shift in the absorption spectrum relative to the monomer. A clear description of molecular exciton theory has recently been given by MASON [1965], which avoids the mathematical treatment essential for the detailed theory.

The life of an exciton may be terminated either (1) it may decay radiatively with emission of fluorescence, (2) it may undergo non-radiative transition by interaction with a lattice imperfection or by capture at an impurity centre. In the latter instance, if the impurity can itself luminesce, the exciton capture may lead to the emission of fluorescence, characteristic of the impurity, or (3) it may be localised on a molecule to produce chemical change.

KASHA [1963] has summarised the characteristics of the individual energy transfer mechanisms which have been considered (table 2).

TABLE 2

A comparison of energy transfer mechanisms

| Mechanism | Type of interaction | Dependence on $R$ | Transfer rate | Spectral effects |
|---|---|---|---|---|
| Förster* | Very weak | $1/R^6$ | $10^6 - 10^{11}$ | None |
| Exciton | Strong | $1/R^3$ | $10^{12} - 10^{15}$ | Splitting, band shifts |
| Exciton | Weak | $1/R^3$ | $10^{12}$ | None |

* particularly applicable to dissimilar molecules.

## 5.  Excitation energy transfer in radiation chemistry

Despite numerous indications that energy transfer effects are important in radiation chemistry, it has proved difficult to demonstrate these effects unequivocally and to identify the excited states produced by ionizing radiations. MATHESON [1962] in an excellent review has covered this field and here some examples only will be given. The non-linear dependence of product yields upon the electron-fraction in two-component systems has frequently been explained on the basis of energy transfer. Protective effects of this nature will, therefore, be considered first. In all considerations of energy transfer in mixtures, it has been assumed that energy is absorbed in proportion to the electron fraction. LAMBORN and SWALLOW [1961], however, queried this basic assumption and suggested that the protective effect of benzene can be completely accounted for if the cross section for $\pi$-electron excitation in benzene is ten times the cross section for $\sigma$-electron excitation in either compound, and if the polymer yields of the two compounds are independent in the mixture. SWALLOW [1963b, 1965] has recently pointed out that there are two errors in the original calculation. First, the mechanism of polymer formation does not involve simple joining of organic free radicals. Secondly, the cross sections assumed cannot be correct. Nevertheless, these considerations are important if they serve only to point out the complex problems associated with calculating how energy from ionizing radiations is distributed in a mixture.

### 5.1. PROTECTIVE EFFECTS

Cyclohexane-benzene mixtures are the classical example of protection. SCHOEPFLE and FELLOWS [1931] first observed that mixtures of cyclohexane and benzene on cathode ray bombardment, behave more like benzene than a simple mixture of the two as far as gas production is concerned. The hydrogen yield is always less than expected for independent decomposition of the two components [MANION and BURTON, 1952; BURTON and PATRICK, 1954; HARDWICK, 1962; BURTON et al., 1957].

It is well established that benzene is particularly resistant to decomposition by ultraviolet light and $\gamma$-radiation [WEST, 1953; WILSON and NOYES, 1941]. Furthermore, alkyl substituted benzenes are also resistant to radiation damage although the yields are somewhat higher than benzene. Such radiation resistance is conveniently interpreted by postulating energy transfer from the alkyl group to the aromatic nucleus, and there is evidence that when introduced into polymers, aromatic groups confer radiation stability to the molecule [ALEXANDER and CHARLESBY, 1960; GARDNER and EPSTEIN, 1961]. For example, benzene nuclei substituted into polymer chains, as in polystyrene decrease $G$ (cross-links). When a naphthyl group is substituted into dodecane, it protects during radiolysis, and its effectiveness is at a maximum when the group is substituted in the middle of the chain and presumably in this way reducing the energy transfer distance. Rough estimates indicate that the extent of protection extends about 4 or 5 carbon atoms along a main chain. However, CHARLESBY [1960], has expressed doubts whether energy transfer is the true explanation for the observed effects.

Nevertheless, by analogy energy transfer from excited cyclohexane molecules to benzene would offer a reasonable interpretation for benzene-cyclohexane mixtures on $\gamma$-irradiation. The results, however, may be also explained on the basis of radical scavenging [FREEMAN, 1960], and it is now realised that the problem is most complex [GÄUMANN, 1960]. Iodine, for example, will produce a reduction in gas yield in cyclohexane, and while superficially this might indicate radical scavenging, the iodine could also quench excited states of cyclohexane. The most comprehensive review of the possible mechanisms which may account for this type of protection following the addition of an additive in low concentration is by BURTON and LIPSKY [1957]. A summary of their considerations will be given here.

### 5.1.1. *An energy transfer of sponge type mechanism*

If the additive has excited or ionized states lying energetically lower than those of the solvent, energy transfer can occur by resonance energy transfer or charge transfer. Thus an additive of higher radiation stability would then exhibit protective action. A difficulty, however, exists in reconciling the time-scale of such process with the known phenomena. Sensitized luminescence [BURTON et al., 1955; KALL-

MAN and FURST, 1950, 1951, 1952] observed for cyclohexane-scintillator solutions is a relatively slow process, and even for a strongly allowed transition, is rarely less than $10^{-9}$ sec and more generally of the order of $10^{-8}$ sec or more. Energy transfer, can therefore, occur before emission, but is energy transfer possible before dissociation of the cyclohexane? If the initial excitation is to a repulsive state, fast rupture may occur in $\sim 10^{-14}$ sec. For excitation transfer to compete effectively with such a rapid process, it is necessary to have strong coupling between donor and acceptor molecules. There is, however, no spectral evidence of such an interaction. The alternative is to consider excitation to occur initially to an attractive state below its dissociation limit and decomposition slowed down to $\sim 10^{-13}$ sec by the necessary internal conversion to a repulsive state. The necessary condition for resonance energy transfer, namely overlap of the electric fields of the variable electronic oscillators would not appear to be fulfilled either. However, it has been suggested that for condensed systems, the more likely possibility is a series of resonant ionization transfers [GURNEE and MAGEE, 1957] from the solvent molecule to solvent molecule until the charge can be trapped by the additive.

### 5.1.2. *A quenching mechanism*

If the additive cannot trap the electronic excitation, it may alternatively promote distribution of the initially localized energy among vibrational-rotational degrees of freedom of neighbouring solvent molecules. This mechanism is visualized as being akin to types of fluorescence and phosphorescence-quenching phenomena. Here again there is little quantitative information as to whether the necessary interaction between quencher and excited molecule can compete effectively with the relatively rapid rupture process. Careful quantitative studies of high-energy induced luminescence processes [BERRY et al., 1956; KROPP and BURTON, 1962] indicate that certain efficient quenchers, such as $O_2$, $CH_3I$ and aromatic halides, may depopulate excited states of scintillation solvents at rates perhaps 100 times greater than the rates of radiative emission ($10^{-8}-10^{-9}$ sec). Although the ensuing times are still short of fast dissociative rupture, it is possible that quenchers can interfere with the normal course of radiolysis.

It has also been suggested that the action of a quencher is to induce, non-radiatively, spin-prohibited transitions [BOWEN, 1953]. The lifetime of the excited state by conversion to a triplet state would thus be extended and the molecule would then be more available for competing non-radiative processes. Substance to this suggestion in high energy radiation processes comes from the observation of BAKH and SOROKIN [1955] that the hydrogen yield during the radiolysis of ethanol is doubled when the alcohol is saturated with oxygen, a molecule which quenches the triplet state.

### 5.1.3. Negative-ion-formation mechanisms [MAGEE and BURTON, 1951; MAGEE, 1952; WILLIAMS and HAMMILL, 1954; SCHULER, 1957].

It is suggested that the excited state produced by the charge neutralization process

$$M^+ + e \to M_+^*$$

is in general higher than that produced by neutralization involving a negative ion

$$M^+ + N^- \to M^* + N$$

The excitation energies are related by the expression

$$E(M_+^*) - E(M^*) \geqq A(N^-)$$

where $A(N^-)$ is the electron affinity of N.

The negative ion $N^-$ is formed when an added molecule captures an electron before it can recombine with a positive hole. Thus if $E(M^*)$ is sufficiently low, the chemistry can be considerably modified.

### 5.1.4. Ionization transfer and ion-molecule reactions

If the additive B can capture the ionization before neutralization

$$M^+ + B \to M + B^+$$

the resultant chemical reaction can be reduced.

In view of the complex variety of possible mechanisms, it is clear that physical measurements on the behaviour of organic scintillators can provide more significant information about energy transfer in these liquid systems than chemical observations. The events in scintillation processes have been described by BIRKS [1960] and BURTON and DREESKAMP [1959] have related luminescence decay times to energy transfer in radiation chemistry. Chemical effects, however, are not necessarily related to luminescence observations. BURTON and PATRICK [1954] showed that p-terphenyl and anthracene, although efficient scintillators do not protect benzene. BURTON [1960] has suggested that the state transferring energy to the terphenyl is not the one involved in the radiolytic decomposition. To explain the extremely rapid energy migration in benzene, the concept of domains or ordered regions was advanced [NOSWORTHY et al., 1961]. There is some physical evidence [BELL and DAVEY, 1941; HISATSURE and JAYADE-VAPPA, 1960; MUNSTER 1950; COUMON and MACKOR, 1964] for the existence of such domains, through which it is envisaged that energy can freely migrate by an exciton mechanism. Recent estimates indicate that about 2–3 ground-state benzene molecules are included in such domains; the decay time of excited isolated benzene in cyclohexane has been reported to be $33 \times 10^{-9}$ sec [BURTON, 1965; DILLON and BURTON, 1965].

Recently there has been more positive evidence advanced in support of intramolecular energy transfer along polymer chains. GARDNER and EPSTEIN [1961] suggested that after high energy irradiation of polymethyl methacrylate, excited states could migrate over relatively large distances ($\sim 5$ nm) and that about one excited state in thirty leads to a main chain scission. Positive ion transfer, on the other hand, occurred over very much shorter distances, and about one ion in four produced a main chain scission. By the introduction of various kinds of energy sinks, such as benzene and p-terphenyl, the energy could be intercepted during its migration, and quenched before a chain break occurred. More recently GARDNER et al. [1965] have reported that such energy transfer is sensitive to the stereochemical form and degree of crystallinity of the polymethyl methacrylate. GUSYNIN and TAL'ROZE [1960] demonstrated that the quenching cross section for alcohols is proportional to the number of carbon atoms in the alcohol, which suggests that the energy can be readily transferred along the—$CH_2$—chain to the OH group. AGRONOVICH [1960] considers that the transfer of energy along a polymer chain by an exciton mechanism would be important if triplet levels are involved.

## 5.2. CIS-TRANS ISOMERIZATION OF OLEFINS

Several mechanisms other than energy transfer processes have been shown to lead to the *cis-trans* isomerization of olefins. GOLUB [1957, 1958, 1959, 1960, 1962, 1964], for example, showed that the geometrical isomerization of polybutadiene and other macromolecules could occur by way of a free radical mechanism or by intramolecular energy transfer from excited benzene. It has been suggested also that positive ion or electron capture processes may lead to isomerization of liquid butene—2 when irradiated alone in the liquid state [KAUFMAN, 1963; HATANO et al., 1964; CUNDALL and GRIFFITHS, 1963; CHANG et al., 1959; COPPINGER, 1957; GREENE et al., 1961; PORTER, 1963]. In paraffinic solutions also there is evidence for the participation of positive ions.

In benzene solution, however, there is now definite evidence that an electronic energy transfer process is responsible for the isomerization. The triplet rather than the singlet state of the olefin is involved and there is no evidence for any significant contribution by an ionic mechanism. The lack of effect of free radical scavengers such as ferric chloride, iodine and galvinoxyl preclude any radical mechanism for the isomerization. A comparison of the $\gamma$-irradiated system with the corresponding photochemical system shows considerable similarities, and it would appear that the only common excited state which would cause the isomerization is the triplet $^3B_{1u}$. A mechanism which will account for the observations is

$$C_6H_6 \longrightarrow C_6H_6^* \tag{1}$$
$$C_6H_6^* + cis \text{ or } trans \text{ } C_4H_8-2 \rightarrow C_6H_6 + C_4H_8-2^* \quad \text{(2c) or (2t)}$$
$$C_4H_8-2^* \rightarrow cis \text{ or } trans \text{ } C_4H_8-2 \quad \text{(3c) or (3t)}$$
$$C_6H_6^* \rightarrow C_6H_6 \tag{4}$$
$$C_6H_6^* + M \rightarrow C_6H_6 + M \tag{5}$$

where M is an added species which acts as a competitive quencher. For the conversion of originally pure *cis* isomer to the *trans* form

$$\frac{1}{G(trans)} = \frac{k_{3c}+k_{3t}}{Ak_1k_2k_3}\left[k_{2c} + \frac{k_4}{cis\text{-}butene—2}\right]$$

where $A$ is a constant which measures the efficiency of excited state production in benzene. From plots of $G$ (isom)$^{-1}$ against [butene—2 isomer]$^{-1}$ the values of $k_4/k_{2c}$ or $k_4/k_{2t}$ can be determined. $k_{2t}/k_{2c}$ is 0.45 and $k_{3t}/k_{3c}$ has been found by another method to be 1.31. A similar kinetic treatment applied to the photochemical data showed that $k_4/k_{2c}$ is similar to, but slightly lower, than the radiation system ratio.

Thus, it is concluded that the olefin is excited by triplet-triplet interchange in both radiation and photochemical systems with the strong probability that the $^3B_{1u}$ triplet state is involved. The triplet state yield in $\gamma$ and electron irradiated benzene is the sum of

$$G_{cis \to trans} + G_{trans \to cis} = 2.40 + 1.83 = 4.23$$

where 2.40 and 1.83 are the limiting $G$-values. The absence of dose rate effects shows that the excited states are formed outside or escape from the tracks.

The detailed studies in this field provide one of the few systems where electronic energy transfer in radiation chemistry have been unequivocally demonstrated.

## 5.3. EFFECT OF UNSATURATION

During ESR studies [FESSENDEN and SCHULER, 1963a] of transient radicals present during the irradiation of liquid hydrocarbons, unexpectedly intense signals characteristic of vinyl radicals were observed from dilute solutions of ethylene in ethane. The yield of vinyl radicals from ethylene in a 10 mole % solution in ethane were found to be 8 times that observed in pure ethylene, indicating considerable intermolecular energy transfer from ethane to ethylene [FESSENDEN and SCHULER, 1963b]. GOLUB [1963] has pointed out that there are definite similarities between this system, benzene +butene and the behaviour of polybutadiene [1960], polyisoprene [DYNE and DEN HARTOG, 1963] and squalene. For example, polybutadiene and polyisoprene were found to isomerize in 1 % benzene solutions with yields, based on energy absorbed only in the solute which were 8–10 times respectively those of the pure polymers. Squalene and butene−2 gave even higher energy transfer factors of 30 and 15–55. Golub, therefore, concludes that there is highly efficient transfer of excitational and/or ionization energy from either an aliphatic or an aromatic structure to an olefinic group.

A similar situation pertains in the solid state, for it has been suggested that the very high yield for the isomerization of *cis*-polybutadiene in the solid state is due to the double bonds, apart from being excited directly, being also excited by intramolecular energy transfer from the methylenic groups in the polymer.

## 5.4. EFFECT OF PHASE CHANGE

Evidence of a long range energy transport mechanism which is more efficient in a crystalline rather than a glassy state was reported by COLLINSON, CONLEY and DAINTON [1963b]. $G(-S)$ values, where S is ferric chloride, iodine or diphenyl picryl hydrazyl were measured at temperatures in the range $-196°$ to $+30°C$ in various organic solvents. For the liquid or glassy solid phase, $G(-S)$ is largely independent of concentration of S. The crystalline solid solutions fall into two categories. Type-A systems behave similarly to the glasses whereas for type-B systems, comprising solutions of ferric chloride in benzene, diphenyl ether, diphenyl methane and phenetole and iodine in diphenyl ether, initial $G(-S)$ increases proportionally with increase in S concentration, the slope of this line being larger the lower the temperature. Thus values of $G(-S)_0$ for the solid phase may be much larger than $G(-S)$ for the liquid or glassy phases. In benzene at $-196°C$ this factor can be as large as 30; there is a sudden increase of $G(-S)_0$ on freezing.

Clearly, the most interesting group are crystalline systems of type-B. At high concentrations of S, $G(-S)_0$ may attain very large values. At $-196°C$, however, the solute molecules and most ionic and free radical intermediates are largely immobile. However, to account for the high $G(-S)$ values, the production of an intermediate 'entity' from the solvent is necessary which has considerable mobility to enable it to encounter the immobile solute molecules. This entity must have a finite probability of reaching and changing a solute molecule lying within a certain distance of its origin. Since the minimum concentration at which this effect becomes noticeable is $\sim 300$ mM, this probability must be very small at distances greater than about 10 nm.

When considering the nature of this mobile entity Collinson et al. argue that positive hole migration and electron migration are unlikely and that only energy transport can account for type-B phenomenon.

The vibration-relaxation Förster mechanism of energy transfer is excluded on the grounds that the process is favoured by the orderly crystalline structure, which does not appear to be a requirement of the Förster mechanism. The most suitable mechanism on which the results may be interpreted thus involves first, the production of exciton states of the solvent in high yield and that interaction of this state with the solutes ferric chloride and iodine causes chemical quenching of these states with dissociation of the solute. The crystalline condition is essential because any interruption of lattice periodicity would limit exciton transport. Interaction with lattice imperfections may also dissipate the exciton as heat. For the aromatic crystals, triplet energy transfer is not considered likely and for a variety of reasons the participating exciton state is identified as $^1B_{2u}$. There is, however, no spectroscopic evidence which ensures certainty in this identification. The mechanism may, therefore, be represented:

$$C_6H_6 \text{ cryst.} \longrightarrow (C_6H_6)_n^*$$
$$(C_6H_6)_n^* + FeCl_3 \rightarrow C_6H_6 \text{ cryst.} + FeCl_2 + Cl$$

where $(C_6H_6)_n^*$ denotes an exciton state embracing $n$ benzene molecules and most probably related to the $^1B_{2u}$ molecular state. More recent work [DAINTON et al., 1965] however, has queried this assignment, particularly since efficient triplet exciton migration has recently been demonstrated in benzene [NIEMANN and ROBINSON, 1963]. Such excitons may be propagated over distances of 5–10 nm, the actual distance being dependent on any imperfections in the benzene crystal or by impurities or thermal fluctuations which by interrupting the lattice periodicity limit the domain of the exciton.

These studies have been extended to solutions of ferric chloride in solid and liquid solutions in N, N-dimethyl aniline, phenetole and cumene at different solute concentrations and a number of temperatures [DAINTON et al., 1963]. The pattern is similar and exciton transfer appears to be responsible for the high initial $G$ values found in the crystalline solid solutions.

## 5.5. PULSE RADIOLYSIS EVIDENCE

The pulse radiolysis technique has enabled direct identification of the reactive species, including excited molecules which are formed some distance from the initial point of energy deposition. In hydrocarbon media, transient absorptions associated with solute molecules have been observed. Only triplet excited states have a sufficiently long life to be detected by this method [McCOLLUM and WILSON, 1961; NOSWORTHY and KEENE, 1964]. Such triplets can disappear by (a) first-order process as a result of quenching by impurities or free radicals, (b) bimolecular reaction to give delayed fluorescence:

$$A_T + A_T \rightarrow A_S + A_G$$

where A is anthracene in the triplet $(A_T)$, excited singlet $(A_S)$ and ground $(A_G)$ states, (c) energy transfer from one solute to another [DAINTON et al., 1964].

Energy transfer from phenanthrene to anthracene and naphthalene was observed by McCOLLUM and co-workers [1961, 1962] who were also able to estimate the relative yields of singlet and triplet state.

Clearly, the use of pulse radiolysis to study energy transfer processes is in its infancy. However, KEMP, SALMON, LAND and NOSWORTHY [1965] in an admirable review conclude that the rôle of excited states of aromatic solvent molecules as intermediates in the transfer of energy from the place of deposition to a solute molecule is well established, but the position as regards solvents which lack low-lying and relatively long-lived excited states remains unclear. In polar solvents, the yields of detectable excited states of solutes are relatively low with the notable exception of dioxane.

## 6. Energy transport in D-glucose crystals

### 6.1. MOLECULAR AGGREGATION EFFECTS

The physical state in which anhydrous $\alpha$-D-glucose is irradiated with ionizing radiation profoundly influences the extent of the radiation decomposition [PHILLIPS and BAUGH, 1963]. Table 3 shows the acid yields which were obtained from linear yield-dose curves for $\alpha$-D-glucose irradiated in three states of aggregation. $G$(acid) for polycrystalline anhydrous $\alpha$-D-glucose is 3–6 times greater than for the freeze-dried samples, depending on the method of freeze-drying, and more than double the yield for the syrup. Acid yields show no increase when the samples are irradiated in air, in vacuo or when an

TABLE 3

G-values for acid and gas formation during the irradiation of D-glucose.

| | Acid | | | Hydrogen | | | Carbon dioxide total |
| | In vacuo | Air | $CO_2$ | Total | Above solid | Retained by lattice | |
|---|---|---|---|---|---|---|---|
| Polycrystalline | 13.2 | 13.3 | 13.0 | 3.8 | 1.06 | 2.74 | |
| Freeze-dried | 3.7 | 3.7 | | 4.0 | 2.0 | 2.0 | — |
| Monohydrate | 5.2 | 5.0 | — | 4.1 | 1.23 | 2.87 | 0.6 |
| Syrup | 6.5 | — | ca.5 | 4.75 | 0.1 | 4.65 | 0.3 |

atmosphere of carbon dioxide is maintained above the sample. This latter observation, taken in conjunction with the low proportion of carbon dioxide in the gas released, indicates that radiation-induced gas phase carboxylation reactions to produce acid may be discounted [SCHOLES et al., 1960]. Although acid yields were measured after dissolution in water, infra red measurements on dry irradiated solid using potassium bromide discs suggest that acid groups are produced directly in the solid state. The lowest acid yields were found for freeze-dried samples, where the water had been quickly removed on to a liquid nitrogen finger, and the sample maintained completely frozen throughout the freeze-drying operation. Production of acid by gas phase carboxylation was considered because of the variable amounts of gas retained by the three states of aggregation. For the polycrystalline sample, 72 % of the gas is trapped within the crystal lattice and is only released after dissolution in water, while for the syrup, the gas is found mainly above the sample and less than 2 % is trapped. The freeze-dried state is intermediate and about 50 % is retained by the samples. It is highly improbable, therefore, that the extent to which the gas is retained by the solid is a factor determining gas production.

In contrast to acid yields, hydrogen and free radical production are not appreciably influenced by the state in which the solid is irradiated (table 3). No significant difference in initial free radical concentration was observed between the freeze-dried and polycrystalline state, and for all the cases studied, $G(H_2)$ is $\sim 4$; initial $G$(free radicals) is also $\sim 4$. It is reasonable to suppose, therefore, that different processes lead to free radical and hydrogen formation than to acid production. Full details of the chemical changes and nature of the free radicals produced have been given elsewhere [PHILLIPS, 1965]. Here we consider mainly the factors which are responsible for the different behaviour of α-D-glucose when irradiated in different states of molecular aggregation.

Our observation that $G$(acid) is highest for the polycrystalline state is reminiscent of the observations of COLLINSON, CONLAY and DAINTON [1963] on the type-B system, and may provide further evidence for the existence of a mechanism of energy transport which is facilitated by a highly ordered crystalline system. This mechanism requires long range propagation of excitation energy, and on examination, this hypothesis offers the most satisfactory explanation of the results for D-glucose. The subsequent discussion will be concerned with an examination of the rôle of energy transfer processes in the radiation chemistry of solid carbohydrates. Here the basic hypothesis will be outlined and its general applicability will be examined in the following sections. [PHILLIPS, in the press]

## 6.2. EXCITON STATES

Following the initial primary physical act, a collective excitation (which here includes ionization) can extend over possibly 100 cu Å but lasts for only a short period of time ($\sim 10^{-15}$ sec) [FANO, 1960]. As already described the subsequent localization of the energy to individual molecules undergoing chemical change involves a series of energy transfer processes. Little is known about the highly excited states initially produced. Further excited states, however, can arise at some distance from the track of the primary electron by charge neutralization processes and by transfer of energy from the primary electron to molecules lying in their path. Such excitations may involve optically allowed or forbidden transitions. For carbohydrates, there is little spectroscopic information about possible excited states, particularly in the condensed phase. For single molecules, it has been seen that repulsive states may arise during n $\rightarrow$ $\sigma^*$ excitations with light of wavelength *ca.* 240 nm [PHILLIPS, 1963; PHILLIPS and BARBER 1963]. In sugar crystals, it is suggested that non-conducting (or exciton) states can arise where the allowed excited electronic states of the identical molecules in the aggregate interact. This interaction is most probably associated with the extensive three-dimensional hydrogen bonded network in carbohydrate crystals. As previously noted (section 4) several mechanisms have been envisaged whereby such a delocalized exciton can move by resonance transfer through the aggregate. Chemical change will, in our view, be dependent on the efficiency of such energy transfer, which will be at a maximum in a perfect crystal. Dissipation of the excitation at an impurity site or by interaction with a lattice imperfection etc., could thus lead to less efficient localization on a single molecule and thus a reduction in the overall chemical change. However, before the process can be characterized, it will be necessary to elucidate the possible contributions of ionization transfer, free radicals, whether singlet or triplet states participate, and finally the nature of the transfer process.

The initial observations on changes in acid yields following variations in molecular aggregation, which have been described, can be rationalized on the basis of the hypothesis which has been outlined. Consider, for example, the reduced yield for the syrup. The change in crystal regularity and increased intermolecular distance (the syrup may contain up to 1 % water) would significantly modify the exciton spectrum of the aggregate, and would give rise to less efficient energy localization and thus a reduced chemical change.

6.3. LATTICE IMPERFECTIONS AND THE FREEZE-DRIED STATE

The low $G$(acid) for the freeze-dried state is not obviously explicable on the above considerations. X-ray powder photographs demonstrate that indistinguishable chemical and crystallographic forms are present in the polycrystalline and freeze dried anhydrous $\alpha$-D-glucose [PHILLIPS, 1965]. All the main lines on the powder photographs could be indexed on the basis of the established cell dimensions and the calculated d-spacings showed excellent agreement with those which were observed. Furthermore, the line intensities are also in reasonable agreement. This evidence, apart from establishing the identical chemical identity of the two states, demonstrates that no significant proportions of $\alpha$-D-glucose monohydrate is present as impurity, which might contribute to the reduced acid yield. Thus, two indistinguishable chemical and crystallographic forms of $\alpha$-D-glucose behave quite differently on irradiation.

The only additional variable which could easily be observed was the smaller size of crystal present in the freeze-dried sample. Examination of the influence of size, however, did not reveal an effect which would account for the appreciably lower yields after freeze-drying. For crystals which have been sieved to below 200 mesh, $G$(acid) does not decrease by more than 17 % and, furthermore, micromill treatment to reduce the crystal size to that of freeze-dried samples ($>$ 350 mesh) did not reduce the acid yield by more than 20 %.

Finally, therefore, an examination of the freeze-dried crystals by electron microscopy was undertaken as no such information was previously available. In this connection, it was significant that the ESR signal of the radical decreased at a faster rate for the $\gamma$-irradiated freeze dried than the polycrystalline form. This suggested that the molecular aggregation was not identical in the two forms. The results of the microscopic examination are shown in the accompanying photographs. No special features were observed on the plane surface of normal crystalline anhydrous α-D-glucose, but after freeze-drying, a distinctive spherulitic pattern appeared (plate 1). Using a replication technique, it can be demonstrated that the surface striations are due to steps and cracks. Plate 2 shows a positive carbon replica of the surface of the normal crystal and plate 3 a replica of the surface after freeze-drying. The imperfect surface is indicative of a highly dislocated crystal lattice. At higher magnification (plate 4), the deep steps and cracks become quite apparent. The cleavage surface of sucrose after aluminizing and storage shows a similar pattern [DUNNING, 1963]. Steps merging like tributaries to form a characteristic river pattern on the crystal surface [GILMAN, 1953, 1956] are indicative of a textured solid, where the imperfection and disorder in position reach such a degree that a space lattice is no longer a useful approximate representation. Such solids include those which form spherulitic structures. An interesting observation is that when initially examined the freeze-dried mass is amorphous and shows no birefringence. Crystallization can be initiated by a variety of stimuli, and thereafter proceeds quickly. Plate 5 shows crystallization at an early stage to produce the spherulite. The striations we have observed, therefore, most probably represent grain boundaries and sub-boundaries of individual crystallites, each disoriented with respect to its neighbour as occurs in a course spherulite. A series of dislocations would thus be arrayed at the fusion of each crystallite. Direct electron microscopic examination revealed individual crystallites (plates 6 and 7) and plate 8 shows the crystalline mass in various states of disaggregation. From the present evidence, there can be no doubt that the freeze-dried crystals show a considerably greater degree of imperfection than the polycrystalline material.

It is highly probable, therefore, that the greater imperfection in the freeze-dried state is the most likely explanation for the different behaviour on irradiation. The exciton model can thus be extended to our results on the freeze-dried solid, for the crystal defects present can act as efficient exciton traps. Indeed, it is probable that the cross section for the interaction of excited states with defects should be large and probably even larger than that caused by a substantial impurity [HOCHSTRASSER, 1963].

On the above considerations, the extent of decomposition of solid α-D-glucose would be expected to depend on the type of pre-treatment which the crystal has received, as in fact we have observed. The following variations were examined (a) after freeze-drying using a liquid air finger, the mass was finally dried in an oven at 80°C (b) the freeze-dried product which gave initially low $G$(acid)-values was heated at 150°C for 48 hr. (c) fast removal of the liquid nitrogen cold finger and ensuring that the frozen mass did not partially melt at any time during the freeze-drying operation (d) it was observed that if the freeze-dried mass melts during the final stages of the operation, crystallization takes place, and the product is different in appearance from the flocculent material normally produced. From linear yield-dose curves for acid production the $G$(acid)-values are as follows (a) 10.3 (b) 5.6 (c) 2.1 (d) 10.0. Thus, if sufficient time is allowed for normal crystallization high $G$(acid)-values are obtained. Annealing of the crystal at 150°C similarly results in an increase in $G$(acid), due presumably to a reduction in the extent of imperfection in the crystal. Under the most stringent freeze-drying conditions $G$(acid)-values as low as 2 have consistently been obtained. The reduction in acid yield following micromill treatment might also be the result of distortion and damage to the crystal lattice.

From a practical point of view, the reduction in acid yield following freeze-drying could find an application in the radiation sterilization of sugars, where minimal acid formation is desirable [HILLS and JOHNSON, 1961].

### 6.4. RADIATION STABILITY

One objection which might be raised to the above discussion is that the changes in $G$(acid) while indicating a mechanism of radiation

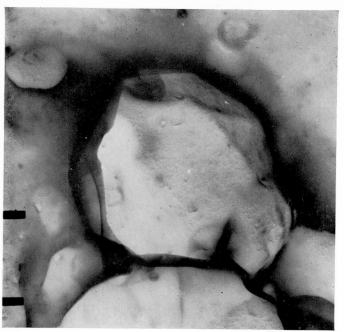

*Plate 2*

*Plate 1*

Plate 1. Direct microscopic examination of surface of freeze-dried α-D-glucose. (×**340**).

Plate 2. Positive carbon replica of surface of polycrystalline anhydrous α-D-glucose crystal (×**23 000**). (Marks indicate 1 micron).

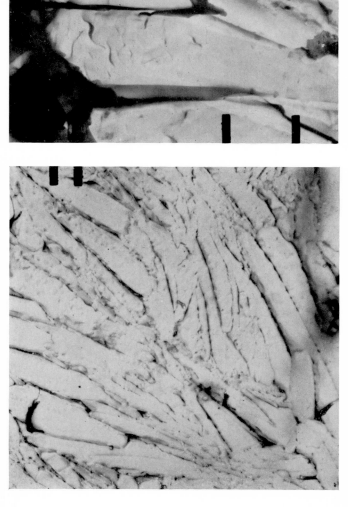

Plate 3. Positive carbon replica of anhydrous polycrystalline α-D-glucose after freeze-drying (×5000). (Marks indicate 1 micron).

Plate 4. Positive carbon replica of anhydrous polycrystalline α-D-glucose after freeze drying (×13 500). (Marks indicate 1 micron).

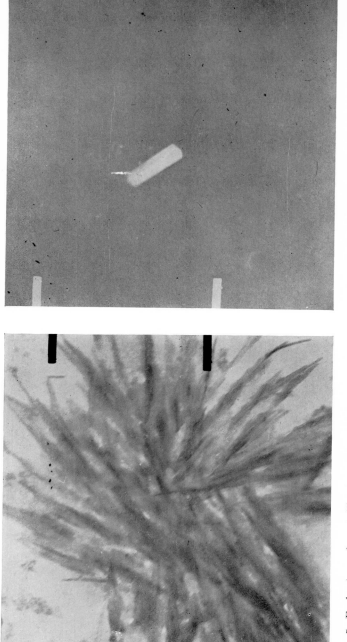

Plate 5. Early stage of crystallisation of freeze dried polycrystalline α-D-glucose. (Marks indicate 1 micron).

Plate 6. Individual crystallite of freeze-dried α-D-glucose.
(Marks indicate 1 micron).

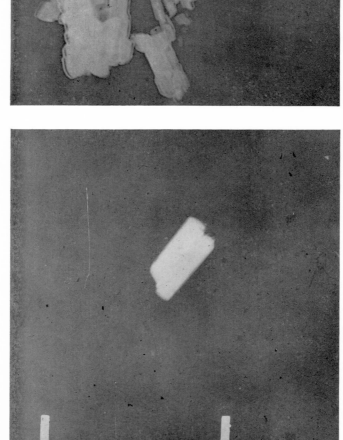

Plate 7. Twin crystal produced by freeze-drying α-D-glucose. (Marks indicate 1 micron).

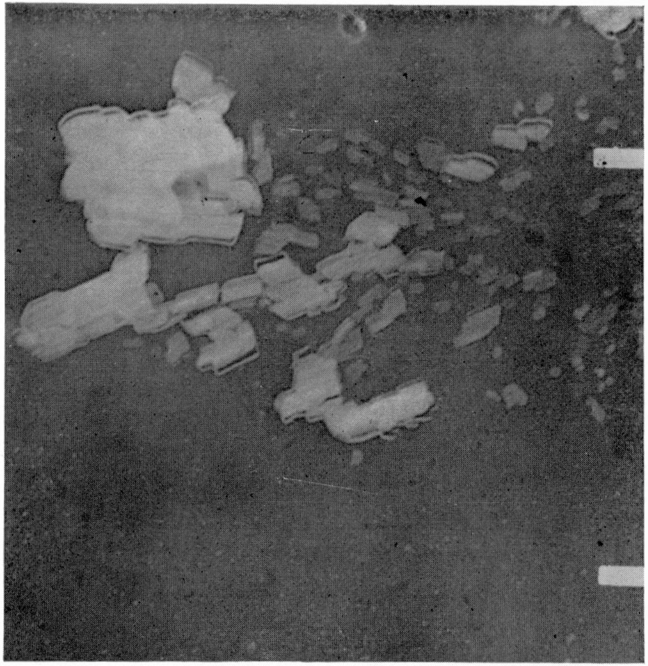

Plate 8. Freeze-dried α-D-glucose in various states of disaggregation (×50 000).

decomposition which is dependent on molecular aggregation, may not truly reflect a difference in the overall radiation stability of the forms investigated. It was for this reason that isotope dilution analysis was used to measure the overall decomposition of polycrystalline α-D-glucose, its monohydrate and its anomer β-D-glucose. The results confirm the conclusions based on acid yields. Polycrystalline anhydrous α-D-glucose is the most susceptible to radiation decomposition and after a dose of $3.7 \times 10^{20}$ eV $g^{-1} \cdot -G$ from the slope of the yield-dose curve is $\sim 20$, which is considerably higher than the acid yield at this dose ($G = 13.2$). Acid production is linear up to this dose and it is probable, therefore, that $-G = 20$ closely approximates the initial $-G$ value. As the dose is increased $-G$ for glucose decomposition decreases (fig. 2) until after a dose of $5.8 \times 10^{21}$ eV $g^{-1} -G$ is $\sim 9$.

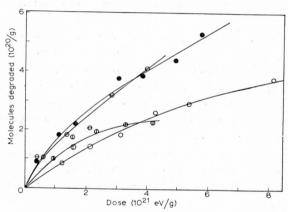

Fig. 2. Radiation degradation of D-glucose
● polycrystalline anhydrous α-D-glucose
⊖ polycrystalline anhydrous β-D-glucose
⊕ polycrystalline α-D-glucose monohydrate
○ freeze dried anhydrous D-glucose
Abscissa: Dose ($10^{21}$ eV/g)
Ordinate: Molecules degraded ($10^{20}$/g.)

This decrease in $-G$ as irradiation proceeds is characteristic of all forms of the hexoses which have been studied, and is probably related to the build-up of irradiation products in the crystal. The lattice defects which would result could act as exciton traps in the manner in which imperfections were seen to stabilize anhydrous D-glucose. A striking feature is the similarity in the behaviour of the anomers anhydrous α-D-glucose and β-D-glucose (fig. 2). The separate identity of all the forms of the hexose examined was established by optical rotation measurements and X-ray powder photography. In each case, the observed $d$-spacings compared well with the $d$-spacings calculated from the known cell dimensions.

The behaviour of α-D-glucose monohydrate is markedly different on γ-irradiation, as, in fact, had been suggested by the lower $G$(acid) of 5.0 for this form. Values for $-G$ at equivalent doses are generally about half those of anhydrous crystals. Here also $-G$ (about 11) is about double $G$(acid).

The freeze-dried state, which as has already been observed is crystallographically indistinguishable from polycrystalline α-D-glucose, proved initially the most radiation resistant of all the forms studied. Initial $-G$ is about 7, which again represents approximately double the acid yield.

Summarizing, therefore, it is clear that the radiation stability of α-D-glucose crystals is dependent on the state of molecular aggregation. The most susceptible to radiation damage is polycrystalline α-D-glucose, and introduction of lattice imperfections by the fast crystallisation following freeze-drying, confers greater radiation stability to the crystal. The β-anomer behaves in a similar fashion to polycrystalline α-D-glucose on irradiation, but the introduction of a molecule of water, as in α-D-glucose monohydrate, also results in higher radiation stability compared with polycrystalline anhydrous D-glucose. The syrup is more stable than the corresponding polycrystalline form.

### 6.5. ENERGY TRANSPORT MECHANISM

For all the crystal forms, the decomposition is unusually high compared with other groups of organic molecules which have been studied [TOLBERT and LEMMON, 1955]. A high efficiency of energy transport and utilization in the crystal is indicated. In these structures there are extensive three-dimensional networks of hydrogen bonds. Such bonds have been shown to execute efficiently the transfer of energy [RIEHL, 1956; REXROAD and GORDY, 1962]. The position of the singlet exciton band of the crystalline aggregate, as a result of hydrogen bonding, would be expected to show a pronounced red-shift compared with the absorption spectrum of the monomer. The exciton band width is given by $\Delta E = 2M_1^2/R^3$, where $M_1$ is the transition moment integral for the absorption of the monomer, and $R$ is the intermolecular separation [AVERY and MASON, 1965; MASON, 1965]. The triplet band width will be very small, and the excited triplet level would thus be hardly modified on aggregation. An important variable controlling energy transfer is thus $R$.

For $\alpha$-D-glucose, four oxygen atoms (at $C_6$, $C_4$, $C_3$ and $C_2$) are directly hydrogen bonded to two oxygen atoms of other molecules. In addition, there appear to be bonds between the ring oxygen atoms and the hydroxyl groups at $C_1$ of the neighbouring molecules. For $\beta$-D-glucose [FERRIER, 1960], four pairs of intermolecular oxygen separations have values in the region of 0.27–0.28 nm and must, therefore, correspond to hydrogen bonds. These are directed from $O_5 - O_3$, $O_6 - O_2$ and $O_2 - O_3$. The fourth hydrogen bond associated with each D-glucose molecule is between oxygen atoms of the identical oriented molecule shifted one cell length along the C axis $(O_6 - O_1)$. The glucose molecules are, therefore, closely joined to adjacent molecules and thus present suitable conditions for efficient energy transfer. Such resonance interaction requires no orbital overlap and can lead to energy migration over the entire molecular aggregate [FÖRSTER, 1946, 1960, 1948, 1959; KASHA, 1963]. For $\alpha$-D-glucose monohydrate there is also a fully hydrogen bonded structure [KILLEAN et al., 1962], but due to the presence of the additional water molecule, the distance between atoms of adjacent D-glucose molecules will be greater than in anhydrous crystals. Oxygen atoms at $C_3$, $C_2$ and $C_0$ are linked by hydrogen bonds through water to adjoining D-glucose molecules. Such hydrogen bonds form two separate infinite chains about two of the screw axes. The greater displacement of individual molecules in the monohydrate is further indicated by the volume of monohydrate unit cell (437 cu Å) containing 2 glucose units, compared with $\alpha$-D-glucose (758 cu Å) and anhydrous $\beta$-D-glucose (785 cu Å), both containing 4 glucose units.

According to each of the resonance energy transfer mechanisms which have been envisaged, the transfer efficiency would be expected to be critically dependent on intermolecular separations. No clear distinction can be made which particular one of the resonance transfer mechanisms is operative, if, indeed, this is a meaningful consideration. On the basis of the exciton model, the transfer rate is proportional to

$R^{-3}$ and according to the Förster mechanism to $R^{-6}$. Thus in each case, if $-G$ is an indication of transfer efficiency, the lower value for the monohydrate, compared with $\alpha$- and $\beta$-D-glucose, could directly result from the greater distance between D-glucose molecules in certain directions in the monohydrate crystal. The observed critical dependence of $-G$ on degree of ordered crystallinity is not a requirement of the Förster mechanism, and would accord better with an exciton model. This observation, however, cannot be considered to distinguish unequivocally between the possible mechanisms, because removal of crystallinity as, for example, in the syrup, may also involve a change in intermolecular separations.

The results may be rationalized if it is postulated that as a result of $\gamma$-irradiation a delocalized excitation (or exciton) extends initially over a domain in which the conduction band electron and valence-band hole may not necessarily be bound together. No single molecule need be considered as the excited one and the excitation is associated with several molecules. Such a WANNIER [1937] exciton differs physically from the Frenkel exciton [FRENKEL, 1931, 1936] only in the degree of separation of the electron and hole. Chemical change will be dependent on whether exciton transport is trapped and dissipated at a dislocation or whether exciton transport is facilitated in more perfect crystals to become localized by dissociation of individual D-glucose molecules somewhere in the region of the excitation. Transformation of excitons into heat would occur to a greater extent as the accumulating products of irradiation cause further lattice dislocations, or, indeed, as a result of any factor which would cause an increased interruption of lattice periodicity. Such exciton dissipation would reduce the chemical decomposition of glucose molecules.

## 6.6. CHEMICAL CHANGES

The nature of the chemical changes [PHILLIPS, 1965] will not be dealt with in detail here. Two relevant points only will be noted. First, although the overall yields of irradiation products varied for the various forms examined, no difference was observed in the nature of the products. Secondly, during the initial chemical act, fragmentation of the molecule occurs to give lower aldehydic fragments. Indeed, the wide spectrum of products is indicative of excitation of the entire ring rather than at one specific group, as occurs during photolysis with light which is absorbed specifically at the $C_1$ acetal chromophore [PHILLIPS, 1963].

## 7. Energy transfer in cycloamylose complexes

In the above discussion, it has been suggested that the major effect of ionizing radiations on solid D-glucose is to produce in high yield exciton states extending over a domain in the crystal. On this view, chemical change is dependent on whether the excitation energy is transformed into heat at lattice imperfections and other traps or whether exciton transport is facilitated in more perfect crystals to become localized by dissociations of individual D-glucose molecules. While the existence of such exciton states has been demonstrated in aromatic crystals, there is no information about their existence in carbohydrate systems. If our explanation is correct and a collective yet coherent excitation is transferable in carbohydrate crystals, then it should be possible to transfer this excitation energy to other molecules. To demonstrate such energy transfer and so further examine the above postulates, carbohydrate systems were sought where close association in the solid state is possible between carbohydrate and a wide range of other molecules. To this end, the unusual cyclic oligo-saccharides formed by the action of *Bacillus macerans* amylose on potato starch, the Schardinger dextrins [FRENCH, 1957] were selected for detailed study (fig. 3). It appeared that these molecules would be particularly suitable for two reasons. First, these cyclic molecules in which D-glucose units are joined by $\alpha1 \rightarrow 4$ glucosidic links, do not contain a free reducing group where radiation induced oxidation reactions are generally dominant in the sugars. Secondly unique inclusion complexes with organic molecules can be formed with these cyclic molecules [FRENCH, 1957; CRAMER, 1955, 1956; PULLEY and FRENCH, 1963; LUTTRINGHAUS et al., 1958].

### 7.1. CHEMICAL CHANGES

When cycloheptaamylose is $\gamma$-irradiated in the solid state, rupture of the cyclic system occurs. No glucose is produced and the main initial

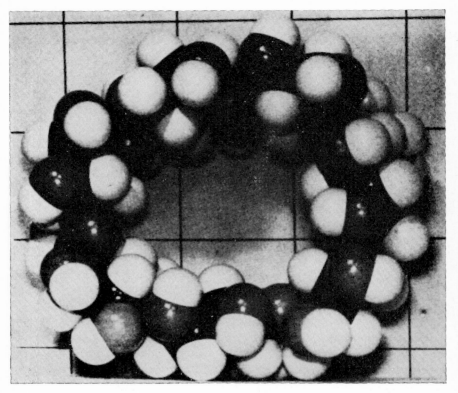

Fig. 3. Model of cycloheptaamylose (1 Division = 0.55 nm).

product is maltahexaose. Simple hydrolysis of the $\alpha 1 \rightarrow 4$ glycosidic linkages, therefore, does not occur. The initial chemical effects of $\gamma$-irradiation may be represented:

Gluconic acid is the main acid produced, although the presence of another acid, particularly at high doses, has been detected. There is no significant difference in the behaviour of cycloheptaamylose and cyclohexaamylose.

The presence of water in the crystalline cycloheptaamylose inhibits the radiation decomposition. Freeze-drying followed by rigorous drying *in vacuo* removed all water from cycloheptaamylose and it is this dry sample which shows the highest $-G$ value (14.6). When water is present in the molar ratio cycloheptaamylose to water of 1 : 1, the $-G$ value is reduced by 7.5. Further amounts of water, until a molar ratio of 10 water molecules to 1 molecule cyclic dextrin is attained, do not significantly reduce $-G$ further, when values are related to energy absorbed in the dextrin only. The radiation stabilization due to 1 molar proportion of water is significant, and appears to be a general phenomenon for carbohydrates. EHRENBERG et al. [1957] showed that on decreasing the water content of starch, amylose and amylopectin, the degradation increases as did the production of acid groups.

For polysaccharides $-G$ values have been generally deduced from viscosity changes following $\gamma$-irradiation, and $-G$ ranges from 5.2 for solid dextran with intermediate molecular weight and low degree of branching, 7.6 for dextran of low molecular weight and high degree of branching, 11.0 for dextran of high molecular weight [GRANATH and KINELL, 1961] and moderate branching to $-G = 14.5$ for amylopectin [WILLIAMS et al., 1959]. The values for cycloheptaamylose and cyclohexaamylose by direct measurement fall in the same range and further demonstrate the marked susceptibility of carbohydrates to radiation damage.

## 7.2. ELECTRON SPIN RESONANCE EFFECTS OF ENERGY TRANSFER

The ESR spectrum of $\gamma$-irradiated cycloheptaamylose shows mainly a hyperfine structure doublet with a splitting of 3–4 gauss and line width 24 gauss (fig. 4). Qualitatively the spectrum compares with irradiated disaccharides, dextran and amylose where the spectra also correspond mainly to a doublet. The splitting is given as 3–5 gauss for dextran [WILLIAMS et al., 1959] and less than 5 gauss for $\beta$-maltose monohydrate [GRANATH and KINELL, 1960; 1961] and $\beta$-cellobiose [MISHINA, 1965]. It is doubtful if the doublet is indicative of interaction of the magnetic moment of the unpaired electron single proton as in the radical:

This suggestion was advanced to account for the hydrolysis which accompanies the $\gamma$-irradiation of disaccharides [WILLIAMS et al., 1959]. The small hyperfine splitting is indicative of only weak interaction with the proton and a radical which more probably accounts for the ESR evidence is a glycosoxyl radical of the type:

where there is only weak interaction with the proton at $C_1$. Extreme excitation leading to the removal of a p electron from the glycosidic oxygen by $\gamma$-radiation could give rise to a radical of this type. A possible reaction scheme is as follows:

The intermediate radical (II) would give rise to a carbonium ion (III) at $C_4$ which would react rapidly with water to produce the corresponding alcohol (IV). The glycosoxyl radical site is the most likely intermediate for the production of the gluconic acid. The additional product would be maltahexaose (IV) as, in fact, has been observed.

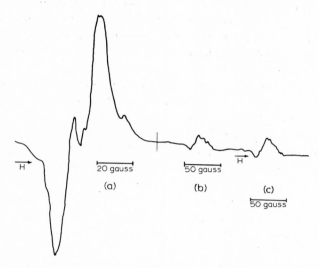

Fig. 4. Electron spin resonance spectra of $\gamma$-irradiated (a) cycloheptaamylose, (b) p-nitrophenol, (c) cycloheptaamylose-p-nitrophenol complex.

The radical formed on irradiation is thus indicative of the chemical changes induced. On $\gamma$-irradiation of the inclusion complexes with nitrophenol and iodobenzene, the ESR spectrum of the cycloheptaamylose disappears and a spectrum considerably different in character and intensity is obtained. There is good evidence that the new spectrum is associated with the aromatic moeity. Modification of the ESR spectrum and the accompanying chemical protection (section 7.3) of the dextrin is in our view the result of energy transfer processes. No such effects were observed in the complexes with $n$-octanol.

Here the ESR data will be examined. Nitrophenol complexes, when the ratio of nitrophenol to cycloheptaamylose is varied from 2.5 to 0.6 all show the modified spectrum on $\gamma$-irradiation (fig. 4). When the central channel of cycloheptaamylose accommodates 1 molecule of p-nitrophenol, on the basis of valence electron fraction of the components

[SWALLOW, 1963a], 79 % of the energy would be deposited in the carbohydrate. In the absence of energy transfer, therefore, the ESR spectrum of the complex should approximate to the spectrum of irradiated cycloheptaamylose reduced by *ca*. 20 %. That only simple mixtures of p-nitrophenol and cycloheptaamylose behave in this anticipated manner demonstrates that some intermolecular interaction is necessary for energy transfer. Complexes with m-nitrophenol show the same effects, and with this complex the ESR spectra are sufficiently distinctive to enable reasonable identification with the spectrum of m-nitrophenol irradiated alone. A similar behaviour, consistent with energy transfer effects, is encountered with iodobenzene complexes, where $\sim$ 20 % of the energy would be absorbed in the iodobenzene on the basis of the electron fraction law. The ESR spectrum is different in form and very much less in intensity. For cycloheptaamylose alone initial $G$ (radicals) is not less than 5, for nitrophenol complexes 0.8 and for the iodobenzene complex no significant increase in radical concentration with dose was detectable. The behaviour of n-octanol complexes is not indicative of preferential energy transfer from host to guest molecules. The ESR spectrum consists of a well-defined doublet and differs from irradiated cycloheptaamylose only in having a somewhat larger hyperfine splitting (7–10 gauss). Approximately 14 % of the energy would be deposited in the n-octanol and the increased hyperfine splitting may be due to an overlapping contribution from radicals of the RCHOH type. Although the yield-dose curves deviate at high doses, the initial $G$(radicals) for the n-octanol complex is the same ($G = 5$) as the cycloheptaamylose alone.

A significant observation is the extremely low $G$ for radical production when p-nitrophenol is irradiated alone ($G$ 0.02), which is typical of aromatic solids [VOEVODSKY, 1962]. In the complex ($G$ 0.8) one possibility is that the energy is directed to bonds weakened by interaction with cycloheptaamylose, and thus provides evidence for a definite association between dextrin and included molecules. Another possible explanation for the high yield of aromatic radicals is discussed later.

## 7.3. CHEMICAL EFFECTS OF ENERGY TRANSFER

For anhydrous cycloheptaamylose $-G$ is 14.5 and shows no significant difference when complexed with n-octanol. Significant protection is produced by complexing with p-nitrophenol ($-G$ 1.1), m-nitrophenol ($-G$ 2.4) and iodobenzene ($-G$ 5.8). This chemical protection, therefore, supports the evidence from ESR that in the complexes with the aromatics there is facile transfer of energy away from the carbohydrate. For mixtures of p-nitrophenol and m-nitrophenol with cycloheptaamylose monohydrate, $-G$ (dextrin) are 6.8 and 7.5 which are not significantly different from the monohydrate alone ($-G$ 7.5), and thus confirm the evidence from ESR that some form of intermolecular interaction is a necessary condition for energy transfer. These observations indicate a most promising method of protecting carbohydrates from radiation damage, for after irradiation of the complex, unchanged dextrin may be conveniently recorded by treatment with water. Reduction from $-G$ 14.5 to 1.1 as for the p-nitrophenol complex represents a degree of protection which has not previously been achieved. Energy scavenging in this manner promises to be more efficient than conventional radical scavenging methods in biological systems, where protection generally is not more than *ca.* 50 % at best.

## 7.4. CHARACTERIZATION OF THE INCLUDED AROMATIC FREE RADICAL

The weak ESR signals which nitrophenol and iodobenzene complexes exhibit after $\gamma$-irradiation make it difficult to make a positive assignment for the radical, although the general form clearly indicates that the signal is associated with the aromatic moiety. More definite evidence for this postulate can be obtained with complexes such as that with 1-methyl naphthalene. The ESR spectrum of irradiated cycloheptaamylose — 1-methyl naphthalene complex (fig. 5) consists of at least 9 lines and extends over a total width of *ca* 160 gauss, which is, therefore, quite distinct from the doublet with total width *ca* 86 gauss from $\gamma$-irradiated cycloheptaamylose alone. Thus for the 1-methyl naphthalene complex the signal is associated with the aromatic moeity despite the fact that 92.9 % of the energy was initially absorbed in the cyclic dextrin. Moreover, on the basis of the low radical yields reported for aromatic hydrocarbons irradiated alone [VOEVODSKY, 1962], it is most surprising that such a strong signal is associated with the 1-methyl naphthalene moeity. When the energy of the first excited level is less than 4.4 eV, the C–H bond dissociation energy, $G_R$ for aromatic hydrocarbons is $\sim$ 0.05, and at the doses we have used a signal would be undetectable for 1-methyl naphthalene ($E_1$ 3.83 eV) alone. Furthermore, on energetic considerations, an additional 30

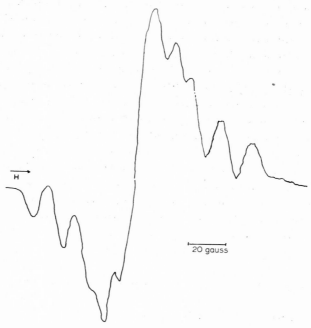

Fig. 5. Electron spin resonance spectrum of $\gamma$-irradiated cycloheptaamylose-1-methyl naphthalene complexes.

kcal/mole would be required to remove a hydrogen atom from the aromatic nucleus compared with the removal from the 1-methyl group. The most probable radical on energetic grounds which would be produced by hydrogen abstraction is thus

Based on the coupling constants for a ·$CH_2$ fragment in a similar environment, the spectrum should approximate to a basic triplet with a splitting of 16–20 gauss, with further splitting by weaker coupling with protons in the nucleus. The ortho and para protons which show strong coupling would lead to a splitting of *ca.* 7 gauss and the meta, which couple weakly, not more than 2 gauss [SOGO et al., 1957; CARRINGTON, 1963]. Therefore, it is highly unlikely that the ESR spectrum of radical I could extend more than *ca.* 60 gauss in total width. It was, therefore, necessary to consider radicals formed by H atom addition to the aromatic molecule (II)

The ESR spectrum of benzene irradiated below −80°C consists of 12 broad lines. It was suggested [FISCHER, 1962a and b; TOLKACHEV, 1961] that the spectrum consists of quartets and on this basis was assigned to the cyclohexadienyl radical, to which the following coupling constants were assigned: for the protons of the methylene group $50 \pm 2$ gauss, for the nuclei of the ortho and para hydrogens $10.6 \pm 0.5$ gauss and for the nuclei of the meta hydrogens $2.6 \pm 0.2$ gauss. Although doubt has been cast by FESSENDEN and SCHULER [1963a] on the detailed assignment of the radical, they also observed similar spectra with three groups of lines separated by 48 gauss with relative intensities 1 : 2 : 1. By analogy it is clear that the ESR spectrum we have observed in irradiated 1-methyl naphthalene complex is compatible with structures II. The nine lines may be derived by an initial triplet due to the methylene group, which is further split by strong coupling with protons at positions 6 and 8. Further splitting may occur which cannot be resolved in our solid samples. On this assignment the coupling constants for the methylene group would be *ca.* 40 gauss and *ca.* 12 gauss for the ortho and para hydrogens. Anisotropy in the g-factor and hyperfine splitting constants, strong intermolecular dipolar broadening and electron exchange reactions tend to reduce the hyperfine structure observable in our polycrystalline samples.

For the complexes where energy transfer is most efficient, the intensities of the ESR spectrum are small and the lack of resolution does not permit an accurate assignment to be made. However, it is quite clear that the species that is formed is different from the normal $\gamma$-irradiated cyclodextrin doublet. A basic triplet, with splitting *ca.* 14 gauss is detectable in the complexes with nitro compounds after irradiation. This observation is again consistent with the radical being associated with the included moiety when the widely spaced nitrogen triplet would be expected ($a_N$ 13–14 gauss). When energy transfer does not occur to any significant extent, as in complexes with tetrachloroethylene, tetracyanoethylene and anthracene, the ESR spectrum of the irradiated complex does not differ from $\gamma$-irradiated dextrin.

### 7.5. ENERGY TRANSFER MECHANISM

When the included molecule is suitably varied $-G$(dextrin) may be reduced from 17 (cyclohexane and tetrachloroethylene) to 1 (nitrophenol) (table 4). During consideration of the transfer mechanism, it is relevant to consider first whether migration of charge or ionization transfer can account for the observed effects. If electron transfer occurred, the efficiency of chemical protection should be dependent on the electron affinity of the included molecule. However, no such dependence is observed (table 4). For example, although tetracyanoethylene and phenyl acetylene differ in their electron affinities by a factor of at least $10^6$, they confer the same degree of protection on the dextrin. Similarly, tetrachloroethylene and carbon tetrachloride despite their high electron affinities and their facility in capturing electrons [HAMMILL et al., 1963; GUARINO et al., 1962], confer negligible protection. Positive hole migration too is unlikely on similar reasoning, particularly since there is reliable mass spectrometric evidence that molecular fragmentation of (Dextrin)$^+$ would accompany any significant charge separation [BEAMANN et al., 1963; DE JONGH and BEAMANN, 1964]. Indeed if ion-pair formation led to $-G$ of 17, the mean energy for their creation would be $\sim$ 12 eV, which is considerably less than the anticipated value of $\sim$ 30 eV. Finally, if electron migration by diffusion, followed by capture, occurred to any significant extent, the process would be strongly dependent on scavenger concentration [HAMMILL et al., 1963]. However, more than a ten-fold variation in 1-bromonaphthalene to dextrin ratio does not change $-G$(dextrin) (fig. 6), which indicates further that transfer extends over a minimum distance of 1 nm at the lowest ratio of dextrin to included molecule. Ionization transfer [COLLINSON et al., 1962] is, therefore, in our view most unlikely.

The hypothesis that transfer of electronic energy from the carbohydrate to the included molecule satisfactorily accounts for the observed effects. Fig. 7 shows the relation between $-G$ and the energy of the

TABLE 4

Radiation protection of cycloamyloses by complex formation

| Included molecule | Azobenzene | Anthracene | Tetracyanoethylene |
|---|---|---|---|
| Ratio of included molecule to cycloamylose | 0.4 | 0.2 | 0.3 |
| Electron affinity [a] | 9 | 12 | 7000 |
| $E_T(eV)$ [b] | | 1.82 | |
| $E_1(\beta)$ [c] | | 0.82 | |
| $E_1(eV)$ [d] | 2.80 | 3.26 | 3.87 |
| $G_{Radical}$ | | | |
| $-G$ | 11.4 | 12.4 | 8.20 |

| Included molecule | Methyl-naphthalene | p-Nitro-phenol[15] | Nitro-cyclohexane | Nitrobenzene |
|---|---|---|---|---|
| Ratio of included molecule to cycloamylose | 0.6 | | 1.0 | 1.6 |
| Electron affinity [a] | | | | 390 |
| $E_T(eV)$ [b] | 2.62 | | | 2.61 |
| $E_1(\beta)$ [c] | 1.21 | | | |
| $E_1(eV)$ [d] | 3.83 | 3.97 | 4.45 | 4.61 |
| $G_{Radical}$ | 2.55 | | | 0.22 |
| $-G$ | 4.6 | 1.0 | 2.3 | 2.3 |

| Included molecule | Toluene | Chloro-benzene | Iodo-benzene [e] | 1-Bromo-naphthalene |
|---|---|---|---|---|
| Ratio of included molecule to cycloamylose | 0.7 | 1.4 | | see fig. 6 |
| Electron affinity [a] | 0.01 | 1 | 370 | |
| $E_T(eV)$ [b] | 3.58 | | | 2.56 |
| $E_1(\beta)$ [c] | 1.86 | | | |
| $E_1(eV)$ [d] | 4.60 | 4.57 | 4.80 | |
| $G_{Radical}$ | | | | |
| $-G$ | 2.6 | 6.0 | 6.4 | 7.0 |

| Included molecule | Phenyl-acetylene | Carbon tetrachloride | Tetrachloro-ethylene | Cyclohexane |
|---|---|---|---|---|
| Ratio of included molecule to cycloamylose | 1.2 | 0.3 | 1.3 | 0.4 |
| Electron affinity [a] | 0.01 | 7000 | ca. 7000 | 0.01 |
| $E_T(eV)$ [b] | | | ca. 3.13 | |
| $E_1(\beta)$ [c] | | | | |
| $E_1(eV)$ [d] | 4.76 | ca 6.5 | ca. 7.0 | 7.5 |
| $G_{Radical}$ | 1.65 | | 3.4 | |
| $-G$ | 8.9 | 14.5 | 16.0 | 16.0 |

[a] Values relative to chorobenzene [LOVELOCK, 1961].
[b] Calculated from the wavenumber of the phosphorescence band [KASHA 1944].
[c] Calculated by L.A.C.O. molecular orbital method [COULSON, 1964; STREIT-WIESER, 1961] and quoted in terms of the resonance integral ($\beta$).
[d] Calculated from absorption spectral data [GILLAM and STERN, 1954].
[e] [BAUGH, 1964].

first singlet level $(E_1)$ of the included molecule. Values of $E_1$ were calculated from measured excitation frequencies. Where it is meaning-

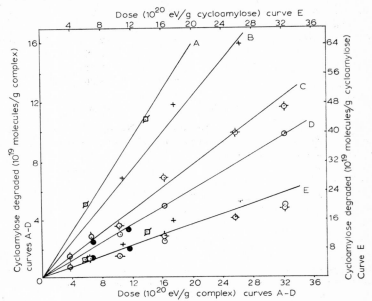

Fig. 6. Radiation degradation of cycloamylose complexes: effect of varying cycloamylose/1-bromonaphthalene

Ratio: 1-bromonaphthalene/cycloamylose

|   |   |
|---|---|
| A | 0.4 : 1 |
| B | 1.3 : 1 |
| C | 4.5 : 1 |
|   | 3.6 : 1 |
| D | 5.6 : 1 |
|   | 7.0 : 1 |

E  Combined results where energy deposition was related to 1g cycloamylose.
Abscissae: Dose ($10^{20}$ eV/g complex) Curves A-D
            Dose ($10^{20}$ eV/g cycloamylose) Curve E
Ordinates: Cycloamylose degraded ($10^{19}$ molecules/g complex) Curves A-D.
          Cycloamylose degraded ($10^{19}$ molecules/g cycloamylose). (See text).

ful for the series anthracene, 1-methyl naphthalene and toluene we have calculated $E_1$ using simple molecular orbital theory. The observations (table 4) are useful in confirming the relative positions of the first singlet level of these hydrocarbons. The first singlet level is used here since it is now well-established that when an organic molecule is excited to a high singlet electronic level, there is a very rapid ($10^{-13}$—$10^{-12}$ sec) cascade to the lowest singlet level.

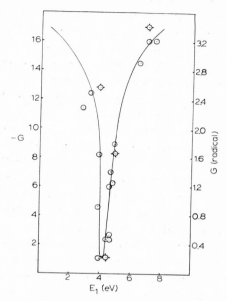

Fig. 7. Resonance energy transfer leading to protection of cycloamylose when complexed with organic molecules.

 ◯ Chemical yield.    Abscissa: $E_1$(eV)
 -◌̣- Radical yield.    Ordinates: $-G$
                $G$(radical)

A resonance energy transfer mechanism is indicated from fig. 7 which may function as follows. The primary physical act can lead to a collective excitation (including ionization) with a lifetime of $10^{-15}$—$10^{-14}$ sec in the dextrin molecule [FANO, 1960]. The mechanism by which such Fano collective excitations of high energy are rapidly converted into states which have lower energy, more akin to states excited by photochemical means is not well understood. Nevertheless, excitation transfer by inductive resonance between like and unlike molecules may then occur with speeds which depend on the particular transfer mechanism. In any event the rates of transfer by each of the possible mechanisms can be faster than the lifetime of the excited molecules, which usually are of the order of $10^{-8}$ sec. Unless transfer occurs faster than thermal relaxation ($\sim 10^{-12}$ sec) the lowest excited level, singlet or triplet will be involved in a transfer of this type. Conditions for excitation transfer are optional if the electronic level of the acceptor is somewhat lower than that of the sensitizer, and for energetic reasons transfer must occur to an acceptor with lower energy gap, with the condition that transfer is most favourable when there is maximum overlap of the electric dipole fields of emitter and acceptor molecules. From fig. 7 transfer begins when the acceptor has $E_1 \sim 5$ eV. and is a maximum at 4 eV, which sets limiting values on the energy of the excited states in the dextrin. More precise assignment is not possible. The Förster mechanism provides the most detailed theory for energy transfer between unlike molecules, and here the interaction energy is less than the vibrational band width, and only small regions of corresponding bands are in resonance. Thus for molecules with broad spectra, such as those involved in the complex, several transitions may coincide when there is overlap between the absorption spectrum of the donor and fluorescence spectrum of the acceptor.

In an attempt to distinguish between the Förster vibrational relation mechanism and energy transfer mechanisms based on the exciton model, temperature effects were examined. At low temperatures the lower vibrational levels would be populated and hence would create unfavourable conditions for the Förster mechanism. From the results, it appears that a reduction in energy transfer occurs at low temperature in uncomplexed dextrin and cycloamylose-nitrobenzene complex, which is in keeping with the Förster mechanism.

Finally, an attempt was made to elucidate whether any significant transfer occurs via triplet states. Such transfer, as described, is now well established. However, in the cycloamylose complexes, there is no indication that triplet states of the aromatic hydrocarbons are involved since there is no regular correlation between $-G$(dextrin) with the first triplet energy levels (calculated from phosphorescence spectra) of the included molecules. Confirmation of this view comes from the experiment where the 1-methyl was replaced by bromine in the naphthalene nucleus. Although the change should enhance the $S \rightarrow T$ transition it results in less efficient energy transfer since $-G$ (dextrin) for the 1-bromonaphthalene complex is 7.0 compared with 4.6 for 1-methyl naphthalene.

It is our conclusion, therefore, that on $\gamma$-irradiation of cycloamylose complexes singlet-singlet resonance energy transfer occurs which leads to efficient radiation protection of the carbohydrate. After the transfer of energy, migration of energy in the included molecule can occur, and for aromatic molecules any quantum will make about $10^5$ hops to neighbouring centres before the energy can be dissipated,—most probably by fluorescence [LYONS, 1957].

It should also be pointed out that a similar correlation between radical yield and $E_1$ and between chemical yield and $E_1$ (fig. 7) is found. If, however, radical formation is due to hydrogen attachment to the aromatic, this process may only be related to energy transfer as a result of a lower yield of primary H atoms in the carbohydrate moiety when efficient transfer occurs. Following rupture of a C–H bond to form a radical, the excess energy would be carried as kinetic energy in the H atom. Since the activation energy of the process H+ aromatics → is close to zero, H atom attachment would be favoured with H atoms which do not possess sufficient energy to initiate further abstraction reactions in the carbohydrate. Indeed if an excitation of *ca.* 4–5 eV in the dextrin could be sufficient to cause bond rupture and simultaneously produce H atoms with excess energy of only *ca* 0.5 eV, then the capture reaction would be more favourable than abstraction. Therefore radical yields, albeit indirectly may be dependent on energy transfer efficiency.

## 8. Intramolecular energy transfer

Intermolecular energy transfer has been demonstrated in cycloamylose complexes from the carbohydrate host to the aromatic guest molecule. The carbohydrates are also particularly suitable molecules for studying the effect of substituent groups on the chemical changes initiated by ionising radiations, since the structure of the molecules is well established and systematic variation in particular substituent groups is possible.

The radiation stabilization of glycosides has been studied from this point of view [PHILLIPS et al., 1964]. During $\gamma$-irradiation of glycosides, the dominant radiation induced-process is scission at the glycosidic group. The extent to which this scission process occurs can be significantly reduced by substitution of aromatic groups into the molecule and their behaviour is closely analogous to the energy transfer effects reported in the previous section. For example, methyl α-D-gluco-pyranoside on γ-irradiation gives glucose with $G$ 2.3. Replacement of the methyl group by phenyl protected the glucosidic bond and for phenyl β-D-glucoside $G$ (glucose) is 0.8. The hydrolytic nature of the cleavage was demonstrated by $G$ (glucose) 0.8 and $G$ (phenol) 0.8, with no other detectable products. The introduction of benzoyl groups into this molecule led to further radiation stabilization. For tetra-0-benzoyl phenyl β-D-glucopyranoside, the phenol production was further reduced ($G$ 0.05) (table 5). It is interesting to observe that

TABLE 5

Effect of aromatic groups on the radiation protection of solid glycosides

| Irradiated glycoside | | Products | $G$ |
|---|---|---|---|
| methyl α-D-gluco-pyranoside | | glucose<br>acid | 2.3<br>1.5 |
| tetra-0-acetyl methyl α-D-glucopyranoside | | glucose<br>deacetylation<br>mannose | 2.3<br>7.9<br>2.0 |
| methyl α-D-manno pyranoside | | glucose<br>phenol | 0.8<br>0.8 |
| phenyl β-D-gluco-pyranoside | | glucose | a |
| tetra-0-benzoyl phenyl β-D-glucopyranoside | | phenol | 0.05 |
| hepta-0-acetyl phenyl β-maltoside | | glycosidic cleavage at (1)<br>(2) | 0.10<br>0.05 |

a not detectable. (1) glycosidic group. (2) disaccharide link.

the stabilization due to the aromatic groups is not due to a bond strength effect. It is well established that 0-aryl glycosides are more rapidly hydrolysed than 0-alkyl glycosides by aqueous acid [FOSTER and OVEREND, 1955]. With hepta-0-acetyl phenyl $\beta$-maltoside, it may be demonstrated that protection can be extended beyond the length of one glucose molecule compared with the unprotected disaccharide [PHILLIPS, 1961] where scission at the glycosidic link occurs with $G$ 2.1, introduction of a phenyl group at $C_1$ stabilises the glycosidic at $C_1$ ($G$ 0.05) and the disaccharide link ($G$ 0.1). Further examples are given in table 5.

The criteria which were used to demonstrate energy transfer in cycloamylose complexes were chemical protection and changes in form and intensity of ESR spectra. According to these same criteria, it would appear that intramolecular energy transfer is responsible for the protective effects which have been described. Chemical protection has already been mentioned. The ESR effects may be illustrated by reference to phenyl $\beta$-D-glucoside. For disaccharides and glycosides generally on $\gamma$-irradiation in the solid state, the ESR spectrum of the radical produced consists of a doublet [WILLIAMS et al., 1959] with hyperfine splitting of *ca.* 3 gauss and total line width of not more than 86 gauss, $G$ (radical) is *ca.* 3 [PHILLIPS, 1964]. For phenyl $\beta$-D-glucoside the ESR spectrum (fig. 8) consists of nine lines made

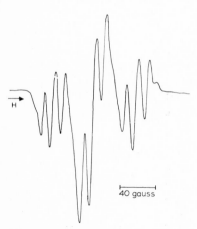

Fig. 8. Electron spin resonance spectrum of $\gamma$-irradiated phenyl $\beta$-D-glucoside. |—| 40 gauss

up of a trio of triplets in the ratio of intensities of $1 : 2 : 1$ and total line width *ca.* 160 gauss; $G$ (radical) is $\sim 0.1$. We consider that this ESR spectrum may be accounted for by a radical formed by H atom addition to the phenyl group:

On this assignment the coupling constants for the methylene protons would be 52 gauss and for an aromatic ring proton 12 gauss. For the cyclohexadienyl radical [FISCHER, 1962; TOLKACHEV et al., 1961; FESSENDEN and SCHULER, 1963] the coupling constants of the methylene group were $50\pm2$ gauss and for the ortho and para hydrogens $10.6\pm0.5$ gauss and the meta hydrogens $2.6\pm0.2$ gauss and our estimates are, therefore, in reasonable agreement with these values.

In the typical case of phenyl $\beta$-D-glucoside, therefore, the protection due to the phenyl group could be the result of intramolecular energy transfer from the glucose ring to the aromatic group. The fluorescence spectrum of this was seen to have a maximum at 290 nm, in relation to the absorption spectral maximum at 271.7 nm. If the energy transfered was of these proportions, the excited molecule could be deactivated by fluorescence without resulting chemical change. Therefore, to obtain estimates of the magnitude of the energy of the excited state in the sugar moiety, the aglycon was varied and table 6 shows the relation between $G$ for scission at the glycosidic linkage and $E_1$ for

TABLE 6

Radiation protection of glycosides by aromatic groups.

| Glycoside | $E_1(eV)^a$ | $E_1(\beta)^b$ | $G$(Glycosidic-scission) | $G$ (Radical) |
|---|---|---|---|---|
| phenyl $\beta$-D-glucopyranoside | 4.55 | 1.83 | 0.6 | 0.1 |
| o-cresyl $\beta$-D-glucopyranoside | 4.53 | 1.79 | 0.75 | |
| m-cresyl $\beta$-D-glucopyranoside | 4.54 | 1.82 | 0.83 | |
| p-cresyl $\beta$-D-glucopyranoside | 4.43 | 1.72 | 1.2 | |
| 2.4 dimethyl phenyl $\beta$-D-glucopyranoside | 4.42 | 1.73 | 1.1 | |
| p-nitrophenyl $\beta$-D-glucopyranoside | 4.09 | | 0.4 | 0.43 |
| m-nitrophenyl $\beta$-D-glucopyranoside | 4.57 | | 0.7 | 0.53 |
| 2-naphthyl $\beta$-D-glucopyranoside | 3.82 | 1.21 | 0.34 | 0.13 |
| benzyl $\beta$-D-arabinopyranoside | 4.81 | | 1.8 | 0.6 |
| p-methoxyphenyl $\beta$-D-glucopyranoside | 4.39 | | 0.8 | |
| p-chlorophenyl $\beta$-D-glucopyranoside | 4.67 | | 0.75 | 0.8 |
| anthranol $\beta$-D-glucopyranoside | 3.19 | 0.81 | 3.2 | 0.4 |

a  calculated from absorption spectral data.
b  calculated by L.C.A.O. molecular orbital method and quoted in terms of resonance integral ($\beta$).
  [KLOTZ, 1958].

the aglycon. Although broadly the results show $G$ (glycosidic scission) is critically dependent on $E_1$ there are anomalous cases at $E_1 \sim 4.5$ eV (275.1 nm) where $G$ values range from 0.6 to 1.2. At the moment singlet-

singlet resonance energy transfer from the sugar moiety to the aromatic group appears to offer the best explanation for our results, and on this basis a discrete energy level of *ca.* 4.25–4.5 eV (291.2–275.1 nm) in the sugar would be indicated. It is noteworthy that the energy limits for the excitation level in the solid carbohydrate are consistent in the two chemical systems which have been examined, namely sugar glycosides where the group is substituted in the molecule and the cyclo-amylose complexes, where the nature of the association is less definite.

Estimates of the distance over which energy transfer can occur in carbohydrates may be obtained using fibrous cotton cellulose. Here the degree of substitution (*d.s.*) of aromatic groups can be varied and protection studied as a function of *d.s.* The effects of $\gamma$-radiation on the breaking strength of fibrous benzoylated cellulose polymer are shown in fig. 9. At the lower dose, *d.s.* of as low as 0.2 of benzoyl groups on the

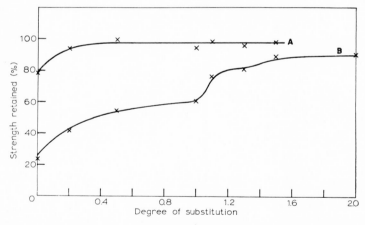

Fig. 9. Effects of $\gamma$-radiation on the breaking strength retained by fibrous benzo-ylated cotton cellulose as a function of the degree of substitution and dose.
Dose A 1.2 × 10²⁰ eV/g;
B 1.3 × 10²¹ eV/g.

cellulose molecule offered some radiation protection of the fibrous cellulose. Considerable protection was observed also at the higher dose. Assuming that the benzoyl groups are randomly substituted on the cellulose molecule, the maximum distance between benzoyl groups may be calculated as a function of degree of substitution and as a binominal distribution with a probability of reaction $\geq$ 0.95. At *d.s.*

of 0.2, the calculated maximum spacing of benzoyl groups on the cellulose molecule was 7.2–8.2 nm; at $d.s.$ 0.5, 3.1–4.1 nm; at $d.s.$ 1.1. 1.0–2.1 nm; and at $d.s.$ 1.5 and 0.2. 0.1. nm. In the experimental case, the assumptions of random substitution of benzoyl groups will not be exactly true, since the physical structure of the fibrous cellulose will limit the accessibility of highly ordered regions to reaction with benzoyl chloride. Therefore, in the experimental case, maximum spacings of benzoyl groups will tend to be greater than those indicated. Assuming that the breaking strength of the benzoylated cotton cellulose is related to its molecular weight [SIPPEL, 1949, ARTHUR, 1958], the following relationships can be calculated: at a dose of $1.3 \times 10^{21}$ eV/g cellulose, the average estimated distances between molecular cleavages were increased from about 50 cellobiose units (50 nm) for unsubstituted cellulose to about 300 cellobiose units (300 nm) for benzoylated cellulose ($d.s.$ 2.0).

On the basis of the results for benzoylated cellulose, therefore, energy transfer of at least 7–8 nm can be envisaged ($d.s.$ 0.2) before protection ceases. Recent observations [ARTHUR, 1965] have shown that the protective effects of groups are in the order benzoyl ≫ benzyl > naphthoyl.

## References

AGRONOVICH, V. M. 1960. Optical Spectroscopy (U.S.S.R.), (English Translation.) 9 59.

ALEXANDER, P. and CHARLESBY, A. 1954. Nature 173 578.

ARTHUR JR., J. C. and MARES, T. 1965. J. Appl. Polymer Sci. in the press.

ARTHUR Jr., J. C. 1958. Textile Res. J. 28 204.

ARTHUR JR. J. C., personal communication.

AUGENSTEIN, L. G., BRUSTAD, T. and MASON, R. 1964. Advances in Radiation Biology, 1 228.

AVAKIAN, P. and MERRIFIELD, R. E. 1964. Phys. Rev. 13 541.

AVERY, J. S. and MASON, R. J. Chem. Phys. in the press.

BAKH, N. A. and Sorokin, Y. I. 1955. Symposium on Radiation Chemistry. (Acad. Sci. U.S.S.R.) 135.

BALAZS, E. A., BOTHNERBY, A. A. and GERGELY, J. 1959. J. Mol. Biol. 1 147.

BANNISTER, T. T. 1954. Arch. Biochem. Biophys. 49 222.

BAUGH, P. 1964. Ph. D. Thesis (University of Wales).

BEAMANN, K., DE JONGH, D. C. and SCHOENS, H. K. 1963. J. Amer. Chem. Soc. 85 1763; [1964, de Jongh, D. C., and Beamann K., ibid., 87 67].

BELL, P. H. and DAVEY, W. P. 1941. J. Chem. Phys. 9 441.

BERRY, P. J. LIPSKY, S. L. and BURTON, M. 1956. Trans. Farad. Soc. 52 311.

BIRKS, J. B. 1960. IRE Trans. Nuclear Sci. **NS-7** No. 2-3, 11.

BOWEN, E. J. 1938. Nature **142** 108.

BOWEN, E. J. 1944. Nature **153** 623.

BOWEN, E. J. 1945. J. Chem. Phys. **13** 306.

BOWEN, E. J. 1947. Nature **159** 706.

BOWEN, E. J. 1953. Fluorescence of Solutions. (Longmans Green, London) pp. 25.

BOWEN, E. J. Proc. Symposium on Energy Transfer Processes. Ed. Phillips G. O. (Cardiff 1965) in the press.

BOWEN, E. J. and BROCKLEHURST, B. 1953. Trans. Farad. Soc. **49** 1131.

BOWEN, E. J. and BROCKLEHURST, B. 1955. Trans. Farad. Soc. **51** 774.

BOWEN, E. J. and LIVINGSTON, R. 1954. J. Amer. Chem. Soc. **76** 6330.

BOWEN, E. J., MIKIEWICZ, E. and SMITH, F. 1949. Proc. Rog. Phys. (London) **62A** 26.

BUCHLER, TH. and KASPERS, J. 1947. Biochim. et Biophys. Acta. **1** 21.

BURTON, M. 1960. Z. Elektrochem. **64** 975.

BURTON, M. 1965. (Acad. Press) 259. Pulse Radiolysis. Ed. EBERT, M. Keene, J. P., Swallow, A. J., Baxendale, J. H., as on page 190 under Dillon.

BURTON, M., BERRY, P. J. and LIPSKY, S. 1955. J. Chim. Physique **52** 657.

BURTON, M. and DREESKAMP, H. 1959. Disc. Farad. Soc. **27** 64.

BURTON, M., CHANG, J., LIPSKY, S. and REDDY, M. P. 1957.

BURTON, M. and LIPSKY, S. 1957. J. Phys. Chem. **61** 1461.

BURTON, M. and PATRICK, W. M. 1954. J. Phys. Chem. **58** 421.

CARIO, G. and FRANCK, J. 1923. Z. f. Physik **17** 202.

CARRINGTON, A. 1963. Quart Rev. **17** 67.

CHANG, P. C., YANG, N. C. and WAGNER, C. D. 1959. J. Amer. Chem. Soc. **81** 2060.

CHARLESBY, A. 1960. In: Comparative Effects of Radiation. Eds. Burton, M., Kirby-Smith, J. S. and Magee, J. L. (Wiley, New York) pp. 259.

COLLINSON, E., CONLAY, J. J. and DAINTON, F. S. 1963a. Disc. Farad. Soc. **36** 153.

COLLINSON, E., CONLAY, J. J. and DAINTON, F. S. 1963b. Disc. Farad. Soc. **36**.

COLLINSON, E., DAINTON, F. S., SMITH, D. R. and TAZUKE, S. 1962. Proc. Chem. Soc. **140**.

COPPINGER, G. M. 1957. J. Amer. Chem. Soc. **79** 501.

COULSON, C. A. 1964. Dictionary of molecular constants (personally communicated).

COUMON, D. J. and MACKOR, E. L. 1964. Trans. Farad. Soc. **60** 1726.

CRAMER, F. D. 1955. Rev. Pure and Appl. Chem. **5** 143.

CRAMER, F. D. 1956. Angew. Chem. **68** 115.

CUNDALL, R. B. 1964. In: Progress in Reaction Kinetics, Vol. II. Ed. Porter, G. (Pergamon Press, Oxford).

CUNDALL, R. B. and GRIFFITHS, P. A. 1963a. Disc. Farad. Soc. **36** 120.

CUNDALL, R. B. and GRIFFITHS, P. A. 1963b. J. Amer. Chem. Soc. **85** 1211.

CUNDALL, R. B. and GRIFFITHS, P. A. 1963c. Disc. Farad. Soc. **36** 111.

CUNDALL, R. B. and GRIFFITHS, P. A. Proc. Symposium on Energy Transfer Processes. Ed. Phillips, G.O. (Cardiff 1965) in the press.

CZAPSKI, G. and SCHWARZ, H. A. 1962. J. Phys. Chem. **66** 471.

DAINTON, F. S., Introduction at Proc. Symposium on Energy Transfer Processes Ed. Phillips, G.O. (Cardiff 1965), in the press.

DAINTON, F. S., KEMP, T. J., SALMON, G. A. and KEENE, J. P. 1964. Nature **203** 1050.

DAINTON, F. S., KOSA-SOMOGYI, I. and SALMON, G. A. 1965. Trans. Farad. Soc. **61** 871.

DAVYDOV, A. S., 1962. Zhur. Eksptl. Teoret. Fiz. ,18, 210; translated by Kasha M. and Oppenheimer M., 1962. Theory of Molecular Excitons, 172 pp. (McGraw-Hill).

DE JONGH, D. C. and BEAMANN, K. 1964. J. Amer. Chem. Soc. **87** 67.

DEXTER, D. L. 1953. J. Chem. Phys. **21** 836.

DILLON, M. A. and BURTON M. 1965. Pulse Radiolysis. Ed. Ebert, M., Keene, J. P., Swallow, A. J. and Baxendale, J. H. (Acad. Press) **259**.

DUNNING, W. J. 1963. In: Physics and Chemistry of the Organic Solid State, Vol. 1. Ed. Fox, D., Labes, M. M. and Weissberger, A. (Wiley, New York) p. 411.

DUTTON, H. J., MANNING, W. M. and DUGGAR, B. M. 1943. J. Phys. Chem. **47** 308.

DYNE, P. J. and DENHARTOG, 1963. Can. J. Chem. **41** 1794.

DYNE, P. J., SMITH, D. R. and STONE, J. A. 1963. Ann. Rev. Phys. Chem. **14** 313.

EHRENBERG, L., JAARMA, M. and ZIMMER, E. C. 1957. Acta Chem. Scand. **11** 950.

ELEY, D. D. and CARDEW, M. H. 1959. Disc. Farad. Soc. **27**.

ELEY, D. D., PARFITT, G. D., PERRY, M. J. and TAYSUM, D. H. 1953. Trans. Farad. Soc. **49** 79.

FANO, U. 1960. In: Comparative Effects of Radiation, Burton, M., Kirby-Smith, J. S. and Magee, J. L. (Wiley, New York) pp. 14.

FERRIER, W. G. 1960. Acta Cryst. **13** 678.

FESSENDEN, R. W. and SCHULER, R. H. 1963a. J. Chem. Phys. **39** 2147.

FESSENDEN, R. W. and SCHULER, R. H. 1963b. Disc. Farad. Soc. **36** 147.

FISCHER, H. 1962a. J. Chem. Phys. **37** 1094.

FISCHER, H. 1962b. Kolloid-Z. **180** 64.

FÖRSTER, TH. 1946. Naturwiss. **33** 166.

FÖRSTER, TH. 1948. Ann. d. Physik. **2** 55.

FÖRSTER, TH. 1949. Z. Electrochem. **53** 93.

FÖRSTER, TH. 1959. Disc. Farad. Soc. **27** 7.

FÖRSTER, TH. 1960. Rad. Res. Suppl. **2** 326.

FOSTER, A. B. and OVEREND, W. G. 1955. Chemistry and Industry (London) 566.

FOX, D. and SCHNAPP, O. 1955. J. Chem. Phys. **23** 767.

FREEMAN, G. R. 1960. J. Chem. Phys. **33** 71.

FRENCH, D. 1957. Advan. Carbohyd. Chem. **12** 189.

FRENKEL, J. 1931. Phys. Rev. **37** 17.

FRENKEL, J. 1936. Phys. Z. Sowjetunion **9** 138.

GÄUMANN, T. 1961. Helv. chim. acta. **44** 1337.

GARDNER, D. G. and EPSTEIN, L. M. 1961. J. Chem. Phys. **34** 1653.

GARDNER, D. G., HENRY, G. and WARD, D. Proc. Symposium on Energy Transfer Processes. Ed. Phillips, G. O. (Cardiff 1965) in the press.

GILLAM, A. and STERN, E. S. 1954. Electronic Absorption Spectroscopy (Arnold, London).

GILMAN, A. 1953. Trans. Am. Inst. Mining Met. Engrs. **203** 1252.

GILMAN, A. 1956. J. Appl. Phys. **27** 1018, 1262.

GOLUB, M. A. 1957. J. Polymer Sci. **25** 373.

GOLUB, M. A. 1958. J. Amer. Chem. Soc. **80** 1794.

GOLUB, M. A. 1959. J. Amer. Chem. Soc. **81** 54.

GOLUB, M. A. 1960. J. Amer. Chem. Soc. **82** 5093.

GOLUB, M. A. 1962. J. Phys. Chem. **66** 1202.

GOLUB, M. A. 1963. Disc. Farad. Soc. **36** 276.

GOLUB, M. A. 1964. J. Phys. Chem. **68** 2360.

GRANATH, K. A. and KINELL, P. 1960. Riso Report No. **16** 23.

GRANATH, K. A. and KINELL, P. 1961. Acta. Chem. Scand. **15** 141.

GREEN, F. D., ADAM, W. and CANTRILL, J. E. 1961. J. Amer. Chem. Soc. **83** 3461.

GURAINO, J. P., RONAYNE, M. R. and HAMMILL, W. H. 1962. Radiation Res. **17** 379.

GURNEE, E. F. and MAGEE, J. L. 1957. J. Chem. Phys. **26** 1237.

GUSYNIN, V. I. and TAL'ROZE, V. L. 1960. Doklady Akad. Nauk. S.S.S.R. **135** 1160.

HAMMILL, W. H., GUARINO, J. P., RONAYNE, M. R. and WARD, J. A. 1963. Disc. Farad. Soc. **36** 169.

HAMMOND, G. S., STOUT, C. A. and LAMOLA, A. A. 1964. J. Amer. Chem. Soc. **86** 3103.

HARBURY, H. A. and FOLEY, K. A. 1958, Proc. Nat. Acad. Sci. U.S. **44** 662.

HARDWICK, T. 1962. J. Phys. Chem. **66** 232.

HART, E. J. and BOAG, J. W. 1963. Nature **197** 45.

HATANO, Y., SHIDA, S. and SATO, S. 1964. Bull. Chem. Soc. (Japan) **37** 1854.

HICKAM, W. M. and BERG, D. 1958. J. Chem. Phys. **29** 517.

HILLS, P. and JOHNSON, R. 1961. United Kingdom Atomic Energy Authority (Research Group) Report, R 3750.

HISATSURE, J. and JAYADEVAPPA, E. S. 1960. J. Chem. Phys. **32** 565.

HOCHSTRASSER, R. M. 1963. Radiation Res. **20** 107.

HOCHSTRASSER, R. M. 1964. J. Chem. Phys. **40** 1038.

ISENBERG, I. and SZENT-GYORGI, A. 1958. Proc. Nat. Acad. Sci. U.S. **44** 857;

ISENBERG, I. and SZENT-GYORGI, A. 1959. Proc. Nat. Acad. Sci. U.S. **45** 1232.

KALLMAN, H. and FURST, M. 1950. Phys. Rev. **79** 857.

KALLMAN, H. and FURST, M. 1951. Phys. Rev. **81** 853.

KALLMAN, H. and FURST, M. 1952. Phys. Rev. **85** 816.

KASHA, M. 1944. J. Amer. Chem. Soc. **66** 2100.

KASHA, M. 1950. Disc. Farad. Soc. **9** 14.

KASHA, M. 1963. Rad. Res. **20** 55.

KAUFMAN, P. C. 1963. J. Phys. Chem. **67** 1671.

KEENE, J. P. 1963. Nature **197** 47.

KEMP, T. J., SALMON, G. A., LAND, E. J. and NOSWORTHY, J. M. Proc. Symposium on Energy Transfer Processes. Ed. Phillips. G.O. (Cardiff, 1965) in the press.

KILLEAN, R. C. G., FERRIER, W. G. and YOUNG, D. W. 1962. Acta Cryst. **15** 911.

KLOTZ, I. M. 1958. J. Amer. Chem. Soc. **80** 2132.

KROPP, J. L. and BURTON, M. 1962. J. Chem. Phys. **37** 1742.

LAMBORN, J. and SWALLOW, A. J. 1961. J. Phys. Chem. **65** 920.

LAUTSCH, W., BROSER, W., GODICKE, V. 1957. Z. Naturforsch. **126** 303.

LAUTSCH, W., BROSER, W. 1958. Kolloid-Z. **161** 10.

LINSCHITZ, H. 1960. Rad. Res. Suppl. **2** 182.

LIVINGSTON, R. 1960. Rad. Res. Suppl. **2** 196.

LOVELOCK, J. 1961. Nature. **189** 729.

LUTTRINGHAUS, H., CRAMER, F. D., PRINZBACH, T. and HENGLEIN, A.1958. Ann. Chem. **613** 185.

LYONS, L. E., 1957. J. Chem. Soc. 5003.

MAGEE, J. L. 1952. Disc. Farad. Soc. **12** 33.

MAGEE, J. L. and BURTON, M. 1951. J. Amer. Chem. Soc. **73** 523.

MANION, J. P. and BURTON, M. 1952. J. Phys. Chem. **56** 560.

MASON, R. 1965. Proc. Symposium Energy Transfer Processes. Ed. Phillips, G. O. (Cardiff) in the press.

MATHESON, M. 1962. Ann. Rev. Phys. Chem. **13** 77.

McCOLLUM, J. D. and NEVITT, T. D. 1963. ADS Technical Report, ASD-TDR-63–616.

McCOLLUM, J. D. and WILSON, W. A. 1961. United States ASD Technical Report, ASD-TDR 61–170.

McCOLLUM, J. D. and WILSON, W. A. 1962. United States AD Technical Report 274, 901.

McCLURE, D. S. 1959. In: Solid State Physics, Vol. 8 (Academic Press, New York) Part I.

McDONALD, T. R. R. and BEEVERS, C. A. 1950. Acta Cryst. **3** 394.

MISHINA, A. personal communication.

MUNSTER, A. 1950. Trans. Farad., Soc. **46** 165.

NOSWORTHY, J. M. and KEENE, J. P. 1964. Proc. Chem. Soc. 114.

NOSWORTHY, J. M., MAGEE, J. L. and BURTON, M. 1961. J. Chem. Phys. **34** 83.

NIEMANN, G. C. and ROBINSON, G. W. 1963. J. Chem. Phys. **39** 1298.

ORE, A. 1959. J. Chem. Phys. **31** 442.

PARKER, C. A. and HATCHARD, C. G. 1963. Trans. Farad. Soc. **59** 284.

PERRIN, J. 1925. 2me conseil de chim. Solvay (Gauthiers and Villars, Paris) p. 322.

PHILLIPS, G. O. 1961. Advan. Carbohyd. Chem. **16** 13.

PHILLIPS, G. O. 1963. Advan. Carbohyd. Chem. **18** 9.

PHILLIPS, G. O. Energy Transport in Carbohydrates, Parts I-VI, J. Chem. Soc. (in the press).

PHILLIPS, G. O. and BARBER, P. 1963. J. Chem. Soc. 3900.

PHILLIPS, G. O. and BAUGH, P. J. 1963a. Nature **198** 262;.

PHILLIPS, G. O. and BAUGH, P. J. 1963b. Disc. Farad. Soc. **36** 281.

PHILLIPS, G. O., BLOUIN, F. A. and ARTHUR JR., JETT C. 1964. Radiation Res. **23** 527.

PORTER, G. 1963. Investigation of Rates and Mechanisms of Reactions, Vol. VIII, Part II in Techniques of Organic Chemistry. Ed. Weissberger, A. (Wiley, New York).

PULLEY, and FRENCH, D. 1963. Biochem. Biophys. Res. Communs. **5** 11.

RABINOWITCH, E. 1957. J. Phys. Chem. **61** 870.

RABINOWITCH, E. 1963. Proc. 5th Intern. Congress Biochem. Vol. 6 (Pergamon Press).

RABINOWITCH, E. 1964. In: Proceedings Symposium on Physical Processes in Radiation Biology. Eds. Augustein, L. G., Mason, R. and Rosenberg, B. (Academic Press, New York).

REXROAD, H. N. and GORDY, W. 1962. Phys. Rev. **125** 242.

RIEHL, N. 1956. Naturwissenschaften **43** 145.

SCHOEPFLE, C. S. and FELLOWS, C. H. 1931. J. Ind. Eng. Chem. **23** 1396.

SCHOLES, G., SIMIC, M. and WEISS, J. 1960. Nature **188** 1019.

SCHULER, R. H. 1957. J. Phys. Chem. **61** 1472.

SHORE, V. G. and PARDEE, A. B. 1956. ARCH. Biochem. Biophys. **62** 335.

SIMPSON, O. 1956. Proc. Roy. Soc. (London) **A 238** 402.

SIMPSON, W. T. and PETERSON, D. L. 1957. J. Chem. Phys. **26** 588.

SIPPEL, A. 1949. Kolloid Z. **112** 80.

SOGO, P. B., NAKAZAKI, M. and CALVIN, M. 1957. J. Chem. Phys. **26** 1343.

STREITWIESER, A. 1961. Molecular Orbital Theory for Chemists (Wiley, New York).

STRYER, L. 1960. Rad. Res. Suppl. **2** 432.

SWALLOW, A. J. 1963a. Disc. Farad. Soc. **36** 273.

SWALLOW, A. J. 1963b. Proc. Intern. Conf. Rad. Res. (Natick, Mass.) pp. 49.

SWALLOW, A. J., 1965 Proc. Symposium on Energy Transfer Processes. Ed. Phillips. (Cardiff).

TEALE, F. J. W. and WEBER, G. 1957. Biochem. J. **65** 476.

TERENIN, A. and ERMOLAEV, V. 1956. Trans. Farad. Soc. **52** 1042.

TOLBERT, B. M. and LEMMON, R. M. 1955. Radiation Res. **3** 22.

TOLKACHEV, V. A., MOLIN, YU., TCHKEIDZE, YU. D., YA. BUBEN and VOEVODSKY, V. V. 1961. Doklady, Akad. Nauk U.S.S.R. **141** 911.

VAVILOV, S. I. 1943. J. Phys. (U.S.S.R.) **7** 141.

VOEVODSKY, V. V. 1962. Radiation Res. **17** 366.

WANNIER, G. H. 1937. Phys. Rev. **52** 191.

WEBER, G. 1952. Biochem. J. **51** 155.

WEBER, G. and TEALE, F. J. W. 1958. Trans. Farad. Soc. **54** 640.

WEBER, G. and TEALE, F. J. W. 1959a. Disc. Farad. Soc. **27**

WEBER, G. and TEALE, F. J. W., 1959b. Biochem. J. **67** 15P.

WEST, W. 1935. J. Amer. Chem. Soc. **57** 1931.

WIGNER, E. 1927. Göttinger Nachrichten. 375.

WILLIAMS, R. R. and HAMMILL, W. H. 1954. Rad. Res. **158** 1.

WILLIAMS, W., SCHMIDT, B., WOLFROM, M. L., MICKELAKIS, A. and McCABE, L. J. 1959. Proc. Nat. Acad. Sci. **45** 1744.

WILSON, J. E. and NOYES, W. A. 1941. J. Amer. Chem. Soc. **63** 3024.

WOLFROM, M. L., BINKLEY, W. W. and McCABE, L. J. 1959. J. Amer. Chem. Soc. **81** 1442.

WOLF, H. C. 1959. In: Solid State Physics, Vol. 9 (Academic Press, New York) Vol. 9.

See also Symposium on Bioenergetis 1960, Rad. Res. Supplement **2**.

# IV

# THE MOLECULAR BASIS OF BIOLOGICAL EFFECTS OF ULTRAVIOLET RADIATION AND PHOTO-REACTIVATION *

JANE K. SETLOW

*Biology Division, Oak Ridge National Laboratory, Oak Ridge, Tennessee, U.S.A.*

\* Research sponsored by the U. S. Atomic Energy Commission under contract with the Union Carbide Corporation.

# CONTENTS

# 1. Introduction

Ultraviolet action spectra obtained from 1928 to 1939 indicated that lethal [GATES, 1928] and mutagenic [EMMONS and HOLLAENDER, 1939; KNAPP et al., 1939] effects of ultraviolet (UV) radiation result from the absorption of photons in nucleic acids. The ratios of the sensitivities at different wavelengths were similar to the ratios of the absorption coefficients of nucleic acid.

Within the past decade it has become possible to begin to explain certain biological effects of UV radiation in terms of specific changes in DNA. A considerable number of different UV-induced alterations in DNA can now be measured chemically. However, the problem of determining which of the observed changes is responsible for a given biological effect is a very difficult one, especially when this effect is likely to involve only a tiny fraction of the chemically determined changes, as in the case of a mutation which may result from a change in a particular one out of as many as $10^7$ nucleotide pairs. Consequently much more progress has been made in determining the changes in DNA responsible for the lethal than for the mutagenic action of UV.

The problem of equating chemical alterations in DNA and biological effects is further complicated by the discovery that cells have a number of methods for decreasing markedly the potential biological effects of UV-induced changes. A study of these repair processes, may, however, produce information which is valuable not only for the solution of specific radiobiological problems, but also of problems of more general biological importance. For example, it is possible that genetic continuity is preserved partly by means of error-correcting mechanisms similar to or the same as those used by the cell to repair UV damage. The investigation of the repair of UV-induced blocks to DNA synthesis may be important for an understanding of DNA synthesis itself.

The most useful biological systems used in studies of the molecular basis of biological effects of UV have been single cells and their components, mainly bacteria, bacterial viruses, and transforming DNA. Some of the basic principles obtained have been extended to work with higher organisms, but the present discussion will be limited to the simpler systems.

## 2. UV-induced physical and chemical changes in nucleic acid and nucleic acid components

Many different UV-induced changes in physical and chemical properties of nucleic acid have been proposed as the cause of biological effects. A description of these changes, with some indication of how they are measured, is presented here.

### 2.1. CHAIN BREAKS

It was early observed that UV causes a decrease in the viscosity and the streaming birefringence of nucleic acids [HOLLAENDER, GREENSTEIN and JENRETTE, 1941]. This was considered to be the result of a depolymerization. MOROSON and ALEXANDER [1961] analyzed the UV-induced decrease in viscosity as due to chain breaks (calculated from light-scattering data) and to a decrease in stiffness, as judged by the decrease in radius of gyration calculated from light-scattering measurements. Many more chain breaks can be detected, by the decrease in sedimentation coefficient [MARMUR et al., 1961], when the DNA is denatured after irradiation, indicating that most UV-induced breaks are in one chain, without a break in the opposite strand in a corresponding position.

### 2.2. DENATURATION

After irradiation, DNA shows an increased ability to react with formaldehyde [SAUERBIER, 1960; MARMUR et al., 1961], suggesting partial denaturation, since heat-denatured DNA also reacts better with this substance. Other evidence for partial denaturation is that the melting temperature of DNA is decreased by UV, and acid denaturation can occur at a higher $p$H than for unirradiated DNA. The observed UV-induced increase in buoyant density of DNA may also be explained partially as a denaturation effect [MARMUR et al., 1961].

### 2.3. DNA CROSS-LINKS

After irradiation, dry DNA becomes insoluble [R. B. SETLOW and

DOYLE, 1953]. DNA irradiated in solution becomes resistant to strand separation, as judged by the lack of separation of strands of hybrid $N^{14}$–$N^{15}$ *Escherichia coli* DNA in a cesium chloride density gradient after formamide treatment [MARMUR and GROSSMAN, 1961]. Both these phenomena may be interpreted as the result of UV-induced bonds between polynucleotide chains. The insoluble dry DNA is presumed to contain intermolecular links, but experiments with two DNA's of different densities indicate that in solution only intramolecular links are formed, since no UV-induced hybrid-density material was found [MARMUR and GROSSMAN, 1961].

More cross-links are produced if the DNA is heated during irradiation, up to a temperature at which denaturation is 20 % complete [GLISIN and DOTY, 1962]. Above this temperature the amount of cross-linking decreases. Thus a disturbance in the local structural organization of the DNA apparently favours formation of cross-links, unless it has gone so far that the strands have begun to come apart. Cross-links are produced more readily in DNA with high A–T content [MARMUR et al.,1961]. The temperature dependence and the base-composition dependence of cross-linking may be two indications of the same phenomenon. A high A–T DNA and a heated DNA both contain more local denatured regions, increasing the probability of the existence of a particular configuration necessary for formation of the UV-induced bond across the chains.

MARMUR and GROSSMAN [1961] reported that crosslinks are photo-reactivable, implicating pyrimidine dimers in cross-linking (see sections 2.6 and 4.1). However, as pointed out by SMITH [1964], the criterion used by Marmur and Grossman for loss of cross-linking after treatment with yeast photoreactivating enzyme was increased sensitivity to the enzyme phosphodiesterase from *E. coli*, rather than the criterion of increased separation of strands of hybrid-density *E. coli* DNA in a cesium chloride gradient. The increased sensitivity to phosphodiesterase after enzymatic photoreactivation may be the result of elimination of cross-links *or* elimination of alterations in single chains. OPARA-KUBINSKA, KURYLO-BOROWSKA and SZYBALSKI [1963] found more cross-links with increasing substitution of 5-bromouracil for thymine in DNA, indicating that thymine dimers cannot be the only cause of cross-linking.

Cross-links, unlike pyrimidine dimers, are not eliminated by short-wavelength irradiation [R. B. SETLOW, 1964a]. The fact that the most cross-links are produced when DNA is irradiated dry, although there are few dimers produced [RIKLIS and SIMSON, 1964], also argues against the hypothesis that cross-links are thymine dimers. Furthermore, T1 bacteriophage which is irradiated dry is not photoreactivable after resuspension and absorption to the host cell [HILL and ROSSI, 1952], again suggesting that cross-links are not dimers (see section 4.1). It is concluded that the chemical nature of cross-linking remains an unsolved problem.

## 2.4. NUCLEIC ACID-PROTEIN CROSS-LINKS

When certain extraction procedures are used, DNA in whole irradiated cells becomes less extractable [SMITH, 1962b; ALEXANDER and MOROSON, 1962]. The *Escherichia coli* cells must apparently be lysed with detergent for the effect to be observed: irradiated cells ground with alumina [SMITH, 1962b] or extracted with 2M NaCl [ALEXANDER and MOROSON, 1962] showed no decrease in extractability. The fact that treatment of the lysed cell suspension with trypsin before deproteinization eliminates the effect suggests that a DNA-protein interaction is responsible for the decrease in extractability [SMITH, 1962b]. Detergent treatment of purified DNA irradiated *in vitro* results in no loss of DNA when the detergent is removed, showing that it is not the detergent itself that removes some of the DNA [SMITH, 1962b].

The extractability effect has been reproduced *in vitro* with a mixture of DNA and bovine serum albumin [SMITH, 1964], although the shape of the dose response curve is different from that obtained with whole cells. The components of the mixture can be irradiated before mixing without loss of the effect, suggesting a long-lived precursor for the bond between DNA and protein. The effect is greater if the protein alone is irradiated, rather than the DNA alone.

The chemical nature of the bonding is unknown, although there is some suggestion that thymine may play a role, since an unidentified thymine photoproduct (not a dimer) appears to be concentrated with the DNA bound to protein [SMITH, 1964]. The effect is greatly modified when bromouracil is substituted for thymine in the bacterial DNA. The substituted DNA is initially more sensitive, and at higher doses less sensitive [SMITH, 1964], also suggesting that thymine might be involved in the protein binding. A mixed photoproduct of uracil and cysteine, which possibly could be a model for the DNA-protein linking, has been found after irradiation of a solution of these substances [SMITH, 1965].

## 2.5. HYDRATES OF CYTOSINE AND URACIL

A UV-photoproduct of uracil, initially identified by the decrease in UV absorbance, was shown to revert to the original compound either by heat or acid treatment [SINSHEIMER and HASTINGS, 1949]. Similar photoproducts were found in irradiated uridine and cytidylic acid. It was suggested that this photoproduct is a water addition at the 5–6 position of the ring [SINSHEIMER, 1954], and later the photoproduct of uracil was shown by organic synthesis of a compound identical to the photoproduct [MOORE, 1958] to be a 6-hydroxy compound. By analogy, the similarly reversible photoproducts of the other compounds are considered to be hydrates at the same position [SHUGAR, 1962], although WANG [1959] believes that the cytosine photoproducts are not hydrates at all, but ring compounds with a shift in the double bond to the 6–1 position. Cytidine or deoxycytidine irradiated in tritium water acquire a radioactive label [WACKER, 1963]. Furthermore, fewer of these photoproducts are formed in heavy water, which is to be expected if they are hydrates, since more energy is required to remove deuterium than hydrogen from oxygen [SHUGAR and WIERZCHOWSKI, 1957].

The possibility that the water addition is in the 5 position has been eliminated in the case of uridine [WANG, 1962] and poly U [WIERZCHOWSKI and SHUGAR, 1962], since MOORE and THOMSON [1955] showed that the 5 hydroxy compound is not heat-reversible.

Cytosine nucleosides and nucleotides, but not cytosine, differ from the corresponding uracil compounds in that a new absorbing peak appears at around 236 nm after irradiation. This new peak is heat- and acid-reversible [SINSHEIMER, 1957]. The existence of the cytosine hydrate in irradiated denatured DNA was inferred from the appearance of a heat-reversible absorption peak around 240 nm [R. B. SETLOW and CARRIER, 1963], not found in glucosylated hydroxymethyl-cytosine-containing DNA from T4 bacteriophage. However, irradiated native DNA showed no such heat-reversible spectroscopic change typical of the deoxycytidine (CdR) photoproduct. Likewise, although evidence of reversible hydrate formation was obtained in the homo-polymer ribo C, none was found in the homocopolymer dI : dC (with inosine in one chain, cytosine in the other), [WIERZCHOWSKI and SHUGAR, 1962; R. B. SETLOW, CARRIER and BOLLUM, 1965b].

No evidence for hydrates of thymine has been found [MOORE and THOMSON, 1957; JOHNS et al., 1964].

It is concluded that few if any pyrimidine hydrates may be found in native DNA.

### 2.6. PYRIMIDINE DIMERS

In addition to the discovery of thymine dimers resulting from UV-irradiation of frozen thymine [BEUKERS, YLSTRA and BERENDS, 1959], evidence for four other types of pyrimidine dimers has been obtained. These are dimers of cytosine [WACKER, 1963; R. B. SETLOW, CARRIER and BOLLUM, 1965b], uracil (WANG, 1961; SMIETANOWSKA and SHUGAR, 1961; SMITH, 1963], uracil-thymine (BEUKERS and BERENDS, 1960; WACKER et al., 1961; SMITH, 1963] and cytosine-thymine [SETLOW, CARRIER and BOLLUM, 1965a]. The initial observation was a decrease in UV absorbance of the irradiated pyrimidines [BEUKERS, YLSTRA and BERENDS, 1958]. Later the thymine photoproduct was isolated by ethanol extraction of irradiated thymine and recrystallization of the residue in water [BEUKERS and BERENDS, 1960]. It was identified as a dimer from information obtained by elementary analysis, molecular weight determination, and crystallographic analysis [BEUKERS and BERENDS, 1960]. The infrared spectrum suggested that the compound contained a cyclobutane ring [BEUKERS and BERENDS, 1960]. Later studies with nuclear magnetic resonance have confirmed the proposed cyclobutane structure [WULFF and FRAENKEL, 1961].

From considerations of electronic structure using molecular orbital method calculations, MANTIONE and PULLMAN [1964] have concluded that the triplet state of pyrimidine residues is necessary for dimeriza-tion. By this criterion, cytosine is less likely to undergo dimerization than uracil and thymine.

Thymine dimers are remarkably stable to acid hydrolysis (enabling them to be removed intact from irradiated DNA) and may be readily separated from thymine by paper chromatography [WACKER, DELL-

WEG and WEINBLUM, 1960]. This property of a photoproduct in DNA has been of tremendous importance for a series of experiments which have provided new information not only on the molecular basis of UV action, but also on two different types of repair processes (see section 4). Many cells can be specifically labeled in their DNA with radioactive thymidine, making it possible to measure very small amounts of thymine dimers induced in their DNA by UV doses which are only partially lethal.

Recently it has been found that one type of thymine photoproduct is not heat resistant (and thus cannot survive acid hydrolysis). This is a dimer which is not a cyclobutane type, but is apparently linked through the carbons in the four position of the ring by an oxygen atom [PEARSON, OTTENSMEYER and JOHNS, 1965]. Obviously caution should be employed in basing all conclusions about the biological importance of photoproducts in DNA on acid-hydrolyzed samples alone.

The cyclobutane-type thymine dimer is both formed and monomerized by ultraviolet radiation, but the wavelength-dependences for the forward and back reaction are different. At long UV wavelengths more dimers are formed, whereas at short wavelengths the back reaction predominates and there are fewer dimers. These reactions have been studied in detail in irradiated thymine [WANG, 1961; R. B. SETLOW, 1961], thymidine [WEINBLUM and JOHNS, 1965], thymine dinucleotides [JOHNS, RAPAPORT and DELBRÜCK, 1962; SZTUMPF and SHUGAR, 1962; DEERING and SETLOW, 1963; JOHNS et al., 1964], polythymidylic acid [DEERING and SETLOW, 1963], and in DNA [R. B. SETLOW and CARRIER, 1963; WULFF, 1963a]. A number of general conclusions may be drawn from this work: (1) Thymine dimers are formed readily in DNA and in frozen thymine solutions, but not in thymine in solution, because a particular relative orientation of two thymines is necessary for dimerization. (2) In dissolved DNA, dimers are formed between adjacent thymines on the same chain. rather than across two chains. (3) There is little change in quantum yield with wavelength for either the forward or the back reaction, and the difference in photosteady state at different wavelengths is the result of the differences in the absorption spectra of the dimer and thymine. (4) The wavelength dependence for dimer formation in DNA more nearly parallels thymidine absorption than DNA absorption, indicating that photons absorbed in other bases are not likely to produce dimers between adjacent thymines. (5) In frozen thymidine and in TpT*, a number of chromatographically separable dimers are formed.

Dimerization of uracil has also been studied in detail by irradiation of dUpU** [HELLEINER, PEARSON and JOHNS, 1963] and poly U [GROSS-MAN, 1962; SWENSON and SETLOW, 1963]. The wavelength dependences of the forward and back reactions are somewhat similar to those found for thymine, in that the short wavelengths are more efficient in mono-merizing the dimers. The uracil dimer reaction is complicated by the production of hydrates, which form from the adjacent uracil residues and prevent them from taking part in dimer formation.

The quantum yield for uracil dimers differs markedly with wave-length, unlike the quantum yield for thymine dimers, and is smaller at longer wavelengths in the case of two types of uracil dimers found in irradiated dUpU. The quantum yield for uracil hydrate formation, however, increases at longer wavelengths [HELLEINER, PEARSON and JOHNS, 1963]. The result of the wavelength relations is that there are more dimers than hydrates after relatively small doses of short-wavelength irradiation, but that relatively more hydrates are produced by long-wavelength irradiation according to HELLEINER, PEARSON and JOHNS [1963] and SWENSON and SETLOW [1963], although GROSSMAN [1963] finds the opposite result (see section 3.5).

The quantum yield for dimer monomerization at short wavelengths is probably smaller than the corresponding one for thymine [HELLEI-NER, PEARSON and JOHNS, 1963; SWENSON and SETLOW, 1963].

The detection of cytosine dimers is complicated not only by the hydrate reaction, but also by the fact that when the 5–6 double bond is saturated, cytosine tends to deaminate [GREEN and COHEN, 1957]. Thus cytosine dimers are readily converted to uracil dimers by heat, as judged by the appearance of uracil dimers after irradiation of frozen cytosine [SMITH, 1963], CpC*** [FREEMAN, HARIHARAN and JOHNS, 1965], poly dI : dC [R. B. SETLOW, CARRIER and BOLLUM, 1965b], and DNA [DELLWEG and WACKER, 1962; SAUERBIER, 1964b; SETLOW, CARRIER and BOLLUM, 1965a]. Furthermore, uracil may be recovered from the dimer region of chromatograms by elution and reirradiation [SAUERBIER, 1964b; SETLOW, CARRIER and BOLLUM,

---

  * Thymidylyl— (3′ → 5′) — thymidine.
 ** Deoxyuridylyl (3′ → 5′) deoxyuridine.
*** Cytidylyl-cytidine.

1965b]. The latter authors have presented the following additional evidence that the original photoproduct is a cytosine dimer. (1) The short-wavelength reversibility of dimers in poly dI : dC is decreased after heating, because the uracil dimers produced from cytosine dimers by heat are less susceptible to monomerization than the cytosine dimers. (2) The amount of uracil recovered by short-wavelength irradiation when the polymer has been heated is quantitatively equivalent to the amount of dimer that disappears. Only if irradiated poly dI : dC has been heated can uracil be recovered after photoreactivation with yeast enzyme, a treatment which eliminates various types of pyrimidine dimers from polynucleotides (see section 4.1).

Monomerization of dimers in irradiated and heated poly dI : dC may be observed directly, because it is possible to measure the amount of uracil that appears after photoreactivation. However, it is not possible to prove from the thymine dimer experiments that the dimers are monomerized in DNA by photoreactivation. The disappearance of dimers can be observed, but *not* the appearance of thymine, since the amount of thymine from monomerized dimer is too small relative to that of originally undimerized thymine. One can infer that monomerization of thymine dimers in DNA has occurred. Similarly one can infer that there is monomerization of cytosine dimers in irradiated, unheated poly dI : dC during photoreactivation, since the cytosine dimers are eliminated, although at a slower rate than the uracil dimers.

Mixed pyrimidine dimers have been obtained after irradiation of frozen solutions [SMITH, 1963; WACKER, 1963], and evidence for mixed dimers in irradiated DNA has been obtained by R. B. SETLOW, CARRIER and BOLLUM [1965a]. The latter authors have made synthetic DNA specifically labelled with tritiated cytosine, using calf thymus DNA polymerase, E. coli primer, and labelled triphosphate as precursor. After irradiation of a mixture of E. coli DNA, labelled with $^{14}$C in the thymine, and the synthetic DNA, labelled with tritium in the cytosine, the mixture was hydrolyzed and chromatographed. In addition to the $^{14}$C-thymine and $^{3}$H-uracil dimers, another photoproduct, which involved both radioactive labels, appeared on the chromatograms. Irradiation of the isolated photoproduct caused a separation of the two labels into compounds with the chromatographic mobilities of uracil and thymine, indicating that the original photoproduct was a mixed dimer. Treatment with photoreactivating enzyme from yeast also eliminated the mixed dimers. Heating DNA after irradiation converts the CT dimers to UT dimers, as judged by the appearance of uracil on chromatograms of irradiated, heated DNA treated with short-wavelength UV. Thus there are five types of pyrimidine dimers which may be found in irradiated DNA: $\widehat{TT}$, $\widehat{CC}$, $\widehat{UU}$, $\widehat{CT}$ and $\widehat{UT}$, all of which are apparently monomerized by photoreactivating enzyme and short-wavelength UV.

## 3. Correlation between observed changes in nucleic acid and biological effects

### 3.1. CHAIN BREAKS

The UV-induced production of chain breaks has been reported to be strongly oxygen-dependent [MOROSON and ALEXANDER, 1961], whereas UV inactivation of transforming DNA is not [MARMUR et al., 1961; JAGGER and J. K. SETLOW, unpublished]. Biological effects of UV radiation on whole cells are similarly unaffected by the presence of oxygen during irradiation, even under conditions of high oxygen pressure [DEWEY and BOAG, 1960]. These data indicate that chain breaks may be eliminated from consideration of biological effects of UV.

Some of the results of MARMUR et al. [1961] conflict with those of MOROSON and ALEXANDER [1961] and are compatible with the notion that chain breaks are of biological importance. Marmur et al., who present little experimental detail, claim to get the same UV-induced viscosity changes in DNA whether nitrogen or oxygen was bubbled through the solution during irradiation. One possible explanation of the discrepancy in the results of the two sets of investigators is that their samples were irradiated at different wavelengths. However, they used the same type of UV source and filters to eliminate radiation of wavelengths below 240 nm. Moroson and Alexander irradiated a higher concentration of DNA (100 $\gamma$/ml, as opposed to 20 $\gamma$/ml in the Marmur experiments), but the path length through the samples was so short that the wavelengths of the radiation absorbed by the DNA were presumably similar to those in the Marmur work. Possibly Marmur et al. failed to get rid of oxygen when they bubbled with nitrogen. Moroson and Alexander bubbled their solutions with nitrogen for an hour before irradiation to drive off all the oxygen, and found that a particular viscosity change required about 10 times the UV dose in nitrogen as in oxygen.

It is concluded that chain breaks probably do not contribute to the biological effects of UV, despite the results of Marmur et al., for the following reasons. (1) The oxygen effect on chain breaks obtained by Moroson and Alexander is a very large one, although there is no oxygen effect on biological changes. (2) The doses required to produce a measurable number of chain breaks are out of the normal biological range [$10^5$ ergs/mm², MARMUR et al., 1961; FREIFELDER and DAVISON, 1963].

## 3.2. DENATURATION

The doses required to produce chemically observable changes are very large [more than $10^5$ ergs/mm², MARMUR et al., 1961], but the possibility cannot be excluded that a relatively small number of UV-induced local regions of denaturation may contribute to biological effects. For example, UV-induced stimulation of recombination in *E. coli* [HAAS, WYSS and STONE, 1948], yeast [ROMAN and JACOB, 1957], and bacteriophage [JACOB and WOLLMAN, 1955] could be indirectly the result of such small denatured areas, which might increase the probability of pairing between non-homologous DNA strands.

## 3.3. DNA CROSS-LINKS

The doses to produce cross-links between strands are large [with a 1/e dose of about $10^5$ ergs/mm², GLISIN and DOTY, 1962], whereas some bacteria are inactivated by as few as 2 ergs/mm² [HILL and SIMSON, 1961; R. B. SETLOW, SWENSON and CARRIER, 1963]. MARMUR and GROSSMAN [1961] report cross-linking after doses comparable to those which inactivate transforming DNA from *Bacillus subtilis*. This DNA is extremely resistant, so that after a dose of $10^5$ ergs/mm² at 260 nm almost 0.05 % of the original activity remains [HAUG and GOES, 1963]. It is possible that some of the biological effect on this DNA at such doses could result from cross-links, although it is known that cross-links can be produced in large amounts by another agent, mitomycin, without a large decrease in the transforming activity of DNA [IYER and SZYBALSKI, 1963].

Cross-links in bacteriophage T7 have been eliminated as a possible explanation for the lethal effects of UV, since there are no cross-links at a dose which kills 99 % of the virus, and there is approximately one cross-link per molecule when the survival is down to $10^{-8}$ [FREI-FELDER and DAVISON, 1963].

ALEXANDER and MOROSON [1962] found that there is less cross-linking of DNA in sperm heads in the presence of oxygen (relative to irradiation in nitrogen). This could be an important clue to the chemical nature of the linkage, and provides further evidence that cross-links have nothing to do with biological effects, which exhibit no oxygen effect.

It is concluded that cross-links are of no biological significance in UV effects, except possibly in the case of extremely UV-resistant transforming DNA.

### 3.4. NUCLEIC ACID-PROTEIN CROSS-LINKS

It has been argued that since DNA and protein are apparently cross-linked by doses similar to those which kill bacteria, therefore this UV change may well be important in killing bacteria [SMITH, 1964]. However, in assigning lethal effects to particular chemical changes, the criterion of similarity of dose range cannot be the only one (although, as previously noted, some UV-induced alterations can be excluded because the doses required are enormously larger than those for biological changes).

Two different strains of *Escherichia coli* (B and B/r) with very different sensitivities to UV killing have the same sensitivity to loss of extractability [SMITH, 1962b]. However, this does not necessarily eliminate the DNA-protein cross-links from consideration as possible contributors to lethality, since different strains may contain the same number of initial lesions and yet have widely varying abilities to repair the damage [R. B. SETLOW and CARRIER, 1964]. However, the long (one hour) detergent treatment required to show a loss of extractability might be expected to permit some repair enzymes to act. The phenomenon is not photoreactivable, which supports the idea that dimers are not involved [SMITH, 1964].

GODDARD, STREETER and GORDON [1964] have observed protein-RNA binding in irradiated tobacco mosaic virus at doses in the range of lethal hits. The linkage is apparently not covalent.

It is possible that the protein-DNA binding is a secondary effect of UV. SMITH [1964] has found that the sensitivity to loss of extractability increases in a thymineless mutant of *E. coli* under conditions of thymine starvation. It might be assumed that when normal DNA synthesis is stopped in this way more protein can bind to the previously damaged DNA. There is some evidence that when irradiated cells are lysed more rapidly with detergent, the loss of extractability is observed only if the cells are allowed to grow following irradiation and before the detergent treatment [R. B. SETLOW, unpublished].

Action spectra for UV killing of *E. coli* and other bacteria [GATES, 1930; WYCKOFF, 1932] suggest that nucleic acid and not protein is the absorbing material, although it has been indicated that protein is the more important target in DNA-protein cross-linking [SMITH, 1964]. An exception is the action spectrum for killing of the extraordinarily resistant *Micrococcus radiodurans*, which is approximately as sensitive to irradiation at 280 nm (an absorption peak for protein) as at 265 nm, the wavelength strongly absorbed by nucleic acid [J. K. SETLOW and BOLING, 1965].

It is therefore unlikely that DNA-protein binding is an important factor in bacterial killing by UV, except possibly in the case of extremely UV-resistant cells such as *M. radiodurans*.

### 3.5. HYDRATES OF CYTOSINE AND URACIL

One would expect that heat reversal of biological effects of UV should be readily observable if hydrate formation were an important factor. In view of what is now known about repair processes in bacteria, it is not possible to conclude that because a UV-induced cellular effect is heat-reversible it must therefore be the result of hydrate formation. Any change in the postirradiation environment of the cell, including heat, can be expected to change the relative kinetics of repair enzymes and DNA synthesis, and thus might alter the observed biological effect of UV. Irradiated cells have been observed to be reactivated [ANDERSON, 1949], unaffected [ANDERSON, 1949], and sensitized [LATARJET, 1943; J. K. SETLOW, 1959] by post-irradiation heat. Therefore one must search for heat-reversible biological effects of UV among subcellular systems, such as transforming DNA or viruses.

Transforming DNA from *Hemophilus influenzae* has been reported to be about as sensitive to inactivation at 85°C as at room temperature [J. K. SETLOW and R. B. SETLOW, 1961]. LERMAN and TOLMACH [1959] found that pneumococcus DNA inactivates slightly faster at 58°C than at room temperature. Some bacteriophage may be heat-reactivated only after they are absorbed to the cellular host [BRESCH, 1950], indicating a cellular mechanism for the effect. Similar results, have been obtained with a variety of other phages [SHUGAR, 1962]. These data suggest that cytosine hydrate formation is *not* an important contributor to UV inactivation in these systems. Only in the case of mutation of a phage of Serratia has extracellular heat reversibility been observed [KAPLAN, WINKLER and WOLF-ELLMAUER, 1960]. This particular UV-induced mutation occurs at high frequency (up to 2 %), unlike the other examples of UV mutation of extracellular phage [TESSMAN, 1956; KRIEG, 1959]. The result of Kaplan et al. is puzzling in that the authors also report extracellular photoreactivation of the UV-induced mutations. A possible change in DNA which would fit both these phenomena is a thymine photoproduct of TpT* [PEARSON, OTTENSMEYER and JOHNS, 1965] which is altered by heat, and probably by photoreactivating wavelengths as well [SMITH, 1963]. Thus none of these examples of heat reactivation is explicable in terms of the cytosine hydrate.

GROSSMAN [1962, 1963] has presented evidence that the uracil hydrate is responsible for the UV-induced change in coding properties of poly U based on studies on wavelength dependence and base-catalyzed heat reversal of the coding and of the spectral changes. He observed that the spectral changes caused by irradiation of poly U at 285 nm are *not* affected by heating, unlike those produced at 245 nm, which he claimed to be a less efficient wavelength in causing the spectral changes. The amount of phenylalanine incorporated by a fraction from an *E. coli* extract was decreased when poly U as an RNA template had been previously irradiated with either of these wavelengths, but a heat-reversible increase in serine incorporation was observed after the shorter wavelength alone. Grossman concluded that 245 nm radiation causes a heat-reversible mutation in poly U from the normal code for

* A type of dimer which these authors call TpT[4].

phenylalanine (UUU) to that for serine (2U, 1C), whereas at 285 nm only the ability of poly U to act as a template is decreased, presumably as a result of the production of non heat-reversible uracil dimers at this wavelength.

A number of questions can be raised concerning Grossman's conclusion.

(1) Other work shows that both dimers and hydrates are formed at the long as well as the short wavelengths. SWENSON and SETLOW [1963] found heat-reversible spectral changes after irradiation at all the UV wavelengths investigated, although the proportion of the absorbance change which was reversible depended on the dose and the wavelength. The change was *smaller* at 280 than at 248 nm. Although these authors presented no data for 285 nm, extrapolation of their data at other wavelengths suggests that this wavelength would be even less effective than 280 nm. Grossman's data, showing the greater effectiveness of 285 nm for decreasing absorbance, are presumably the result of higher intensity of the irradiation at this wavelength. Swenson and Setlow calculated from their data at low doses that *more* dimers are produced at 248 than at 280 nm. Similarly HELLEINER, PEARSON and JOHNS [1963] found the quantum yield for dimers in dUpU to be higher at the shorter wavelength. Since it appears that hydrates are not exclusively produced at 245 nm, as claimed by Grossman, it is not certain that the observed coding change in poly U is the result of the hydrate.

(2) It is not clear that uracil dimers are entirely responsible for the decrease in the ability of poly U to act as a template. LOGAN and WHITMORE [1965] found part of the decrease in incorporation to be due to changes in the length of poly U resulting from base-catalyzed dehydration of the irradiated polymer, and they also observed that the dehydration rate varies with the chain length.

(3) The increased incorporation of serine may not be a mutation in poly U. The amino acid-incorporating system used by Grossman is an impure one, presumably containing a mixture of many enzymes, including a possible end-addition enzyme, which could add serine in response to uracil hydrate.

(4) It is possible that there is a heat-reversible photoproduct of poly U which is not a hydrate, analogous to the heat-sensitive thymine photoproduct discovered by PEARSON, OTTENSMEYER and JOHNS, [1965].

Thus the increased incorporation of serine may or may not be the direct result of hydrate formation in poly U.

ONO, WILSON and GROSSMAN [1965] have also investigated the effect of UV on the template properties of poly C with RNA polymerase. The irradiated polymer loses the ability to incorporate GTP, but more ATP is incorporated. The authors conclude that the code change is the result of cytosine hydrate, because (1) the increase in ATP incorporation is heat reversible, and (2) there is more incorporation of ATP when the $p$H of the mixture containing irradiated primer and RNA polymerase is decreased from 7.5 to 6.0, although the $p$H change does not affect the decrease in GTP incorporation. The measured $p$H for dihydrocytidine was 6.1, and by analogy this was considered to be the same for the photoproduct responsible for the coding change. It is surprising that all the AMP incorporation is reversed by heat, since it might be assumed that heat would cause some deamination of the hydrate as well as reversion to the original cytosine. These studies do, however, show a heat-reversible coding change, which, because of the $p$H effect, presumably cannot be explained in terms of a possible end-addition contaminant in the RNA polymerase preparation.

It is concluded that no clear evidence for a biological effect of hydrated pyrimidines has been obtained, with the possible exception of the experiments of ONO, WILSON and GROSSMAN [1965]. Since native DNA does not exhibit the spectroscopic changes characteristic of cytosine hydrate [SETLOW and CARRIER, 1963], it seems improbable that this photoproduct is important in lethal damage, although the possibility that it could be responsible for some mutations is not excluded.

### 3.6. PYRIMIDINE DIMERS

#### 3.6.1. *Occurrence of thymine dimers in bacterial cells*

Thymine dimers were first found in irradiated bacteria by WACKER, DELLWEG and JACHERTS [1962]. The numbers of dimers increased with dose, a behaviour expected for all photoproducts, including those of no biological importance. These authors presented data to show that when *E. coli* T$^-$ cells were synchronized by cold treatment, the number of thymine dimers was larger in cells irradiated during the more UV-sensitive part of the division cycle. The change in the sensitivity of the cells to killing was a little more than a factor of two, while the amount of thymine dimer changed by about 12 %. The authors have explained the increase in dimers and sensitivity at a certain stage in the division cycle in terms of separation of DNA strands during DNA replication, and they further observe that denatured DNA contains more dimers than native DNA after irradiation with the same dose of UV. This explanation would require that during the most sensitive part of the division cycle about one quarter of the cell's genome should behave like denatured DNA—a very improbable figure, expecially in view of HANAWALT and RAY's [1964] inability to detect any denatured DNA in replicating cells.

During the course of the cell division cycle one would expect changes to occur which would affect the number of dimers and the survival, but not necessarily by the same process. Enlargement of the cell just before division should decrease the number of dimers slightly because of an increased absorption by the cells, resulting in a smaller dose to the DNA, presumably smaller numbers of all types of photoproducts. Doubling of the cell genome before cell division might result in an apparent increased resistance by a factor of two [as also observed by HELMSTETTER and URETZ, 1963, for *E. coli* strain B]. It is concluded that assigning the lethal photochemical events to the formation of thymine dimers is not possible from these experiments of Wacker et al.

### 3.6.2. *Short-wavelength reversal*

The number of dimers in irradiated DNA may be decreased without apparently decreasing the number of other photoproducts [R. B. SETLOW and J. K. SETLOW, 1962]. This may be done by short-wavelength radiation, such as 240 nm, applied after irradiation with a long wavelength, such as 280.5 nm. The shift in equilibrium of the forward and back reaction (see section 2.6) results in the disappearance of a large fraction of the dimers. To obtain this effect the initial dose of the long wavelength must be large enough (more than $10^4$ ergs/mm²) so that the number of dimers is considerably greater than the number of dimers formed by the short-wavelength irradiation at equilibrium. Unfortunately it is impossible to measure survival in most species of bacteria after such doses, but transforming DNA from *Hemophilus influenzae* is relatively resistant to UV-induced loss of transforming ability and has measurable activity remaining even following a dose at 280.5 nm well above $10^4$ ergs/mm². Subsequent short-wavelength irradiation eliminates dimers in the DNA and also restores biological activity (see also fig. 1). Furthermore, the kinetics of reactivation and of elimination of dimers by different short-wavelength doses are quantitatively similar, providing strong evidence that the dimers induced by the long-wavelength radiation are responsible for a large part of the inactivation of the DNA (estimated to be 50–70% of the total biological inactivation) [SETLOW and SETLOW, 1963].

HAUG and GOES [1963] have reported that *Bacillus subtilis* transforming DNA fails to show similar short-wavelength reactivation, and they concluded from this and from their action spectrum for inactivation of transforming ability that *B. subtilis* DNA is inactivated mostly by damage to cytosine. It is known that two of the possible UV-induced changes in cytosine (the cytosine-cytosine and thymine-cytosine dimers) are reversible by short wavelengths [SETLOW, CARRIER and BOLLUM, 1965a]. Furthermore, *B. subtilis* DNA has almost as high an A–T content as *H. influenzae* [BELOZERSKY and SPIRIN, 1960], and thus one would not expect the ratio of different types of lesions to differ appreciably in the two DNA's. Haug and Goes used very large doses of 285 nm radiation ($3-6 \times 10^5$ ergs/mm²), and subsequent irradiation at 240 nm produced further inactivation. Fig. 1 shows that after considerably lower doses at 285 nm, *B subtilis* DNA is reactivated by 240 nm radiation. The lack of reversibility after the large doses used by Haug and Goes may be the result of other classes of damage which begin to appear at these enormous dose levels.

An attempt has been made to demonstrate short-wavelength reversal of UV killing in a bacterial cell. Since the long-wavelength dose must be very large, in order to have measurable survival levels it is necessary to use a highly resistant microorganism such as *Micrococcus radiodurans*, which is able to tolerate the conversion of more than 1% of its thymine to dimer without any loss of viability [J. K. SETLOW and DUGGAN, 1964]. However, no reactivating effect of short-wavelength following long-wavelength irradiation was found for this microorganism [SETLOW and DUGGAN, unpublished]. It is possible that the micrococcus has a repair mechanism for thymine dimers so efficient (see section 4.2) that the viability level is unaffected by the

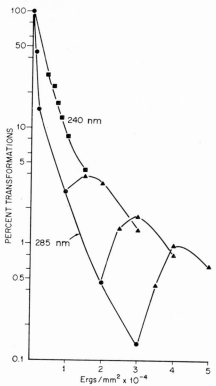

Fig. 1. Short-wavelength reactivation of *Bacillus subtilis* transforming DNA. Cells were *B. subtilis* strain ≠ 168, transformed to prototrophy. ● 285 nm irradiation alone; ■ 240 nm irradiation alone; ▲ 240 nm radiation following 285 nm radiation, doses plotted as the sum of the 285 and 240 nm doses [BOLING and SETLOW, unpublished].

initial level of dimers. This is a probable explanation, since there is evidence that thymine dimers are not responsible for most of the UV killing in this microorganism [J. K. SETLOW and BOLING, 1965], in that the wavelength dependencies for formation of thymine dimers and for killing are markedly different.

### 3.6.3. *Lack of dimers in spores and dry DNA*

Some bacterial spores are unusually UV-resistant [STUY, 1956]. *Bacillus megaterium* spores irradiated in liquid suspension do not contain dimers [DONNELLAN and SETLOW, 1965], indicating that at least some of their resistance to inactivation is caused by resistance to dimerization. It is known that DNA in the dry state is resistant to dimerization [RIKLIS and SIMSON, 1964; RIKLIS, 1965], suggesting that DNA which is dry and in spores does not have a configuration which readily permits thymine residues to come together in an orientation suitable for dimerization.

### 3.6.4. *Blocks to DNA synthesis*

DNA irradiated with UV loses its ability to function as a primer in *in vitro* enzymatic DNA synthesis. Evidence that dimers are blocks to DNA synthesis comes primarily from the fact that the decrease in priming ability by 280 nm radiation is restored by subsequent 240 nm radiation [BOLLUM and SETLOW, 1963]. Other evidence is the following. The sensitivity of different DNA's to loss of priming ability increases with A–T content, and furthermore the product made from irradiated primer shows an increased G/A ratio, suggesting that the presence of thymine dimers in the primer prevents the correct incorporation of A opposite T. Nearest-neighbour analysis of the product shows a deficiency of AA sequences [SETLOW, 1964b].

Some experiments with UV-sensitive and resistant strains of *E. coli* suggest that dimers may also block DNA synthesis in cells [R. B. SETLOW, SWENSON and CARRIER, 1963]. The number of dimers induced in the two strains is approximately the same after the same dose of UV. In the sensitive strain DNA synthesis stops after a small initial synthesis and never starts again, after a dose which induces the formation of one dimer per $350\mu$ of DNA strand (about half the total length). In the resistant strain DNA synthesis also stops after irradiation, but later resumes. The proposed explanation for these phenomena is that in the irradiated sensitive strain DNA can be synthesized only up to the dimer, and hence there is a small amount of initial synthesis, but the cells die because DNA synthesis cannot go beyond the block. In the resistant strain, however, DNA synthesis can resume because the blocks are removed (see section 4.2), and the cells may survive the initial blocks. The implication of these experiments is that thymine dimers may kill cells if the cells cannot remove them as a block to DNA synthesis.

### 3.6.5. *Phage killing*

A number of studies have been done on the possible relationship between thymine dimers and killing in bacterial viruses. WULFF [1963b] has carefully measured the thymine dimers and the lethal effect on the same population of irradiated T4v⁻, a mutant of T4 which is believed not to carry information for a repair enzyme, unlike the more resistant parent strain [HARM, 1963a]. Wulff found that 4.8 thymine dimers are produced for every phage lethal hit. If thymine dimers can kill phages, why do most of them (about 4 out of 5) fail to kill? One possibility, discussed by Wulff, is that the function of the DNA region containing the dimer may sometimes be assumed by the dimer-less region of the opposite strand. One can only conclude from Wulff's experiment that there are more than enough, indeed too many, dimers formed to acount for lethality in T4v⁻; but the conclusion that dimers are lethal events in this phage cannot be drawn.

SAUERBIER [1964c] has made similar measurements on the bacteriophage T4v⁻x⁻, which is a still more sensitive mutant with two independent and additive genotypic changes. He found 2.4 thymine dimers per lethal hit in this phage and pointed out that this is close to the value which would be obtained from a "two-hit" model for phage inactivation, although the observed phage survival curves are actually about 1.6-hit [WULFF, 1963b]. Again one can conclude only that there are enough dimers to explain the lethal events. This is not the case for the single-stranded bacteriophage $\phi \times 174$. DAVID [1964] found only 0.38 dimers per lethal hit, which presumably means that other photoproducts must be responsible for more than half of the lethal effect. Action spectra for inactivation of this virus at different $p$H's suggest that cytosine as well as thymine photoproducts are important [R. SETLOW and BOYCE, 1960].

SAUERBIER and HAUG [1964] have estimated the maximum fraction of the lethal effect on phage T4v⁻x⁻ due to thymine dimers after 260 nm irradiation to be 0.34. Their estimate is based on a comparison of thymine dimers per phage lethal hit produced in the phage under two conditions: (1) at 315 nm, $p$H 3.5, in a nitrogen atmosphere, and (2) at 260 nm, $p$H7, in air. The first condition was chosen so as to minimize the contribution to lethality of a hypothetical photoproduct, which the authors believe involves cytosine, and they observed that the number of thymine dimers formed after 315 nm irradiation at

$p$H 3.5 is twice as large in nitrogen as in oxygen. They found that only about one-seventh of the thymine dimers are lethal after irradiation under the first condition. They argued that the maximum fraction of thymine dimers which are lethal must be the same for both conditions. Since they have observed 2.4 thymine dimers per lethal hit at 260 nm, $p$H 7, in air, the maximum contribution of these dimers to lethal action of 260 nm radiation under these conditions must be 2.4/7.1, or 0.34.

### 3.6.6. *Other pyrimidine dimers in DNA*

In all of these investigations, thymine dimers have been isolated by chromatographic procedures which do not separate thymine-thymine dimers from uracil-thymine dimers [R. B. SETLOW, CARRIER and BOLLUM, 1965b]. Thus what is measured as thymine dimer after hydrolysis is actually a mixture of thymine-thymine and thymine-uracil dimers, the latter type resulting from heating the originally induced thymine-cytosine dimer (see section 2.6), or in the case of T4 DNA, possibly a thymine-hydroxymethylcytosine dimer. Since the DNA is labelled only in thymine, the mixed pyrimidine dimers would contain half as much radioactivity as the thymine-thymine dimers. Thus the total number of dimers would be underestimated, especially at wavelengths at which relatively more mixed dimers are produced. More mixed dimers are produced in *E. coli* DNA at 260 nm $p$H 8 than at 313 nm $p$H 3.5 [R.B. SETLOW, unpublished]. Assuming that hydroxymethylcytosine (HMC) dimerizes like cytosine in DNA, one would conclude that Sauerbier and Haug's calculated figure for the maximum fraction of damage resulting from dimers may well be too low.

There is some indirect indication that hydroxymethylcytosine in DNA behaves like cytosine in its ability to dimerize. Irradiated T2 bacteriophage DNA (which also contains HMC), like cytosine-containing DNA, shows increasing competition with transforming DNA for photoreactivating enzyme from yeast [J. K. SETLOW and BOLING, unpublished] at doses which produce a constant level of thymine dimers. This phenomenon may be explained in terms of dimers of cytosine or their heat product, uracil dimers. However, until there has been direct measurement of the hypothetical HMC-HMC and HMC-T dimers, the evaluation of the contribution of thymine-thymine dimers to lethality in HMC-containing bacterial viruses cannot be made. It is possible also that the glucosylation of the DNA of these viruses [VOLKIN, 1954] may affect their pyrimidine photochemistry.

SAUERBIER [1964b] irradiated T1 with a radioactive label, mostly in cytosine except for a small amount in thymine. Following acid hydrolysis and chromatography of the phage DNA, radioactive material that appeared in the dimer region of the chromatograms was reirradiated with UV and rechromatographed. He found a considerable amount of radioactivity in the cytosine region of the chromatogram and concluded that a cytosine photoproduct, presumably a dimer, had been formed in the original DNA. It is very puzzling that cytosine appeared in these chromatograms, since R. B. SETLOW, CARRIER and BOLLUM [1965a] found that all the cytosine in dimer form was deaminated by acid hydrolysis of DNA.

The correlation of the mixed pyrimidine dimers and cytosine and uracil dimers with biological effects can be made at present only indirectly. These dimers are all monomerized by photoreactivating enzyme and apparently are involved in the biological effects of enzymatic photoreactivation [J. K. SETLOW, BOLING and BOLLUM, 1965]. It is known that C-T dimers are excised from the DNA of resistant bacteria [R. B. SETLOW, CARRIER and BOLLUM, 1965a]. In these respects these dimers appear to behave like thymine-thymine dimers.

### 3.6.7. *UV sensitivity and base composition*

It has been observed by Haynes [1964] that the sensitivity of a large number of different bacteria to UV killing at 253.7 nm is linearly related to A-T content. However, one would expect the sensitivity to increase with the square of the A-T content if the thymine dimer were the only lethal photoproduct. If the other types of pyrimidine dimers are included, it turns out that the total number of dimers increases linearly with A-T content (this calculation allows for the fact that TT dimers in DNA are more readily formed than CC dimers), as observed by R. B. SETLOW [unpublished]. Thus the data on base ratio and UV sensitivity make quantitative sense if the other pyrimidine dimers are added to thymine dimers as lethal lesions.

### 3.6.8. Uracil dimers in RNA

Uracil dimers have been isolated from RNA [SCHUSTER, 1964]. KLECZKOWSKI [1963] found, however, that after irradiation at 285 nm the infectivity of tobacco mosaic virus (TMV) was not increased by subsequent short-wavelength irradiation. He expected to find such an increase if uracil dimers in the viral RNA were lethal. However, the dose of 285 nm used was too low by about an order of magnitude to achieve dimer reversal at the shorter wavelength, and therefore no biological effect would be expected. From the data on loss of infectivity after irradiation, the number of all types of pyrimidine dimers per mean lethal dose to TMV has been calculated to be about one [R. B. SETLOW, personal communication], with an estimate of the relationship between dose and number of dimers formed in RNA obtained from the base composition of TMV RNA and the number of dimers formed in poly U [SWENSON and SETLOW, 1963]. Thus there are sufficient uracil dimers to account for the lethal effect, but one cannot conclude that they are the cause of the lethal effect on the basis of sufficient numbers alone, and unfortunately the dose required to do the short-wavelength reversal experiment eliminates all measurable biological activity. The photoreactivability of TMV RNA in the tobacco leaf [BAWDEN and KLECZKOWSKI, 1959] also suggests pyrimidine dimers as lethal lesions.

## 4. Enzymatic repair of UV-induced lesions

### 4.1. PHOTOREACTIVATION

An important advance in the study of cellular repair mechanisms was the discovery that UV-inactivated transforming DNA recovers some of its activity when illuminated in the presence of an extract of *E. coli* [GOODGAL, RUPERT and HERRIOTT, 1957]. It was first believed that the active agent in the extract consisted of a dialyzable and a nondialyzable (enzymatic) fraction, since the rate and the final level of reactivation obtained depends on the amount of the dialyzed component added back to the mixture [RUPERT, GOODGAL and HERRIOTT, 1958]. Later experiments, however, suggested another interpretation of the data, namely that the crude extract contains inhibitory substances for the reaction, since it was found that the amount of photoreactivation of transforming DNA with limited amounts of dialyzed fraction increased with increasing DNA concentration [RUPERT, 1964a]. Another interpretation, which explains why the final level of activity, and not just the rate of the reaction, varies with amount of dialyzed material present, is that this material contains an inhibitor for the nuclease inactivation of transforming DNA. The inactivation rate would be expected to decrease with increasing amount of transforming DNA, thus making the observed reactivation rate higher, as found by RUPERT [1964a]. The practical problem of the nucleases in the *E. coli* extracts can be solved by the addition of large amounts of unirradiated DNA of another type to the mixture of transforming DNA and cell extract [J. K. SETLOW and BOLING, unpublished].

Because of the nucleases in *E. coli*, most of the work on *in vitro* photoreactivation has been done with yeast extract, the activity of which is not affected by dialysis [RUPERT, 1960]. The main results of a series of papers on this extract by RUPERT [1960, 1961, 1962a and b] may be summarized as follows. (1) The active agent is an enzyme. (2) Kinetic studies with fairly crude enzyme preparations indicate that the Michaelis-Menten scheme can be applied to the increase in transforming ability observed after incubation of irradiated DNA in the light in the presence of extract. (3) The enzyme forms a complex with irradiated, but not unirradiated, DNA in the dark, and the enzyme in the complex is protected against inactivation by heat and heavy metals. (4) The complex separates during illumination, and if the illumination is carried on for a sufficient time the DNA loses its ability to complex with the enzyme. Thus it is reasonable to suppose that the enzyme binds to specific sites on DNA which contain UV damages, and that these damages are somehow removed by illumination. Almost nothing is known about the mechanism of this light-induced reaction. Apparently only one photon is required, because unless saturating intensities are reached the amount of reactivation increases linearly with the total number of photons and is independent of the intensity. This has been found to be the case for *in vitro* photoreactivation [J. K. SETLOW and BOLING, 1963], *in vivo* photoreactivation in *E. coli* B/r [JAGGER and LATARJET, 1956], and T2 bacteriophage DNA photoreactivation inside the host cell [DULBECCO, 1950].

Studies of photoreactivation in whole cells are complicated by an

indirect type of photoreactivation which does not involve photoreactivating enzymes [JAGGER and STAFFORD, 1965]. The wavelength,
dose, dose-rate, and temperature dependencies of this indirect photoreactivation differ from those of direct photoreactivation, and the
indirect type is presumed to operate by means of induction of growth
and division delay [JAGGER and STAFFORD, 1965], by the same mechanism as photoprotection [WEATHERWAX, 1956], in which cells irradiated with visible light before UV show higher survival. Indirect
photoreactivation can be observed in a "photoreactivationless"
mutant of *E. coli* [HARM and HILLEBRANDT, 1962], which is believed
to lack a functional photoreactivating enzyme as judged by the
inability of its extract to photoreactivate transforming DNA [RUPERT,
1964a; J. K. SETLOW, 1964]. The studies by JAGGER and STAFFORD
[1965] suggest that much of the earlier work on photoreactivation of
whole cells should be reevaluated in terms of the two types of photoreactivation.

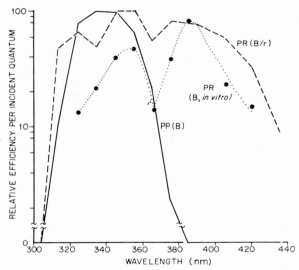

Fig. 2. Action spectra for photoprotection (PP) in *E. coli* B (solid line; JAGGER
and STAFFORD [1962]), photoreactivation (PR) in B/r (dashed line; JAGGER and
LATARJET, [1956]), and PR of *Hemophilus influenzae* transforming DNA by an
extract of *E. coli* B (dotted line; SETLOW and BOLING, unpublished).

Action spectra for photoreactivation of UV killing in whole cells
[KELNER, 1951; JAGGER and LATARJET, 1956] and in bacteriophage

[DULBECCO, 1950; JAGGER and LATARJET, 1956], which may be photoreactivated intracellularly, suggest that the absorbing unit is different in different types of microorganisms, although it is possible that some of the observed photoreactivation is of the indirect type. The action spectrum for photoreactivation of killing in E. coli [JAGGER and LATARJET, 1956] is not just the sum of the photoprotection action spectrum [JAGGER and STAFFORD, 1962] and the direct enzymatic action spectrum [J. K. SETLOW and BOLING, unpublished], obtained from in vitro photoreactivation of transforming DNA with an extract of E. coli B. There is a third peak in the photoreactivation of killing in E. coli B/r at 324 nm, where the action spectra for photoprotection and in vitro photoreactivation are dropping off sharply (fig. 2). This peak may be explained in terms of a type of indirect photoreactivation which can only function if the photoreactivating light follows UV irradiation. An alternative explanation is that there is another photoreactivating enzyme in E. coli which does not affect the biological activity of transforming DNA, and that the peak in the action spectrum involves this enzyme alone. In any case the action spectra for photoreactivation have been unsuccessful in suggesting the nature of the absorbing unit for the reaction, usually assumed to be part of the photoreactivating enzyme, although the shapes of the spectra have evoked considerable speculation [see the review by JAGGER, 1958]. The absorbing unit could possibly be the complex of enzyme and substrate. The final solution of the problem must await further purification of the enzyme. MUHAMMED [1965] has achieved an increase in specific activity over the crude yeast extract of about 6 000, without finding a substance which has an absorption spectrum resembling the action spectrum for in vitro photoreactivation with yeast extract [J. K. SETLOW and BOLING, 1963] when the extract is alone or in a complex with irradiated DNA. The highly purified enzyme preparation shows a large homogeneous peak on ultracentrifugation (molecular weight $\sim$ 30,000) and another small component, probably a contaminant, which does not peak and which absorbs at 546 nm.

The nature of the ultraviolet lesions in DNA which are repaired by the photoreactivating enzyme has been an intriguing problem since the enzymatic nature of photoreactivation was discovered. WACKER [1961] and WULFF and RUPERT [1962] found that thymine dimers were eliminated from DNA by treatment with relatively crude yeast extract in the light. These experiments suggest, but do not prove, that elimination of dimers is the cause of the biological effect of *in vitro* photoreactivation. Later it was found that there is overlap in the biological effect of short-wavelength reversal and photoreactivation, in that transforming DNA which had been photoreactivated was no longer reactivable by short-wavelength irradiation and the photoreactivability was decreased by previous short-wavelength irradiation [J. K. SETLOW and R. B. SETLOW, 1963]. These data are evidence that dimers are involved in the biological effect of photoreactivation. Before the discovery of other types of pyrimidine dimers in DNA (see section 2.6), it appeared that thymine dimers could account for all the photoreactivable damage in transforming DNA. However, two pieces of experimental data, based on an ingenious method developed by RUPERT [1961], contradict this hypothesis. He showed that some UV-irradiated polydeoxynucleotides lacking the ability to transform could be considered photoreactivable if (1) they competed for photoreactivating enzyme with irradiated transforming DNA, as judged by the decrease in rate of biological reactivation, and (2) they lost their ability to compete as a result of illumination in the presence of photoreactivating enzyme. He found that the synthetic deoxypolymer GC is photoreactivable in this sense, although it contains no thymine [RUPERT, 1961, 1964b]. It can be inferred from this experiment that there is a photoreactivable lesion in DNA in addition to the thymine dimer. *E. coli* DNA irradiated with increasingly large doses of short-wavelength UV shows a constant level of thymine dimers but an increasing ability to compete for enzyme [J. K. SETLOW, 1964], again indicating that there is at least one other photoreactivable lesion in DNA besides the thymine dimer. Further experiments on competition by a variety of synthetic polydeoxyribonucleotides have shown that only the polymers containing adjacent pyrimidines are photoreactivable [J. K. SETLOW, BOLING and BOLLUM, 1965]. The homocopolymer dA : dT competes and forms dimers, but the alternating polymer d(AT) : d(AT) does not compete [RUPERT, 1961] and shows no spectroscopic evidence of dimer formation [DEERING and SETLOW, 1963]. Poly dA and poly dI do not compete, but poly dC and poly dI : dC do. Furthermore, the ability to compete is correlated kinetically with dimer formation. In poly dA : dT the dimers and the competing ability reach a constant level after a short-wavelength irradiation at a dose of around $3 \times 10^4$ ergs/mm$^2$, whereas in dI : dC and in DNA they do not, unless the polymers are kept cold, thus preventing the conversion of cytosine dimers to uracil dimers. When poly dI : dC is heated after long-wavelength irradiation, the competing ability and the dimers are less susceptible to short-wavelength reversal, but they are more readily decreased by enzymatic photoreactivation, indicating a greater affinity of the enzyme for uracil dimers than for cytosine dimers. The mixed pyrimidine dimers $\widehat{CT}$ and $\widehat{UT}$ are also presumed to be biologically important substrates for the photoreactivating enzyme in DNA, since they have been shown to be eliminated from DNA by purified photoreactivating enzyme [R. B. SETLOW, CARRIER and BOLLUM, 1965a]. Thymine-thymine dimers in DNA are eliminated considerably more rapidly than the other four types, and the mixed dimers more rapidly than $\widehat{CC}$ and $\widehat{UU}$ [J. K. SETLOW, BOLLUM and BOLING, 1965].

Apparently, a certain chain length is necessary for the photoreactivating enzyme to bind to a pyrimidine dimer in a polynucleotide, since RUPERT [1961] found that irradiated $(pT)_8$ does not compete with transforming DNA for enzyme. Polymers containing ribose also do not compete [RUPERT, 1961].

It is concluded that monomerization of pyrimidine dimers in DNA can probably account for all the biological effects of direct photoreactivation. It is of interest that vegetative cells of different species of *bacillus*, but not *B. subtilis* spores, are photoreactivable [STUY, 1955], and dimers are *not* found in *B. megaterium* spores [DONNELLAN and SETLOW, 1965]. Similarly T1 bacteriophage irradiated dry is not photoreactivable in infected cells [HILL and ROSSI, 1952], and DNA irradiated dry contains few dimers [RIKLIS, 1965].

Photoreactivation of infectious RNA from TMV is also possible, as shown by BAWDEN and KLECZKOWSKI [1959], although unless the protein is removed before irradiation there is no photoreactivation in the leaf, indicating that the protein-RNA linkage or the RNA structure in the whole virus at the time of UV irradiation prevents photoreactivable damage. It is tempting to suppose by analogy with DNA photoreactivation that pyrimidine dimers are monomerized in photoreactivation of TMV. However, it is probable that there is an indirect type of photoreactivation operating in this system, since one would expect the metabolism of a photosynthetic organism to be very different in daylight, which was the photoreactivating illumination used. There has also been a report of photoreactivation of an RNA bacterial virus [PITTMAN, 1964], but it is not yet possible to say whether this is direct enzymatic photoreactivation.

Photoreactivation of whole cells or transforming DNA is never complete, in that there is always residual biological damage after photoreactivation has reached a constant level [JAGGER, 1958; RUPERT, 1960], although all the thymine-thymine and cytosine-thymine dimers have been eliminated [J. K. SETLOW, unpublished]. The fraction of damage which is photoreactivable is called the photoreactivable sector [JAGGER, 1960]. In *E. coli*, with about equal amounts of A-T and G-C in the DNA [BELOZERSKY and SPIRIN, 1960], the photoreactivable sector is about 0.5 [JAGGER, 1960] to 0.8 [CASTELLANI, JAGGER and SETLOW, 1964], depending on photoreactivating conditions. But it is as high as 0.91 in transforming DNA from *Hemophilus influenzae* [J. K. SETLOW, 1963], which is high in AT [BELOZERSKY and SPIRIN, 1960].

CAVILLA and JOHNS [1964] have measured the photoreactivable sectors of T4, T2, and T6 bacteriophages following inactivation with wavelengths ranging from 230 to 302 nm, and find some evidence for a drop in the photoreactivable sector at the lower and higher wavelengths similar to that found for *Hemophilus influenzae* transforming DNA [J. K. SETLOW, 1963]. Although it has been reported that the shorter wavelengths may inactivate T4 by producing protein damage, so that injection of phage DNA is impaired [WINKLER, JOHNS and KELLENBERGER, 1962], it is unlikely that the lower photoreactivable sector observed for phages at 230 relative to 265 nm is entirely the result of the increased proportion of tail damage. The fact that purified transforming DNA photoreactivated with yeast enzyme is also less photoreactivable after inactivation by 230 nm radiation shows that there is a larger fraction of nonphotoreactivable damage in DNA itself at this wavelength. This has been interpreted in terms of the relative absorption coefficients of nucleosides, thymidine absorption falling off more rapidly than cytosine deoxyriboside absorption at the extreme wavelengths [J. K. SETLOW, 1963]. In addition, the quantum yield for thymine dimerization seems to decrease slightly at the longer UV wavelengths [DEERING and SETLOW, 1963].

An action spectrum for nonphotoreactivable damage in *Hemophilus influenzae* DNA suggests that a cytosine alteration is important in this type of damage [J. K. SETLOW, 1963]. Since it is now known that both cytosine-thymine and cytosine-cytosine dimers can be eliminated from DNA by enzymatic photoreactivation, the question is what could this cytosine alteration be? The cytosine hydrate was rejected earlier (see section 3.5). It is possible that a few cytosine-cytosine dimers are immune to monomerization by the photoreactivating enzyme because of a particular sequence in neighbouring bases, such as a long string of thymines on either side of the adjacent cytosines. Alternatively, the nonphotoreactivable cytosine damage may be an unknown photoproduct. However, one cannot at this time reject the possibility that both photoreactivable and nonphotoreactivable damage consists of pyrimidine dimers in DNA. An obvious experimental test of this possibility is the measurement of dimers after maximum *in vitro* photoreactivation of DNA. If they have all been eliminated, one can conclude either that nonphotoreactivable damage is not a dimer, or that some cytosine-cytosine or cytosine-thymine dimers can cause a lethal effect even when monomerized if deamination of cytosine to uracil has occurred before monomerization. These are difficult problems to solve experimentally, because of the small numbers of dimers to be measured and because of the difficulties of obtaining a large percentage of radioactively labelled cytosine components in DNA.

## 4.2. DARK REPAIR

It has long been known that irradiated bacteria [HOLLAENDER and CLAUS, 1937] and yeast [LATARJET, 1943] show different survival levels depending on various postirradiation environmental factors in addition to visible light. This phenomenon was interpreted by many investigators to mean that postirradiation factors can alter the amount of repair of initial UV lesions, especially by introducing a further delay in DNA synthesis, as when irradiated cells are held in nonnutrient medium and show higher survival [ROBERTS and ALDOUS, 1949]. It was later shown, in some related strains of bacteria, that the number of thymine dimers induced in the DNA of whole cells was the same although the survival levels differed by orders of magnitude [R. B. SETLOW, SWENSON and CARRIER, 1963]. There were two clues to the mechanism of repair in the resistant strains. (1) The dimers were conserved in the cells, even after the cells had remained in nutrient medium following irradiation. (2) The dimers became unsusceptible to monomerization

by photoreactivation under these conditions [R. B. SETLOW and
CARRIER, 1964]. Therefore it appeared that the dimers were inside the
cell in a form which was not a substrate for the photoreactivating
enzyme. The dimers in *E. coli* strains B and B/r, but not in the very
sensitive strain $B_{s-1}$, disappear from the acid-insoluble fraction of the
cell (i.e., from native DNA) and appear in the acid-soluble fraction
during postirradiation in nutrient medium. The time taken to transfer
all or almost all of the dimers to the insoluble fraction is about the time
that DNA synthesis takes to resume after the UV-induced delay [R. B.
SETLOW and CARRIER, 1964]. Therefore it is reasonable to conclude that
DNA synthesis can resume because the dimer blocks are excised from
the bacterial DNA, and that this is part of the mechanism which enables
the resistant but not the sensitive cells to survive. It is assumed
that the holes left after dimer excision must be patched in some way.
The fact that dimers are excised at about the same rate in two strains
of *E. coli*, B and B/r, which have different resistance to UV killing,
indicates that dimer excision is only part of the repair process [R. B.
SETLOW and CARRIER, 1964].

PETTIJOHN and HANAWALT [1964] have found evidence of such repair
"patching". They used a density label for DNA synthesis after irradiation, and then analyzed the density distribution in sonicated and
unsonicated DNA extracted at various times during the postirradiation
period in nutrient medium. Their results showed that the newly synthesized material appeared at random points along the DNA in short,
single-stranded segments about 20 nucleotides long. Photoreactivation
of the cells resulted in normal, semiconservative replication. These
experiments provide very convincing evidence of the patching phenomenon, except that the dose of UV they needed to use to obtain a clear
effect eliminated colony formation in 96 % of the cells. Thus one cannot
exclude the possibility that the strange DNA made in a population
which is almost entirely inactivated is not "repair replication" at all.
It would be very desirable to do such experiments with a more resistant
cell, in the hope of observing "repair replication" in a truly recovering
population.

The excision mechanism has also been found in mating strains of
*E. coli* K-12 [BOYCE and HOWARD-FLANDERS, 1964]. Genetic analysis
has shown that the excision mechanism is controlled by a number of
loci [HOWARD-FLANDERS et al., 1962; HOWARD-FLANDERS, 1964].
A number of loci concerned with cellular repair of UV-damaged

bacteriophage have been mapped by VAN DE PUTTE et al. [1965]. Cells which have this ability are called host cell reactivating (hcr+). It is of interest that the single-stranded phage $\phi \times 174$, unlike $\lambda$, T1, and T3 phages [ELLISON, FEINER and HILL, 1960; HARM, 1963b], exhibits hcr only after intracellular irradiation [SAUERBIER, 1964a].

The question may be raised whether there are any mutations affecting UV sensitivity which do not concern DNA repair. In *E. coli* mutations are known which affect cell sensitivity but not the ability to repair UV-irradiated phage, and *vice versa* [HILL, 1964; HOWARD-FLANDERS, SIMSON and THERIOT, 1964; VAN DE PUTTE et al., 1965]. ADLER [1965] has suggested that a gene controlling the rate of synthesis could be important in radiation sensitivity. He discusses the *"lon"* locus in *E. coli* K12 [HOWARD-FLANDERS, SIMSON and THERIOT, 1964; ADLER and HARDIGREE, 1964], which seems to control filament formation in irradiated bacteria, and concludes that this region of the chromosome probably does not directly control a DNA repair process.

In order to evaluate this conclusion, it is important to consider the intimate association between the origination of cross-wall formation and DNA synthesis [see JACOB, BRENNER and CUZIN, 1963, for a discussion]. It is possible to have DNA synthesis without cross walls, but not cross walls without DNA partition, since cells lacking DNA have never been observed. There is strong evidence that filament formation is induced by lesions in DNA. DEERING and SETLOW [1957] found that the action spectrum for production of filaments in *E. coli* B, probably also a *lon*-type mutant [ADLER, 1965], was similar to the nucleic acid absorption spectrum. The doses required to form filaments are too small for consideration of RNA as the target molecule, and furthermore the doses are too small to involve a particular region of the DNA, so that one can assume that a UV lesion anywhere in the DNA will produce filaments in *E. coli* B. The only other effect that is known to result from such doses is a temporary cessation of DNA synthesis due to a pyrimidine block (see section 3.6). Even a dose of 10 ergs/mm$^2$ at 265 nm to *E. coli* B produces a measurable delay in DNA synthesis [R. B. SETLOW, 1964b]. DNA synthesis delay is linearly related to dose in this microorganism [SWENSON and SETLOW, 1965] and also in *Micrococcus radiodurans* [J. K. SETLOW and BOLING, 1965], and by extrapolation it may be inferred that the very small doses causing filament formation in *E. coli* B also temporarily stop DNA synthesis. It is possible, therefore, that the UV-induced delay in DNA synthesis causes filament formation. This hypothesis is strengthened by the fact that both filament formation [ERRERA, 1954] and delay in DNA synthesis [R. B. SETLOW, SWENSON and CARRIER, 1963] are photo-reactivable. It is concluded that the lack of cross-wall formation in irradiated mutants of the *lon* type could be a secondary result of lack of ability to repair UV damage to DNA.

SAUERBIER [1964b] has tried to measure elimination of dimers from T4 bacteriophage of the resistant, compared to the sensitive strain [HARM, 1963a], genetic studies having shown that two loci on the T4 genome control UV sensitivity [HARM, 1963a]. SAUERBIER found no evidence of dimer removal from the phage DNA during the course of infection of *E. coli* B, and concluded that dark repair mechanisms as described in this section do not operate in resistant T4. Two serious objections to this conclusion may be made. In the case of dark repair of the *E. coli* genome, the piece of DNA originally excised may be further degraded by nucleases [SETLOW and CARRIER, 1964]. Native T4 DNA is known to contain blocks to nuclease action [SINSHEIMER, 1960], and it is possible that excision of acid-insoluble material from the phage DNA is not followed by sufficient nuclease action to produce acid-soluble pieces. Sauerbier used cyanide-poisoned host cells. Since energy is apparently required for excision [SETLOW and CARRIER, 1964], the excision mechanism may have been inhibited. Thus whether or not excision is part of the mechanism for T4 repair remains an open question.

CAVILLA and JOHNS [1964] have obtained evidence that there is a lesion produced by 302 nm radiation which is not photoreactivable but which is repaired in the presence of the *v* gene of T4 [HARM, 1963a]. Whereas T4 phage which carry this gene are more sensitive to 265 nm radiation than T2 phage irradiated and maximally photo-reactivated, T4 phage without photoreactivation are considerably more resistant to 302 nm radiation than photoreactivated T2. Identification of the UV lesion, and determination of whether or not the lesion is excised from the phage DNA, would be of considerable interest.

Another UV-induced thymine lesion, not a dimer, which is formed in large quantities in *Bacillus megaterium* spores [DONNELLAN and SET-LOW, 1965], disappears from the DNA during the postirradiation period [DONNELLAN and SETLOW, unpublished]. There is also evidence that lesions induced by other agents are similarly excised. PAPIRMEISTER and DAVISON [1964] have demonstrated excision of sulphur-mustard-induced products from the DNA of *E. coli,* and glucose is required for this process. R. B. SETLOW and CARRIER [unpublished] have found unidentified lesions induced by ionizing radiation in purified DNA to be excised by an extract of *Micrococcus lysodeikticus.* Evidence for excision of nitrogen-mustard lesions has also been obtained [HANA-WALT and HAYNES, 1965; KOHN, STEIGBIGEL and SPEARS, 1965].

We know very little about the excision mechanism itself. It can apparently take place in a thymine-requiring strain of *E. coli* in the absence of thymine [SHUSTER, 1964]. Chloramphenicol does *not* inhibit excision, indicating that protein synthesis is not necessary for the process [R. B. SETLOW, 1964b]. Excision can proceed in the absence of RNA as well as DNA synthesis [R. B. SETLOW, 1964b], but an energy source is apparently required, as judged by the fact that the excision rate is considerably slowed down in a medium lacking glucose [SETLOW and CARRIER, 1964]. The excision rate is also dramatically decreased in the presence of acriflavin [R. B. SETLOW, 1964b], a dye which is known to decrease the survival of UV-irradiated *E. coli* B/r when it is included in the postirradiation plating medium [WITKIN, 1963b].

Further information about dark repair processes can be expected from *in vitro* systems. Two such systems have been described. ELDER and BEERS [1964] have prepared extracts of *Micrococcus lysodeikticus* which increased the transforming ability of UV-irradiated DNA in the dark. Using a similar extract, RÖRSCH, VAN DER KAMP and ADEMA [1964] have been able to restore the infectivity of irradiated double-stranded $\phi \times 174$ bacteriophage DNA tested on *E. coli* spheroplasts from a strain which lacks the ability to repair irradiated phage. It may be assumed that these micrococcus extracts contain one or more en-zymes that can accomplish excision or excision and patching. The patching enzyme is presumably a kind of DNA polymerase. Purification of these extracts would be an important step toward understanding the mechanism of dark repair.

CLARK and MARGULIES [1965] have isolated UV-sensitive mutants of *E. coli* K12 which are deficient in recombination. Their evidence that a single gene mutation is responsible for both characters suggests that excision and recombination have a step in common.

## 5. The effect of bromouracil and iodouracil substitution on UV killing

Cells or bacteriophage in which 5-bromodeoxyuridine (BUdR) is substituted for the thymidine in the DNA are considerably more sensitive to UV killing [GREER and ZAMENHOF, 1957; STAHL et al., 1961]. A similar result has been obtained for transforming DNA [OPARA-KUBINSKA, LORKIEWICZ and SZYBALSKI, 1961]. OPARA-KUBINSKA, KURYLO-BOROWSKA and SZYBALSKI [1963] have found that BUdR DNA has a greater affinity for methylated albumin. The DNA from BUdR *E. coli* irradiated *in vivo* is initially more sensitive to loss of extractability, and at higher doses less sensitive [SMITH, 1964]. These two observations presumably reflect the same phenomenon, namely that certain BUdR photoproducts may have a tendency to form a linkage with basic protein. T2 phage containing BUdR shows a greater degree of sensitization to visible light than to UV [STAHL et al., 1961]. Furthermore, dark repair controlled by the *v* gene in T2 phage is inhibited in substituted phage [STAHL et al., 1961], as well as host cell reactivation (hcr) of T1 phage [SAUERBIER, 1961]. HOWARD-FLANDERS, BOYCE and THERIOT [1962] found that BUdR-substituted T1 were considerably more sensitive than normal T1 when plated on *E. coli* B, a strain which apparently can repair damage to phage DNA, but there was little difference between BUdR and normal T1 plated on the sensitive strain $B_s$, which is hcr⁻. Thus it appears that at least some of the sensitization effect of BUdR is due to the inability of repair enzymes to deal with UV lesions involving this compound.

UV action spectra of BUdR and normal *E. coli* [BOYCE and SETLOW, 1963] and T4 phage [R. SETLOW and BOYCE, 1963] suggest that some of the increase in sensitivity at the longer wavelengths is due to the greater absorption of BUdR compared to thymidine at these wavelengths. Similar action spectra for T4 were obtained by RAPAPORT [1964]. In the case of the phage, but not the cells, the sensitivity to long wavelengths can probably be totally accounted for in terms of the absorption difference [R. SETLOW and BOYCE, 1963].

SMITH [1962a] found both the total number and the number of different types of photoproducts of BU to be greater than those of thymine after irradiation of *E. coli* B/r *in vivo*. He concluded that at least some of the increased sensitivity of cells containing BUdR in their DNA can be attributed to the greater sensitivity of BUdR relative to thymidine. This hypothesis is strengthened by some experiments of HOTZ [1964], who found some degree of UV sensitization in substituted T1 phage plated on $B_{s-1}$, indicating that not all the sensitization can be explained in terms of interference with repair, since $B_{s-1}$ supposedly cannot repair phage DNA. The slopes of normal and BUdR T1 on this host are very similar. The major difference is that the shoulder of the curve is missing in the BUdR phage, T4 [R. SETLOW and BOYCE, 1963] as well as in BUdR T1. The explanation for this phenomenon is not known.

HOTZ [1963] observed that the sensitization of BUdR T1 was eliminated if the phage was irradiated in the presence of cysteamine, a compound which does not affect the survival of normal phage. Hotz postulated a reaction between the sulfhydryl group and irradiated BUdR in the phage DNA. He later [1964] found that cysteamine partially restores the photoreactivability of T1 phage. HAUG [1964a] irradiated the dinucleotide TpBU and found three photoproducts, the principal one of which contained no bromine and appeared to be a dimer as judged by its chromatographic mobility, but which was unlike the usual type of pyrimidine dimer in two respects. It was not monomerized by 240 nm radiation, and its absorption was half that of the original compound. Haug postulated that this photoproduct was a cyclobutene-type dimer, with one double bond in the ring. He further found [1964b] that irradiation of the dinucleotide or the photoproduct in the presence of cysteamine at $pH$ 2 in nitrogen resulted in the formation of another photoproduct which contained sulphur, and which showed little absorption at 271 nm, indicating that the double bond in the cyclobutane ring was no longer present. This new photoproduct was also not reversible by 240 nm radiation. Whether or not the photoproduct is formed in DNA irradiated in the presence of cysteamine at a $pH$ considerably higher than 2 is a question which must be answered before the biological importance of Haug's discovery can be assessed.

RUPERT [1961] found that the photoreactivating enzyme binds to BUdR-DNA, as judged by the ability of the DNA to compete for enzyme with irradiated transforming DNA, but this ability could not be eliminated by a photoreactivating treatment. Thus it is possible that the photoreactivability of BUdR-phage when it is irradiated in the presence of cysteamine can be explained in terms of Haug's second photoproduct, which in DNA could be a substrate for the photoreactivating enzyme, although the dimer containing one double bond in the cyclobutene ring might bind the enzyme without being monomerized. LION [1965], however, found no mixed photoproduct of BU and thymine after irradiation of *E. coli* 15 T⁻-DNA containing ¹⁴C-thymidine and ring-labelled ³H-BUdR, whether the DNA was acid or enzymatically hydrolyzed after irradiation. He found that the presence of cysteamine changed the ratio of the various BU photoproducts, but there was no such effect when whole cells were irradiated in cysteamine. These results indicate that cysteamine probably affects a number of other BU photoproducts in addition to the T-BU dimer.

Iodouracil-substituted T1 phages behave in many respects like BU phages [RUPP and PRUSOFF, 1964]. The phages when plated on a UV-resistant (uvr⁺) strain are sensitized by the IU, but not when irradiated in the presence of cysteamine. There is only a small amount of sensitization when the phages are plated on a uvr⁻ strain, and the cysteamine-protected phages are considerably more sensitive than cysteamine-protected phages or normal phages on the uvr⁺ strain. Iodouracil in solution is more sensitive than bromouracil, as judged by loss of UV absorption [WACKER, 1963]. RUPP and PRUSOFF [1965a, b] have investigated the photochemistry of iodouracil irradiated in solution, and they postulate that a uracil radical is produced by UV which reacts either with oxygen (a lethal event) or, when cysteamine is present, is converted to uracil (which they assume would leave the coding properties intact in phage DNA). Whether this phenomenon actually occurs in DNA is somewhat dubious in view of LION's observation (personal communication) that BU *E. coli* DNA irradiated *in vitro* forms *more* uracil when cysteamine is not present, assuming that BU and IU behave similarly in this respect.

The results of all these investigations may be summarized as follows. The increased sensitivity of halogen-substituted DNA *in vivo* and *in vitro* can be explained in terms of a number of different properties of this DNA, the relative absorption of the halogen pyrimidines, the increased sensitivity of these substances in DNA to formation of various photoproducts, and the lack of susceptibility of these photoproducts in DNA to repair enzymes. A quantitative assessment of the importance of these various factors has not been made. The role of sulphydryl compounds in protection of substituted DNA is not yet clear, and it is probable that a number of different photoproducts of halogen pyrimidines are involved in the protective effect.

## 6. UV-induced mutation and repair of premutational lesions

Mutation of extracellular transforming DNA by UV irradiation has not been reported. LITMAN and EPHRUSSI-TAYLOR [1959] found that it was possible to produce mutations in pneumococcus transforming DNA by chemical treatment, but not by UV. CABRERA-JUÁREZ and HERRIOTT [1963] were unable to produce UV-induced mutations in *Hemophilus influenzae* transforming DNA, using a method that was very successful in chemical induction of mutation in this DNA, namely, treating the DNA in denatured form and then renaturing the DNA before looking for new transformable markers [HORN and HERRIOTT, 1962]. It is possible that UV-induced mutations of transforming DNA are not observed because UV-lesions are not incorporated into the bacterial genome. The UV-inactivation data for transforming DNA quantitatively fit a model in which the probability of incorporation of a marker on a DNA molecule is a function of the distance between the marker and the nearest UV lesion or end of the molecule [J. K. SETLOW, 1963]. Further evidence for this model is that sonication and UV inactivation are quantitatively additive [J. K. SETLOW, 1963]. The model predicts that incorporation would take place up to, but not including, the UV lesion.

The only clear-cut case of UV-induced mutation of extracellular DNA is in bacteriophage [TESSMAN, 1956; KRIEG, 1959; KAPLAN, WINKLER and WOLF-ELLMAUER, 1960; FOLSOME and LEVIN, 1961]. T4 phage is somewhat more sensitive to mutation when irradiated at certain stages of development inside the host cell [J. K. SETLOW, 1962]. With the exception of mutations in Serratia phage [KAPLAN et al., 1960], mutations in phage are produced in very low frequency by UV, either extracellularly or intracellularly administered.

Two methods have been used to attempt to determine the nature of the UV-induced molecular change causing the mutation in phage. One method is to study the reversion of UV-induced mutants by different chemical mutagens, and from the base changes believed to be caused by these chemicals [see KRIEG, 1962 for review] to infer the nature of the UV-induced base changes. DRAKE [1963, 1964], using this method, found that UV-induced rII mutants in T4 fell into two classes. One class seemed to contain small deletions or additions, and the other class (transition mutants) appeared to have in the majority of cases an A-T pair substituted for a G-HMC pair. Drake concluded that the G-HMC pair was the UV-affected one in most of the transition-type UV-induced mutations. A similar method was used by HOWARD and TESSMAN [1964] to investigate UV-induced mutations in the single-stranded bacteriophage S13. The majority of the mutations appeared to be a change from C to T, and the remainder represented either a T to C transition or a base deletion or addition. In the studies by Drake and by Howard and Tessman, both the host cell and the phage were irradiated. In S13, this is necessary to produce measurable mutation [TESSMAN and OZAKI, 1960]. Multiple infection with T4 is apparently necessary for detection of mutants from virus irradiated extracellularly [KRIEG, 1959]. This is a puzzling phenomenon, and suggests that the mechanism of UV-induced mutation in these phages is not a simple one.

Ultraviolet action spectra have also been used to try to determine the base containing the premutational lesion. J. K. SETLOW [1962] found that the relative efficiencies of different UV wavelengths in causing reversion in two T4 rII mutants were somewhat similar to the relative absorption of thymidine at these wavelengths, and concluded that the photons causing the mutations were absorbed in this component of DNA, in accord with the indirect evidence from chemically-induced reversions of these mutants.

None of these studies provides information about how a particular photochemical change in DNA, such as a pyrimidine dimer, could cause a mutation. *In vitro* studies of DNA replication with calf thymus polymerase show that there are fewer AA sequences and more GG sequences in the DNA made from UV-irradiated primer, in which dimers act as partial blocks to DNA synthesis [R. B. SETLOW, 1964b]. Whether base changes in DNA irradiated *in vivo* take place by a similar mechanism is not at all clear. Some, but by no means all, of the base changes in the *in vitro* system can be accounted for in terms of a contaminating "end-addition" enzyme in the DNA polymerase preparation [BOLLUM, 1963]. Whether or not such enzymes contribute to UV mutagenesis *in vivo* is an unsolved problem.

A number of studies of UV-induced mutation in bacteria have suggested that some premutational lesions are very susceptible to cellular repair in the dark, in that certain posttreatments result in a large decrease in the number of observed mutations [see review by KIMBALL, 1965]. It might be expected that these studies, together with current knowledge of DNA repair mechanisms, would provide some information on the mechanisms of UV mutagenesis. Unfortunately this is far from being the case. As pointed out by KIMBALL [1965], one of the difficulties in interpreting experiments in which the frequency of mutations is measured as a function of various treatments of the cells after irradiation is that the effect of the supposed repair is only observed long after the repair processes are complete, usually when a surviving cell has divided many times so as to produce a colony. It is not at all obvious whether the repair takes place at the time of the posttreatment or at some later time, though probably before DNA synthesis.

A frequently-employed experimental technique is to leave irradiated *E. coli* for various times in a low mutation yield medium, followed by plating on a high mutation yield medium. The observed frequency of mutation decreases as a function of time in the first medium, and this phenomenon has been called mutation frequency decline (MFD) by DOUDNEY and HAAS [1958]. Two of the postirradiation conditions which yield a low mutation frequency are (1) minimal medium in bacteria adapted to nutrient broth (and glucose must be present for appreciable MFD) and (2) chloramphenicol in nutrient broth [WITKIN, 1956], suggesting that inhibition of protein synthesis increases repair. Witkin observed that survival is not appreciably affected by these treatments, following a relatively small UV dose, and neither is mutation to streptomycin resistance or streptomycin independence, according to Witkin and THEIL [1960], although SHANKEL and WYSS [1961] have reported MFD for the streptomycin-resistance mutation, using different techniques. The mutation systems which show large MFD are reversions to prototrophy in amino acid-requiring strains. These are probably changes in supersuppressors, rather than true reversions [WITKIN, 1963a]. High frequency of mutation is observed after the following postirradiation conditions: (1) saline solution for bacteria adapted to nutrient broth [WITKIN, 1958], (2) nutrient broth, or minimal medium plus glucose for bacteria adapted to minimal medium [WITKIN, 1956], and (3) caffeine, acriflavine, or 6 azauracil in the postirradiation medium [WITKIN 1961, 1963b]. A number of other factors have a large effect on the amount of reversion to prototrophy in *E. coli*. Cells irradiated in stationary phase are considerably less susceptible to mutation than cells in lag or log phase. Log phase cells are the most sensitive [J. K. SETLOW, unpublished]. WITKIN [unpublished] has isolated several mutants which show a greatly decreased rate of MFD.

It is of interest to try to correlate the effects on mutation of post-treatments and other modifying factors with their effects on the only dark repair process that can be measured directly at present, namely excision of pyrimidine dimers. The results of such correlations do not lend themselves to a clear-cut interpretation of the observed repair phenomena. The experimental procedure consists of measuring excision rates under some of the conditions which have been shown to modify mutation. Witkin has in most cases irradiated bacteria which were emerging from lag phase. The excision rate under these conditions is considerably slower than the rate of MFD, and is lower than when the cells are irradiated in log or in stationary phase [R. B. and J. K. SETLOW, unpublished], although there are more mutations when cells are irradiated in log phase. Obviously a simple correlation between excision rate and mutation frequency cannot be made. The excision rate after irradiation of cells in stationary or log phase is decreased in cells grown in nutrient broth and placed in minimal medium plus glucose after irradiation [J. K. SETLOW, unpublished]. Chloramphenicol has no effect on the excision rate of cells irradiated in log phase [R. B. SETLOW, unpublished], but acriflavine is an inhibitor of excision [R. B. SETLOW, 1964b]. Thus the excision data do not show a correlation with mutation data with respect to sensitivity to different states and the chloramphenicol effect. On the other hand, the requirement of glucose for excision and MFD and the effect of acriflavine seem to be what would be expected if excision were the first step in the repair process reflected in MFD. The observation that one of Witkin's mutants which has a very low MFD also has a slow excision rate [J. K. SETLOW, unpublished] would appear to strengthen this hypothesis. LIEB [1961] has found that the effect of MFD in the presence of chloramphenicol may be reversed by treating the cells with caffeine subsequent to chloramphenicol treatment, suggesting that the increased repair caused by the latter substance takes place after the MFD period.

Some of the mutation and excision data might be reconciled if the excision mechanism is considered a necessary but not sufficient part of the dark repair mechanism. Thus the relative rates of excision and "patching" may be the important parameter in repair. Chloramphenicol, which does not affect the excision rate, might affect the rate of "patching" and thus cause more repair. The lack of correlation between excision rates and mutation frequency at different states of growth might be explained in a similar way. It is also possible that the premutational lesion involved in reversion to prototrophy is specially accessible to repair enzymes under conditions in which protein synthesis is turned off, unlike the lesions in most of the genome. This possibility might be amenable to experimental test, if a large enough region of the chromosomes were more available to repair enzymes. By pulse-labelling cells in which DNA synthesis is phased, it might be possible to show different rates of excision for different parts of the genome. It has been found that DNA polymerase and DNA-primed RNA polymerase compete with each other for the same template, and that the action of some nucleases is inhibited by the RNA-polymerase-DNA complex [BERG et al., 1965]. Similarly, the rate at which repair enzymes can function in a given part of the genome may depend on the metabolic functioning of this part.

None of the investigations so far reported provides information on the nature of the premutational lesion or on how it could be converted into a mutation. Because many mutations are photoreactivable [KIMBALL, 1965] it might be assumed that premutational lesions could be pyrimidine dimers. WITKIN [1964] has argued that the lesion causing prototrophy reversion in *E. coli* is not a dimer, since the degree of photoreversal of the mutation is the same in a strain lacking functional photoreactivating enzyme as in a strain which contains the enzyme, suggesting that all photoreactivation of this mutation is of the indirect type, which causes increased dark repair subsequent to the visible light treatment. The greater efficiency of photoreversal in the presence of photoreactivating enzyme is taken to be an indication that dimers interfere with the dark repair process that eliminates the premutational lesion. WITKIN [1963b] points out that acriflavine treatment after photoreactivation in a strain containing photoreactivating enzyme eliminates much of the photoreversing effect, further strengthening her conclusion that photoreversal of this mutation operates entirely by an indirect mechanism. Another piece of evidence offered by WITKIN [unpublished] is that mutants which are poor in dark repair are also poorly photoreversed, although photoreactivation of killing is normal. However, since we do not know whether all the pyrimidine dimers in the DNA of whole cells can be monomerized by photoreactivation, there must be some reservation concerning her conclusion that the premutational lesion is not a dimer. This lesion in the mutants with poor dark repair may be relatively inaccessible to both the photoreactivating and dark repair enzymes.

It is reasonable to inquire whether excision itself can cause mutations, since there is the possibility that a mistake can be made in "patching". HILL [1965] has found that a sensitive strain of *E. coli*, unable to repair bacteriophage DNA, has apparently lost the ability to repair premutational lesions leading to reversion to prototrophy. Since this same strain is apparently lacking in excision [R. B. SETLOW, unpublished], it is probable that these mutations are not caused by excision. However, one cannot exclude excision as a possible part of the mechanism of some mutations. The fact that at the lower UV doses Hill finds that her dose curves for survival and reversion in her mutant and the less sensitive parent are superimposable when the doses for the resistant parent are divided by the same dose reduction factor argues against Witkin's conclusion that the premutational lesion cannot be a dimer.

A UV-induced change of cytosine to uracil could take place by three different mechanisms: (1) deamination of the cytosine hydrate, with subsequent dehydration * of the resulting uracil hydrate; (2) deamination of a cytosine-cytosine or cytosine-thymine dimer, followed by monomerization of the resulting uracil-uracil or uracil-thymine dimer; and (3) direct deamination of cytosine to uracil. The first mechanism presumably cannot operate in native two-stranded DNA, because there is evidence that hydrates do not form in such material (see section 2.5). However, there may well be hydrate formation in single-stranded bacteriophage DNA, which could account for the large number of apparent UV-induced cytosine to thymine transitions obtained by HOWARD and TESSMAN [1964] in S13 virus, since uracil would be expected to behave like thymine in its base-pairing properties. The dehydration of the cytosine hydrate, however, probably proceeds considerably more rapidly than deamination [SCHUSTER, 1964; JOHNS, LEBLANC and FREEMAN, 1965]. The second mechanism could

---

* It is possible that dehydration is not necessary for a coding change. ONO, WILSON and GROSSMAN [1965] have suggested that the cytosine hydrate in poly C may pair with adenine. Similarly, the uracil hydrate might pair with adenine.

involve monomerization either by UV (since dimer formation is a reversible process) or by photoreactivating enzyme. The cytosine-uracil transition has been shown to take place in irradiated DNA which was first heated and then treated with photoreactivating enzyme to monomerize the resulting uracil-uracil and uracil-thymine dimers. There is no evidence for the third mechanism.

An unsuccessful attempt has been made to make mutations in *Hemophilus influenzae* transforming DNA by UV, followed by heat, followed by photoreactivation with yeast enzyme [J. K. SETLOW, unpublished]. Unfortunately this negative result does not exclude the proposed mechanism, (number 2 above), since the particular mutations looked for in the transforming DNA (resistance to a number of drugs) may not involve a cytosine to uracil change. A similar attempt has been made to demonstrate such a mutational mechanism in a strain of *E. coli* H/r 30 R obtained from Witkin, as shown in table I.

TABLE 1

Modification of UV-induced reversion to prototrophy in *E. coli* strain H/r 30 R

| Treatment | % survival | Mutants/$10^7$ survivors |
|---|---|---|
| UV | 20 | 474 |
| UV plus heat* | 16 | 253 |
| photoreactivation | 83 | 21 |
| photoreactivation plus heat* | 70 | 7 |
| heat* plus photoreactivation | 48 | 145 |

* 45°C for one-half hour.

In accord with the proposed mechanism, the number of mutants observed when the bacteria were heated before photoreactivation was much larger than when these two treatments were in the reverse order. This cannot be explained in terms of heat inactivation of photoreactivating enzyme, since the rate of monomerization of thymine dimers was the same whether or not the cells were heated first. The order of treatment had no effect in a similar strain lacking a functional photoreactivating enzyme. The experiment is suggestive, but not conclusive. Unfortunately heat by itself leaves more mutations than heat plus photoreactivation. The considerable decrease in UV-induced mutation produced by heat is probably not the result of repair

242 JANE K. SETLOW

taking place during heating, because no excision of dimers was detected during this period. The fraction of cytosine dimers deaminated by exposure to 45°C for one-half hour is probably not large [SETLOW, CARRIER and BOLLUM, 1965b], which may account for the fact that the number of observed mutations after heat plus photoreactivation is not very high. Thus deamination of cytosine-cytosine or cytosine thymine dimers may be a mechanism of mutation, but conclusive evidence is not at present available.

## 9. Summary

The importance of a number of different types of UV-induced pyrimidine dimers in lethal effects on many bacteria, bacteriophage, and transforming DNA is now reasonably well established, although an assessment of the fraction of damage due to these dimers has not been made for most of these biological systems. There is at present no proof that any other UV-induced change in DNA can cause lethal effects, nor can one exclude the possibility that all lethal effects in bacteria of normal UV sensitivity are the result of pyrimidine dimers. There is, however, evidence that protein damage may be important in the extremely resistant *Micrococcus radiodurans*.

Repair of UV-damaged bacterial DNA has been shown to take place by two different mechanisms: (1) monomerization of pyrimidine dimers by the action of an enzyme plus light (photoreactivation), and (2) enzymatic excision of pyrimidine dimers from the bacterial DNA in the absence of light, presumably followed by repair of the holes produced by the excision.

The mechanism of UV-induced mutation is still largely a mystery. It is not even known whether or not pyrimidine dimers can cause mutations in biological material, although it has been shown that pyrimidine dimers can cause chemically measurable base changes in DNA.

One can expect a solution to a few of the outstanding problems in the UV field in the near future. Some of these are: the chemical nature of the photoreactivating enzyme, the determination of whether or not the excision mechanism operates in viral DNA-directed repair of bacteriophage DNA, and the demonstration of DNA-repair replication in bacteria from which pyrimidine dimers have been excised. A number of other problems whose solutions seem much remoter may be listed: (1) the chemical mechanism of enzymatic monomerization of pyrimidine dimers in polynucleotides; (2) the nature of the excision and "patching" enzymes, and the details of these mechanisms; (3) a complete list of lethal photoproducts; and (4) the mechanism of UV-induced mutation.

## Acknowledgments

I am grateful to many individuals for allowing me to see and quote their unpublished work. I owe particular thanks to R. B. Setlow, with whom I have had numerous discussions on the material covered in this review.

## References

ADLER, H. I. 1965. In: Advances in Radiation Biology, Vol. 2. Eds. Augenstein, Mason and Zelle. (Academic Press, New York).

ADLER, H. I. and HARDIGREE, A. A. 1964. J. Bact. **87** 720.

ALEXANDER, P. and MOROSON, H. 1962. Nature **194** 882.

ANDERSON, E. H. 1949. Amer. J. Botany **36** 807.

BAWDEN, F. C. and KLECZKOWSKI, A. 1959. Nature **183** 503.

BELOZERSKY, A. N. and SPIRIN, A. S. 1960. In: The Nucleic Acids, Vol. 3. Eds. Chargaff and Davidson. (Academic Press, New York).

BERG, P., KORNBERG, R. D., FANCHER, H. and DIECKMANN, M. 1965. Biochem. Biophys. Res. Commun. **18** 932.

BEUKERS, R. and BERENDS, W. 1960. Biochim. Biophys. Acta **41** 550.

BEUKERS, R., YLSTRA, J. and BERENDS, W. 1958. Rec. Trav. Chim. Pays-Bas **77** 729.

BEUKERS, R., YLSTRA, J. and BERENDS, W. 1959. Rec. Trav. Chim. Pays-Bas **78** 883.

BOLLUM, F. J. 1963. In: Progress in Nucleic Acid Research, Vol. 1. Eds. Davidson and Cohn. (Academic Press, New York).

BOLLUM, F. J. and SETLOW, R. B. 1963. Biochim. Biophys. Acta **68** 599.

BOYCE, R. P. and HOWARD-FLANDERS, P. 1964. Proc. Nat. Acad. Sci. U. S. **51** 293.

BOYCE, R. and SETLOW, R. 1963. Biochim. Biophys. Acta **68** 446.

BRESCH, C. 1950. Z. Naturforsch. **5b** 420.

CABRERA-JÚAREZ, E. and HERRIOTT, R. M. 1963. J. Bact. **85** 671.

CASTELLANI, A., JAGGER, J. and SETLOW, R. B. 1964. Science **143** 1170.

CAVILLA, C. A. and JOHNS, H. E. 1964. Virology **24** 349.

CLARK, A. J. and MARGULIES, A. D. 1965. Proc. Nat. Acad. Sci. U. S. **53** 451.

DAVID, C. N. 1964. Z. Vererbungsl. **95** 318.

DEERING, R. A. and SETLOW, R. B. 1957. Science **126** 397.

DEERING, R. A. and SETLOW, R. B. 1963. Biochim. Biophys. Acta **68** 526.

DELLWEG, H. VON and WACKER, A. 1962. Z. Naturforsch. **17b** 827.

DEWEY, D. L. and BOAG, J. W. 1960. Brit. Emp. Cancer Campaign 38th Ann. Rep. **II** 242.

DONNELLAN, J. E. and SETLOW, R. B. 1965. Science **149** 308.

DOUDNEY, C. O. and HAAS, F. L. 1958. Proc. Nat. Acad. Sci. U. S. **44** 390.

DRAKE, J. W. 1963. J. Mol. Biol. **6** 268.

DRAKE, J. W. 1964. J. Cell Compl Physiol. **64** (Suppl. 1) 19.

DULBECCO, R. 1950. J. Bact. **59** 329.

ELDER, R. and BEERS Jr., R. F. 1964. Fed. Proc. **23** (Part I) 373.

ELLISON, S. A., FEINER, R. R. and HILL, R. F. 1960. Virology **11** 294.

EMMONS, C. W. and HOLLAENDER, A. 1939. Amer. J. Botany **26** 467.

ERRERA, M. 1954. Brit. J. Radiol. **27** 76.

FOLSOME, C. E. and LEVIN, D. 1961. Nature **192** 1306.

FREEMAN, K. B., HARIHARAN, P. V. and JOHNS, H. E. 1965. Abstr. Biophys. Soc. 9th Ann. Meeting, San Francisco.

FREIFELDER, D. and DAVISON, P. F. 1963, Biophys. J. **3** 97.

GATES, F. L. 1928. Science **68** 479.

GATES, F. L. 1930. J. Gen. Physiol. **14** 31.

GLISIN, V. R. and DOTY, P. 1962. Biochim. Biophys. Acta **61** 458.

GODDARD, J., STREETER, D. and GORDON, M. P. 1964. Abstr. 6th Internat. Congr. Biochem. New York.

GOODGAL, S. H., RUPERT, C. S. and HERRIOTT, R. M. 1957. In: The Chemical Basis of Heredity. Eds. McElroy and Glass. (Johns Hopkins Press, Baltimore).

GREEN, M. and COHEN, S. S. 1957. J. Biol. Chem. **228** 601.

GREER, S. and ZAMENHOF, S. 1957. Abstr. Amer. Chem. Soc. 131st Meeting, p. 3C.

GROSSMAN, L. 1962. Proc. Nat. Acad. Sci. U. S. **48** 1609.

GROSSMAN, L. 1963. Proc. Nat. Acad. Sci. U. S. **50** 657.

HAAS, F., WYSS, O. and STONE, W. S. 1948. Proc. Nat. Acad. Sci. U. S. **34** 229.

HANAWALT, P. C. and HAYNES, R. H. 1965. Biochem. Biophys. Res. Commun **19** 462.

HANAWALT, P. C. and RAY, D. S. 1964. Proc. Nat. Acad. Sci. U. S. **52** 125.

HARM, W. 1963a. Virology **19** 66.

HARM, W. 1963b. In: Repair from Genetic Radiation. Ed. Sobels. (Pergamon, New York).

HARM, W. and HILLEBRANDT, B. 1962. Photochem. Photobiol. **1** 271.

HAUG, A. 1964a. Z. Naturforsch. **19** 143.

HAUG, A., 1964b. Biochim. Biophys. Acta **88** 480.

HAUG, A. and GOES, E. 1963. Int. J. Radiat. Biol. **7** 447.

HAYNES, R. H. 1964. In: Physical Processes in Radiation Biology. Ed. Augenstein, Mason and Rosenberg. (Academic Press, New York).

HELLEINER, C. W., PEARSON, M. L. and JOHNS, H. E. 1963. Proc. Nat. Acad. Sci. U. S. **50** 761.

HELMSTETTER, C. E. and URETZ, R. B. 1963. Biophys. J. **3** 35.

HILL, R. F. 1964. J. Bact. **88** 1283.

HILL, R. F. 1965. Photochem. Photobiol. **4** 563.

HILL, R. F. and ROSSI, H. H. 1952. Science **116** 424.

HILL, R. V. and SIMSON, E. 1961. J. Gen. Microbiol. **24** 1.

HOLLAENDER, A. and CLAUS, W. D. 1937. Bull. Nat. Res. Council U. S. **100** 75.

HOLLAENDER, A., GREENSTEIN, J. P. and JENRETTE, W. V. 1941. J. Nat. Cancer Inst. **2** 23.

HORN, E. E. and HERRIOTT, R. M. 1962. Proc. Nat. Acad. Sci. U. S. **48** 1409.

HOTZ, G. 1963. Biochem. Biophys. Res. Commun. **11** 393.

HOTZ, G. 1964. Z. Vererbungsl. **95** 211.

HOWARD, B. D. and TESSMAN, I. 1964. J. Mol. Biol. **9** 372.

HOWARD-FLANDERS, P. 1964. J. Cell. Comp. Physiol. **64** (Suppl. 1) 65.

HOWARD-FLANDERS, P., BOYCE, R. P., SIMSON, E. and THERIOT, L. 1962. Proc. Nat. Acad. Sci. U. S. **48** 2109.

HOWARD-FLANDERS, P., BOYCE, R. P. and THERIOT, L. 1962. Nature **195** 51.

HOWARD-FLANDERS, P., SIMSON, E. and THERIOT, L. 1964. Genetics **49** 237.

IYER, V. N. and SZYBALSKI, W. 1963. Proc. Nat. Acad. Sci. U. S. **50** 355.

JACOB, F., BRENNER, S. and CUZIN, F. 1963. Cold Spring Harbor Symp. **28** 329.

JACOB, F. and WOLLMAN, E. 1955. Ann. Inst. Pasteur **88** 724.

JAGGER, J., 1958. Bact. Rev. **22** 99.

JAGGER, J. 1960. In: Radiation Protection and Recovery. Ed. Hollaender. (Pergamon, Oxford).

JAGGER, J. and LATARJET, R. 1956. Ann. Inst. Pasteur **91** 858.

JAGGER, J. and STAFFORD, R. S. 1962. Photochem. Photobiol. **1** 245.

JAGGER, J. and STAFFORD, R. S. 1965. Biophys. J. **5** 75.

JOHNS, H. E., LeBLANC, J. and FREEMAN, K. 1965. Abstr. Biophys. Soc. 9th Ann. Meeting, San Francisco.

JOHNS, H. E., PEARSON, M. L., LeBLANC, J. C. and HELLEINER, C. W. 1964. J. Mol. Biol. **9** 503.

JOHNS, H. E., RAPAPORT, S. A. and DELBRÜCK, M. 1962. J. Mol. Biol. **4** 104.

KAPLAN, R. W., WINKLER, U. and WOLF-ELLMAUER, H. 1960. Nature **186** 330.

KELNER, A. 1951. J. Gen. Physiol. **34** 835.

KIMBALL, R. F. 1965. In: Advances in Radiation Biology, Vol. 2. Eds. Augenstein, Mason and Zelle. (Academic Press, New York).

KLECZKOWSKI, A. 1963. Photochem. Photobiol. **2** 497.

KNAPP, E., REUSS, A., RISSE, O. and SCHREIBER, H. 1939, Naturwiss. **27** 304.

KOHN, K. W., STEIGBIGEL, N. H. and SPEARS, C. L. 1965. Proc. Nat. Acad. Sci. U.S. **53** 1154.

KRIEG, D. R. 1959. Virology **9** 215.

KRIEG, D. R. 1963. In: Progress in Nucleic Acid Research, Vol. 2. Eds. Davidson and Cohn. (Academic Press, New York).

LATARJET, R. 1943. C. R. Acad. Sci. **217** 186.

LERMAN, L. S. and TOLMACH, L. J. 1959. Biochim. Biophys. Acta **33** 371.

LIEB, M. 1961. Z. Vererbungsl. **92** 416.

LION, M. B. 1965. Abstr. 30th Ann. Meeting Radiat. Res. Soc., Philadelphia.

LITMAN, R. M. and EPHRUSSI-TAYLOR, H. 1959. C. R. Acad. Sci. **249** 838.

LOGAN, D. M. and WHITMORE, G. F. 1965. Abstr. Biophys. Soc. 9th Ann.

Meeting, San Francisco.

MANTIONE, M.-J. and PULLMAN, B. 1964. Biochim. Biophys. Acta **91** 387.

MARMUR, J., ANDERSON, W. F., MATTHEWS, L., BERNS, K., GAJEWSKA, E., LANE, D. and DOTY, P. 1961. J. Cell. Comp. Physiol. **58** (Suppl. 1) 33.

MARMUR, J. and GROSSMAN, L. 1961. Proc. Nat. Acad. Sci. U. S. **47** 778.

MOORE, A. M., 1958. Can. J. Chem. **36** 281.

MOORE, A. M. and THOMSON, C. H. 1955. Science **122** 594.

MOORE, A. M. and THOMSON, C. H. 1957. Can. J. Chem. **35** 163.

MOROSON, H. and ALEXANDER, P. 1961. Rad. Res. **14** 29.

MUHAMMED, A. 1965. Abstr. Biophys. Soc. 9th Ann. Meeting, San Francisco.

ONO, J. WILSON, R. G. and GROSSMAN, L. 1965. J. Mol. Biol. **11** 600.

OPARA-KUBINSKA, Z., KURYLO-BOROWSKA, Z. and SZYBALSKI, W. 1963. Biochim. Biophys. Acta **72** 298.

OPARA-KUBINSKA, Z., LORKIEWICZ, Z. and SZYBALSKI, W. 1961. Biochem. Biophys. Res. Commun. **4** 288.

PAPIRMEISTER, B. and DAVISON, C. L. 1964. Biochem. Biophys. Res. Commun. **17** 608.

PEARSON, M. L., OTTENSMEYER, F. P. and JOHNS, H. E. 1965. Photochem. Photobiol. In the press.

PETTIJOHN, D. and HANAWALT, P. 1964. J. Mol. Biol. **9** 395.

PITTMAN, D. 1964. Abstr. 4th Internat. Photobiol. Congr., Oxford.

RAPAPORT, S. A. 1964. Virology **22** 125.

RIKLIS, E. 1965. Can. J. Biochem. **43** 1207.

RIKLIS, E. and SIMSON, E. 1964. Abstr. Biophys. Soc. 8th Ann. Meeting, Chicago.

ROBERTS, R. B. and ALDOUS, E. 1949. J. Bact. **57** 363.

ROMAN, H. and JACOB, F. 1957. C. R. Acad. Sci. **245** 1032.

RÖRSCH, A., VAN DER KAMP, C. and ADEMA, J. 1964. Biochim. Biophys. Acta **80** 346.

RUPERT, C. S. 1960. J. Gen. Physiol. **43** 573.

RUPERT, C. S. 1961. J. Cell. Comp. Physiol. **58** (Suppl. 1) 57.

RUPERT, C. S. 1962a. J. Gen. Physiol. **45** 703.

RUPERT, C. S. 1962b. J. Gen. Physiol. **45** 725.

RUPERT, C. S. 1964a. In: Photophysiology, Vol. 2. Ed. Giese. (Academic Press, New York).

RUPERT, C. S. 1964b. Photochem. Photobiol. **3** 399.

RUPERT, C. S., GOODGAL, S. H. and HERRIOTT, R. M. 1958. J. Gen. Physiol. **41** 451.

RUPP, W. D. and PRUSOFF, W. H. 1964. Nature **202** 1288.

RUPP, W. D. and PRUSOFF, W. H. 1965a. Biochem. Biophys. Res. Commun. **18** 145.

RUPP, W. D. and PRUSOFF, W. H. 1965b. Biochem. Biophys. Res. Commun. **18** 158.

SAUERBIER, W. 1960. Nature **188** 329.

SAUERBIER, W. 1961. Virology **15** 465.

SAUERBIER, W. 1964a. Z. Vererbungsl. **95** 145.

SAUERBIER, W. 1964b. J. Mol. Biol. **10** 551.

SAUERBIER, W. 1964c. Biochim. Biophys. Acta **87** 356.

SAUERBIER, W. 1964d. Biochim. Biophys. Acta **91** 663.

SAUERBIER, W. and HAUG, A. 1964. J. Mol. Biol. **10** 180.

SCHUSTER, V. H. 1964. Z. Naturforsch. **19b** 815.

SETLOW, J. K. 1959. PhD. Thesis, Yale University.

SETLOW, J. K. 1962. Nature **194** 664.

SETLOW, J. K. 1963. Photochem. Photobiol. **2** 393.

SETLOW, J. K. 1964. Photochem. Photobiol. **3** 405.

SETLOW, J. K. and BOLING, M. E. 1963. Photochem. Photobiol. **2** 471.

SETLOW, J. K. and BOLING, M. E. 1965. Biochim. Biophys. Acta. In the press.

SETLOW, J. K., BOLING, M. E. and BOLLUM, F. J. 1965. Proc. Nat. Acad. Sci. U. S. **53** 1430.

SETLOW, J. K., BOLLUM, F. J. and BOLING, M. E. 1965. Abstr.Biophys.Soc. 9th Ann. Meeting, San Francisco.

SETLOW, J. K. and DUGGAN, D. E. 1964. Biochim. Biophys. Acta **87** 664.

SETLOW, J. K. and SETLOW, R. B. 1961. Proc. Nat. Acad. Sci. U. S. **47** 1619.

SETLOW, J. K. and SETLOW, R. B. 1963. Nature **197** 560.

SETLOW, R. 1961. Biochim. Biophys. Acta **49** 237.

SETLOW, R. B. 1964a. In: Mammalian Cytogenetics and Related Problems in Radiobiology. Eds. Pavan, Chagas, Frota-Pessoa and Caldas. (Pergamon, New York).

SETLOW, R. B. 1964b. J. Cell. Comp. Physiol. **64** (Suppl. 1) 51.

SETLOW, R. and BOYCE, R. 1960. Biophys. J. **1** 29.

SETLOW, R. and BOYCE, R. 1963. Biochim. Biophys. Acta **68** 455.

SETLOW, R. B. and CARRIER, W. L. 1963. Photochem. Photobiol. **2** 49.

SETLOW, R. B. and CARRIER, W. L. 1964. Proc. Nat. Acad. Sci. U. S. **51** 226.

SETLOW, R. B., CARRIER, W. L. and BOLLUM, F. J. 1965a. Abstr. Biophys. Soc. 9th Ann. Meeting, San Francisco.

SETLOW, R. B., CARRIER, W. L. and BOLLUM, F. J. 1965b. Proc. Nat. Acad. Sci. U. S. **53** 1111.

SETLOW, R. and DOYLE, B. 1953. Biochim. Biophys. Acta **12** 508.

SETLOW, R. B. and SETLOW, J. K. 1962. Proc. Nat. Acad. Sci. U. S. **48** 1250.

SETLOW, R. B., SWENSON, P. A. and CARRIER, W. L. 1963. Science **142** 1464.

SHANKEL, D. M. and WYSS, O. 1961. Rad. Res. **14** 605.

SHUGAR, D. 1962. Abh. Deut. Akad. Wissensch. Berlin **1** 72.

SHUGAR, D. and WIERZCHOWSKI, K. 1957. Biochim. Biophys. Acta **23** 657.

SHUSTER, R. 1964. Nature **202** 614.

SINSHEIMER, R. L. 1954. Rad. Res. **1** 505.

SINSHEIMER, R. L. 1957. Rad. Res. **6** 121.

SINSHEIMER, R. L. 1960. In: The Nucleic Acids, Vol. 3. Eds. Chargaff and Davidson. (Academic Press, New York).

SINSHEIMER, R. L. and HASTINGS, R. 1949. Science **110** 525.

SMIETANOWSKA, A. and SHUGAR, D. 1961. Bull. Acad. Polon. Sci. **9** (Cl. II) 375.

SMITH, K. C. 1962a. Biochem. Biophys. Res. Commun. **6** 458.

SMITH, K. C. 1962b. Biochem. Biophys. Res. Commun. **8** 157.

SMITH, K. C. 1963. Photochem. Photobiol. **2** 503.

SMITH, K. C. 1964. In: Photophysiology, Vol. 2. Ed. Giese. (Academic Press, New York).

SMITH, K. C. 1965. Abstr. Biophys. Soc. 9th Ann. Meeting, San Francisco.

STAHL, F. W., CRASEMANN, J. M., OKUN, L. FOX, E. and LAIRD, C. 1961. Virology **13** 98.

STUY, J. H. 1955. Biochim. Biophys. Acta **17** 206.

STUY, J. H. 1956. Biochim. Biophys. Acta **22** 241.

SWENSON, P. A. and SETLOW, R. B. 1963. Photochem. Photobiol. **2** 419.

SWENSON, P. A. and SETLOW, R. B. 1965. J. Mol. Biol. In the press.

SZTUMPF, E. and SHUGAR, D. 1962. Biochim. Biophys. Acta **61** 555.

TESSMAN, E. S. 1956. Virology **2** 679.

TESSMAN, E. S. and OZAKI, T. 1960. Virology **12** 431.

VAN DE PUTTE, P., VAN SLUIS, C. A., VAN DILLEWIJN, J. and RÖRSCH, A. 1965. Mut. Res. **2** 97.

VOLKIN, E. 1954. J. Amer. Chem. Soc. **76** 5892.

WACKER, A. 1961. J. Chim. Phys. **58** 1041.

WACKER, A. 1963. In: Progress in Nucleic Acid Research, Vol. 1. Eds. Davidson and Cohn. (Academic Press, New York)

WACKER, A., DELLWEG, H. and JACHERTS, D. 1962. J. Mol. Biol. **4** 410.

WACKER, A., DELLWEG, H. and WEINBLUM, D. 1960. Naturwiss. **47** 477.

WACKER, A., WEINBLUM, D., TRÄGER, L. and MOUSTAFA, Z. H. 1961. J. Mol. Biol. **3** 790.

WANG, S. Y. 1959. Nature **184** 184.

WANG, S. Y. 1961. Nature **190** 690.

WANG, S. Y. 1962. Photochem. Photobiol. **1** 37.

WEATHERWAX, R. S. 1956. J. Bact. **72** 124.

WEINBLUM, D. and JOHNS, H. E. 1965. Abstr. Biophys. Soc. 9th Ann. Meeting, San Francisco.

WIERZCHOWSKI, K. L. and SHUGAR, D. 1962. Photochem. Photobiol. **1** 21.

WINKLER, U., JOHNS, H. E. and KELLENBERGER, E. 1962. Virology **18** 343.

WITKIN, E. M. 1956. Cold Spring Harbor Symp. **21** 123.

WITKIN, E. M. 1958. Proc. 10th Internat. Congr. Genet. **1** 280.

WITKIN, E. M. 1961. J. Cell. Comp. Physiol. **58** (Suppl. 1) 135.

WITKIN, E. M. 1963a. Genetics **48** 916.

WITKIN, E. M. 1963b. Proc. Nat. Acad. Sci. U. S. **50** 425.

WITKIN, E. M. 1964. Mutation Res. **1** 22.

WITKIN, E. M. and THEIL, E. C. 1960. Proc. Nat. Acad. Sci. U. S. **46** 226.

WULFF, D. L. 1963a. Biophys. J. **3** 355.

WULFF, D. L. 1963b. J. Mol. Biol. **7** 431.

WULFF, D. L. and FRAENKEL, G. 1961. Biochim. Biophys. Acta **51** 332.

WULFF, D. L. and RUPERT, C. S. 1962. Biochem. Biophys. Res. Commun. **7** 237.

WYCKOFF, R. W. G. 1932. J. Gen. Physiol. **15** 351.

V

# APPROACHES TO THE DETERMINATION OF THE INITIAL SITES OF ACTION OF RADIATIONS IN *Escherichia coli* AND YEAST *

F. JOSET, E. MOUSTACCHI and H. MARCOVICH

*Laboratoire Pasteur, Institut du Radium, Paris*

* This investigation was supported by U. S. Atomic Energy Commission grant AT (30-1) 2803 and by the French Commissariat à l'Énergie Atomique grant 6674-r.

# CONTENTS

# 1. Introduction

There is very little information about the cellular sites affected at the very early stages following exposure to X-rays or ultraviolet (UV) light. Experiments generally performed in radiobiology on microorganisms permit one to detect the lethal damage or the induction of a mutation only several generations after the time of irradiation. Interpretation of the dose-effect relationships gives a first approximation of what occurred in the irradiated cell; but it usually does not allow an analysis of what had happened at a given site in a single cell.

The present discussion will deal with some results obtained with microorganisms, essentially *Escherichia coli* and yeast, using the techniques of genetics to analyse, by conjugation between two cells, the damage produced by radiation. We shall consider first the mechanism of X-ray- and UV-induced lethal and mutagenic effects in *E. coli*, at the intracellular level, and secondly the genetic aspects of radiation sensitivity in yeast.

# 2. Chromosomal lesions induced by X-rays and UV light in *E. coli* K12

## 2.1. LETHAL EFFECTS

### 2.1.1. *X-rays*

The survival of *E. coli* K12 after X-rays is an exponential function of the dose. This is observed for various physiological conditions of the bacterial populations, though the number of nuclear bodies per cell varies from one (steady state) to two or three (exponential growth phase). From a formal stand-point, the X-ray-induced lethal lesions have a dominant character. Accordingly, if they are induced on the chromosome it should be possible to detect them by using suitable crosses. Experiments have been carried out by irradiating *E. coli* K12 Hfr male cells, and mating them with non irradiated F⁻ recipient ones.

It is known that during conjugation between an Hfr donor (Hfr for High frequency of recombination) and an F⁻ recipient, the genetic determinants of the donor are transferred to the zygote sequentially and in an order constant for a given Hfr strain. The frequency of transfer of a marker decreases as a function of its distance from the point of the chromosome first transferred, the origin O. One can thus define a gradient of transfer of the male characters, and a degree of linkage between them, expressed as their probability of being simultaneously transmitted to the recombinants. The study of the variation of these two factors as a result of the irradiation of the male or of the female has been used as a tool to analyse the radio-induced lethal damage.

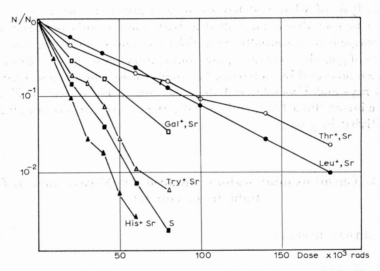

Fig. 1. Survival curves of the recombinants issuing from a mating between X-irradiated Hfr H males and normal PA 309 females. Prototroph Sm$^s$ *E. coli* K12 Hfr H males and auxotroph Sm$^r$ F$^-$ PA 309 females are grown in broth to a concentration of $2 \cdot 10^8$ cells/ml. The males are irradiated and mated with the females at a ratio of 1 male to 10 females, for 90 minutes, with gentle agitation, at 37°C. The 90 minute length of time permits a maximal transfer of the His locus with no appreciable transfer of the Sm one. Aliquots for each dose are then plated on minimal medium enriched with all but one of the growth factors essential to the female and with Sm. Recombinants are counted after 48 hours of growth at 37°C. Survival of males is simultaneously assayed (curve S). Ordinate: frequency of markers in the recombinants, as a fraction of the zero dose frequencies.
Symbols: Thr: Threonine; Leu: Leucine; Gal: Galactose; Try: Tryptophan; His: Histidine; S: Streptomycin; + indicates prototrophy or capacity to ferment a sugar; s and r indicate sensitivity and resistance to an antibiotic, respectively [from MARCOVICH, 1961].

In this system, any dominant lethal lesion induced on the male chromosome should have a lethal effect on the zygote.

In a first set of experiments, the male strain Hfr H was used; it injects its markers in the order, O, Thr, Leu, Gal, Try, His, Sm* [HAYES, 1953]. Increasing doses of X-rays were given [MARCOVICH, 1961] and the probability of transfer to the recombinants of each male marker was scored. Fig. 1 shows that the probability of finding a male marker in the progeny decreases exponentially with dose; the greater the distance of the selected character from the origin O, the steeper the slope of the dose-effect curve. These results eliminate the possibility that X-rays actually destroy each gene independently. But they are still consistent with the possibility of a transfer of dominant lethal lesions, the probability of their concomitant transfer increasing with the length of chromosome transmitted to the recombinants (A dominant lethal lesion, transferred after a given marker, would be able to kill the zygote). It was possible to test this hypothesis by interrupting the mating. The earlier the interruption is effected, the shorter the piece of chromosome transferred, and consequently, the lower the probability for a lethal lesion to be transmitted together with an early marker. Accordingly, an early interruption should yield a less steep survival curve of this marker than a late interruption. This was not actually observed and it was concluded that no such lethal damage was detectable on the irradiated male chromosome. Besides, no lethal effect of the transferred irradiated male chromosome could be detected in the recipient cell itself.

In a cross, the selected male marker determines two regions on the chromosome, the anterior and the posterior ones, respectively transferred before and after it. The loci of the anterior region segregate according to their linkage. Any lethal event induced in it by X-rays should decrease this linkage. This is not observed (fig. 2). It may then be concluded that no such lethal event, if induced on the male chromosome, can be transmitted to the recombinant. It may also be concluded that X-rays induce damage which prevents transfer, that is, operationally, breaks in the chromosome. By comparing the sensitivity of the chromosome to these breakage events with the lethal effect on the male cell, it may be estimated that for each lethal event three such breaks are produced, on the average. It is not possible to say whether

* See fig. 1. for explanations of symbols.

the lethal event is not actually a break which has one chance out of three to kill the cell [MARCOVICH, 1961].

Carrying out the irradiation on the females, and mating them subsequently with normal males yields zygotes bearing the induced lesions.

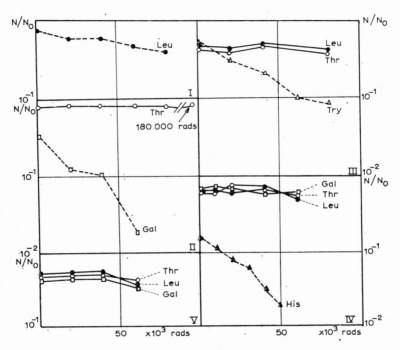

Fig. 2. Effect of X-irradiation of the male on the frequency of unselected markers in a population of recombinants selected for a given character. The recombinant colonies appearing in the experiment described in fig. 1 are isolated and tested, by the replica plating technique, for the presence of unselected markers. Ordinate: percent of selected recombinants having a given unselected marker. Abscissa: dose given to the males. The figures I, II, III, IV, and V correspond to the following selected recombinants, respectively: Thr, Leu, Gal, Try, His. The dotted lines indicate distal markers, the full lines proximal markers [from MARCOVICH, 1961].

By analysing the frequency of appearance of the male markers in the recombinants, it can be seen that the sensitivity of the zygotes decreases when the amount of male genetic material transmitted increases (fig. 3). A rescue effect of the female genetic material by the male chromosome seems to exist. Also, the linkage of the male markers in the zygotes apparently increases with the dose given to the females, suggesting that the X-ray lesions counter-select the female markers [WOOD and MARCOVICH, 1964].

The same results have been obtained using α-particles [WOOD and MARCOVICH, unpub.].

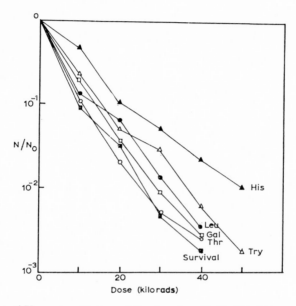

Fig. 3. Effect of X-ray irradiation of the female cells F⁻ PA 309 on the recombination frequencies for selected male markers in a cross with Hfr H males. The experimental conditions are the same as described in fig. 1 except that the female population is irradiated; The survival of the females is shown [from WOOD and MARCOVICH, 1964].

In no case do X-rays or α-particles seem to have any detectable effect on the conjugation process. The curves giving the variation of the gradient of transfer of the Hfr markers as a function of doses received by the male, deduced from the data of fig. 1, show that a marker infinitely close to the origin would be transmitted independently of dose.

The transfer of the male material is hampered in as much as breakage events are made. This conclusion may be analysed in the light of what is known about the mechanism of transfer of the male genetic material in an Hfr × F⁻ cross. According to the model proposed by JACOB et al. [1963], the transfer process requires the synthesis in the males, at the conjugation point, of a hybrid DNA involving a parental strand and a newly formed one. Considering the absence of effect of X-rays on the mating capacity, it may be concluded that the resistance to X-rays of the DNA replicase, in this system, is very high.

It may then be suggested that the lethal effect of X-rays on vegetative cells is not exerted on the replication enzyme. Since no X-ray induced lesions other than chromosome breaks have yet been detected in *E. coli* K12, it may be thought that the lethal event is an interruption of chromosome replication at the place where the DNA replicase reaches a "transfer" lesion. According to this mechanism, the one hit survival curve would mean that the divisions of the nuclei are coordinated, one of them dividing only when the other(s) have accomplished its (their) own division, or that they divide synchronously.

### 2.1.2. *Ultraviolet light*

The same type of experiments have been performed using ultraviolet light. There is, as with X-rays, a decrease in the transfer frequency according to the markers' distances from the origin, after irradiation of the males, and a rescue of the female genetic material when it is irradiated.

However, besides these effects, it has been observed that contrary to X-rays, UV inhibits the conjugation process: the extrapolations to the zero ordinate of the gradient curves (fig. 4) show that the frequency of transfer of a marker near to the origin decreases with the dose received by the males, faster than would be expected considering its distance from the origin. This decrease reflects an inhibition of the capacity of mating of cells. The efficiency of this inhibition is about half that of the killing of the males. Its mechanism is not known, but it is not excluded that the replication system may be involved [JOSET and WOOD, 1965].

### 2.1.3. *Invertant males*

It has recently been found that both X-rays and UV light can, in

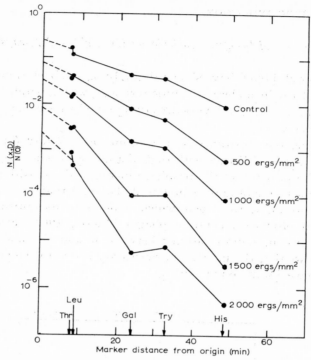

Fig. 4. Effect of ultraviolet irradiation of the donor parent, Hfr, H, on the gradient of transfer of its markers to the recipient. Marker frequency is plotted as a function of marker position for various doses. The experimental conditions are as in fig. 1, except that the irradiation is carried out in saline. The survival of the males is approximately $10^{-2}$ at 2000 ergs/mm² [from JOSET and WOOD, 1965].

some Hfr male strains, produce another type of effect. When these males are irradiated and immediately mated, they are induced to change their origin and sequence of transfer of their markers. If the matings are performed several generations after the irradiation, this effect is considerably decreased, or disappears. Also the proportion of such "invertant" males among the survivors is much smaller than that which would be expected from the marker survival curves. These two facts show that the induced inversion is either unstable or lethal in most cases. The mechanism of its induction is not known; though it may be suggested from the transfer model proposed by JACOB et al. [1963], that the radiations might induce a temporary new origin of DNA replication on the chromosome [JOSET et al., 1964].

## 2.2. LYSOGENIC INDUCTION

### 2.2.1. *Induction of lysogenic bacteria by UV light and X-rays*

LWOFF et al. [1950] have shown that a lysogenic bacterium exposed to ultraviolet light undergoes a lytic response, with a parallel development of mature phages. LATARJET [1951] found that X-rays have the same property.

Comparing the sensitivity of a lysogenic *E. coli* K12 ($\lambda$) strain to the lethal action of X-rays with that of a non-lysogenic one, one may see that the presence of the prophage increases the sensitivity of the former by a factor of approximately 2. The fact that starvation of a lysogenic strain, a treatment which suppresses its aptitude to be induced to produce vegetative phages [JACOB, 1962], also cancels the difference in radiosensitivity between it and the non-lysogenic strain, shows that the increase in sensitivity is due to the presence of the prophage [MARCOVICH, 1957].

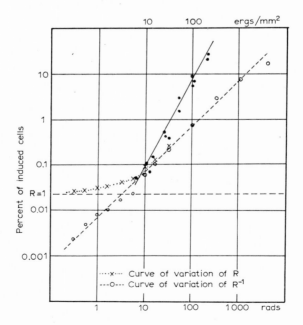

Fig. 5. Kinetics of induction of K12 ($\lambda$) by X-rays (dotted line) and UV light (full line). The free phages have been scored [from MARCOVICH, 1957].

The kinetics of induction by X-rays give a one hit dose-effect relationship [MARCOVICH 1956], fig. 5. On the basis of the target theory, the size of the sensitive site would represent about 10 % of the nucleus. It is consequently much larger than the size that one might assign to the prophage (approximately 1 % of the total DNA), assuming it has the same DNA content as the $\lambda$ phages. The molecular weight of the latter is about $3 \cdot 10^7$ daltons [BURGI and HERSHEY, 1963] as compared to $2.8 \cdot 10^{10}$ daltons for the DNA of one cellular nucleus [CAIRNS, 1963].

The initial site of action of X-rays in this system is not known. According to the model proposed by JACOB and CAMPBELL [1959], the lysogenic state is maintained because of the presence in the cell of a repressor substance produced by the prophage. There is very probably more than one repressor molecule. One way of estimating their number is to infect lysogenic cells with the phage to which they are immune, and to determine the minimal number of phages necessary to overcome immunity. This has been found to be of the order of 30 [JACOB et al., 1962]. Thus a direct destruction by radiation of the repressor molecules cannot explain the one hit dose-effect curve with X-rays and the two hits with UV.

Induction of vegetative development of $\lambda$ bacteriophage in a lysogenic cell may be ascribed to a decrease in the amount of active repressor through an indirect mechanism which might concern its rate of synthesis or its stability.

The repressor model for induction of temperate phages, by radiation or arrest of DNA synthesis, raises a question about the mechanism of depression by these agents. Any such effect has not been described for repressed enzymes except in the case of the galactose operon [BUTTIN, 1960]. In this case, galactokinase is induced by UV only if there is an inducible prophage in the neighbourhood at one side of the operon.


## 2.2.2. Cross induction

In 1958, BOREK and RYAN made the following experiment. A methionine-less F+ male strain of *E. coli* K12 ($\lambda$) was irradiated with UV light under methionine starvation, and mated with a lysogenic recipient *E. coli* K12 ($\lambda$) F−. In these conditions, the starved donor strain could not produce bacteriophage; however the mixture of both strains produced a significant amount of phage, which was demonstrated to be produced by the recipient cells. The authors concluded that there exists a cross-induction effect, carried out from the donor to the recipient cell. In later experiments, [BOREK and RYAN, 1960], they showed that the induction event produced in the donor strain is stable in the cold, unstable at 37°C, and unstable to illumination by visible light. Moreover, cross-induction occurs with the same efficiency whether the donor strain is lysogenic or not.

DEVORET and GEORGE [1946b] have shown that it is actually the F episome which is responsible for cross-induction; Hfr cells irradiated with UV induce the lysogenic recipients with a much lower frequency, corresponding approximately to the proportion of spontaneously occurring F+ cells among them. Other episomes such as colicinogenic factors also cross-induce.

The kinetics of cross-induction have been found to be of the two-hit type, as for direct induction [DEVORET and GEORGE, 1964a].

The phenomenon of cross-induction is in contradiction with the idea that UV induces by altering directly the repressor molecules.

Contrary to UV, X-rays do not produce cross-induction [RYAN, 1962; DEVORET, 1963]. It has been shown in the previous section that no X-ray lesion can be transferred during a mating, while some UV lesions can be. This fact might have some relation to the incapacity of X-rays to cross-induce.

It remains quite difficult to understand why episome but no other DNA transfer may cross-induce. Heavily UV-irradiated λ phage cannot induce a lysogenic strain by infection suggesting that UV'ed DNA, other than episomic, is unable to carry indirect induction [JACOB et al., 1962]. As the buoyant density of the F episome is the same as that of the E. coli chromosome [MARMUR et al. 1961], the specificity of the UV lesion producing cross-induction would lie not in its overall chemical nature. However, it cannot be excluded that a very small region of it, responsible for cross-induction, injected late, could have a different composition.

Let us now consider induction through other, apparently unrelated, mechanisms.

It has been shown that induction can be achieved by several means such as mitomycin treatment [OTSUJI et al., 1959], thymine starvation of a thymine-less strain [KORN and WEISSBACH, 1962], 5-FU or FUDR treatments [MARCOVICH and KAPLAN, 1963] or heating of a thermo-sensitive mutant [CAMPBELL, 1959]. All these treatments block DNA synthesis. It is well known that one of the effects of UV on a cell is to block DNA synthesis [KELNER, 1953]. If this event is the first step leading to the maturation of a prophage, it might be thought that cross-induction is accomplished by an arrest of DNA synthesis in the recipient cell. It has recently been suggested that replication of DNA in *E. coli* occurs on the membrane [JACOB et al., in the press]. It is then not excluded that cross-induction may be linked to an effect of the donor strain on the membrane of the recipient one. The terminal end of the donor replicating DNA might transmit to the female a signal to stop DNA synthesis.

### 2.2.3. *Mutagenic effect*

The use of techniques of conjugation in *E. coli* K12 permits one to localize the initial event induced by radiations on the nuclear or extra nuclear material and leading to mutagenesis. The advantage of this method lies in the fact that no material other than genetic is transferred from the male to the female cell. It is then possible to conceive experiments in which the donor cell is induced to mutate by radiations, and then mated with a non-irradiated recipient one, or in which inversely, the non-irradiated donor is mated with an irradiated recipient. This allows one to detect an initial event induced outside the genetic material, and affecting the genome only after a certain lag.

The experiments performed with this system involved the study of the reversion to prototrophy of the threonineless character, which was chosen because of its high linkage with the leucine determinant; by choosing an adequate repartition of both characters among the parents, it is possible to determine the parental origin and the initial site of the induced mutation.

A first set of experiments consisted in exposing Hfr H Thr⁻ Leu⁺ cells to increasing doses of X-rays, and mating them immediately with Thr⁻ Leu⁻ recipient cells. As appears in fig. 6, the frequency of recombinants carrying the Thr⁺ back mutation, increases with dose at the same rate as that of the induced mutants determined directly in the irradiated males. This suggests that the mutational event induced by X-rays is established with no delay in the transferable genetic material of the male cells. The opposite result has been found after UV irradiation: no Thr⁺ character can be transferred to the females, although the mutagenic effect is very easy to observe in the exposed non-mated males (fig. 6). For the mutagenic event induced by UV to be established in the transferable male genetic material, a delay of several hours is necessary, during which the irradiated population grows. But it can be shown that there is no selective advantage of the mutants over the rest of the population during this lag.

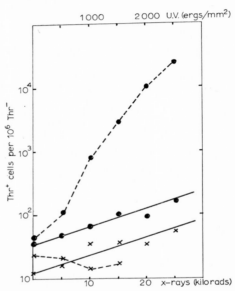

Fig. 6. Transfer to the recombinants of the Thr⁻ → Thr⁺ mutation induced in the males. The strains and techniques are similar to those already described, except that both parents bear the isoallelic Thr⁻ character. Ordinate: number of Thr⁺ Leu⁺ recombinants recovered per 10⁶ Thr⁻ Leu⁺ male cells (X) as compared with the number of mutations observed in the males directly (●). Dotted line: UV. Full line: X-ray [from KADA and MARCOVICH, 1963].

These experiments suggest that X-rays induce the mutation Thr⁻ → Thr⁺ by a direct action on the chromosome, while UV produces a mutagenic intermediate which is incorporated in the genetic material only during DNA synthesis.

Support for this conclusion is given by the observation that the male Thr⁻ locus, injected into an irradiated female, is not affected if

the radiation used was X-rays, while it is mutated if UV was administered (fig. 7).

Comparable results have been obtained by JENSEN and HAAS
[1963], who showed that transforming DNA of UV irradiated *Pneumococcus* cannot transfer the mutation if no cell division occurred before
its extraction. Also, several observations have shown that bacteriophage
is mutated when infecting a UV irradiated sensitive cell [JACOB, 1954].

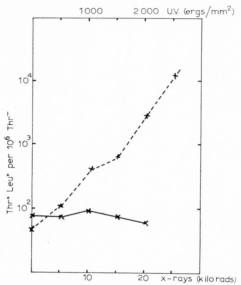

Fig. 7. Modification of the Thr⁻ male character after its transfer into irradiated
females. The strains and procedures are as for fig. 6 [from KADA and MARCOVICH,
1963].

The nature of the bacterial intermediate induced by UV is not known.
It might be a nucleic acid, or one of its precursors. Nor has the X-ray
altered site on the chromosome been defined [KADA and MARCOVICH,
1963].

## 3. Effects of radiations on yeast

The use of yeast cells is very convenient to study the lethal action
of radiations. One can follow specifically, through conjugation and
consecutive meiosis, the fate of induced damage, and determine its

cellular localization. A number of observations have been made on these cells concerning the lethal effect of UV and X-rays.

1) Sporulation of cells of different degrees of ploidy (2 to 8) allows the detection of the lethal damage in the progeny of the irradiated cells. MORTIMER [1955], MAGNI [1956] and LASKOWSKI [1962] have shown that the major part of the lethal action of radiations is related to the appearance of dominant and recessive nuclear damage.

2) Mutants which are resistant to the lethal action of ionizing radiations have been induced [MOUSTACCHI, 1964], showing that there exists a genetic control of "sensitivity to radiations".

3) Yeasts can have a mitotic or a meiotic cycle depending on their growth medium. The phase of the growth cycle influences the radiosensitivity of the cells: for example dividing cells are more resistant to the lethal action of ionizing radiations [LACASSAGNE and HOLWECK, 1930; BEAM et al., 1954]. As we shall see later, some repair mechanism seems to act efficiently during a given period of the division.

4) Recovery of diploid yeasts after irradiation, obtained by keeping the cells for six or more hours in water or buffer, has been reported by KOROGODIN and MALUMINA [1959]. Similar restoration has not been observed for haploid cells. The molecular approach to this problem has been recently developed [PATRICK and HAYNES, 1964].

5) Ultraviolet light [ROMAN and JACOB, 1958] and X-rays [MANNEY and MORTIMER, 1964] stimulate the reversion to the wild type during the mitotic division of heteroallelic diploids. A process of allelic recombination has been suggested to account for this greater sensitivity.

6) Finally the influence of a number of external factors on the radiosensitivity such as anoxia, glycerol, radioprotectors (cysteamine), temperature, etc., has been abundantly studied on this material. It has pointed out several interesting points especially on the role of "linked" water in relation to the size of the "target".

These last three points will not be reported here but one may refer to the following reviews: PATRICK and HAYNES [1964]; WILKIE and LEWIS [1963]; WOOD [1959].

3.1. RADIOBIOLOGICAL STUDIES ON POLYPLOID SERIES OF *Saccharomyces cerevisiae*

Using haploid and diploid cultures, LATARJET and EPHRUSSI [1949] established that haploid cells were inactivated exponentially, while diploid ones exhibited a sigmoidal survival curve. Comparing the shapes of the curves, these authors proposed that inhibition of cell division was due to recessive lethals; they envisaged the possibility of the existence of some dominant lethal lesions. If cells were inactivated exclusively by recessive lethals, the mathematical model proposed by ZIRKLE and TOBIAS [1953], giving the survival as a function of ploidy and dose, predicts that radioresistance has to increase with increasing ploidy. MORTIMER [1958] using a polyploid series, showed that radioresistance did not increase continuously with ploidy. Formally these results show that besides recessive lesions, a fraction of the lethal damage is due to dominant ones.

### 3.1.1. *Nature of the lethal damage in haploid cells*

Compared to the other ploidies, haploid cells of the wild type are the most sensitive. An elegant method to determine the frequency of induction of recessive lethals has been devised by MORTIMER [1955]: haploid cells are irradiated and then mated with unirradiated haploid ones. The zygotes can sporulate and are tested for lethals. If no more than two spores in each ascus are viable, the haploid irradiated parent was carrying a recessive lethal lesion. MORTIMER [1955] found that a much lower frequency of lethals is produced than expected from the assumption of exclusively recessive lethal inactivation. For instance, a dose of 10 krad reduces viability to 10 %. If only recoverable recessive lethals were responsible for the inhibition of cell division, 90 % of the zygotes should contain one or more lethals in heterozygous condition. Instead, only 19 % contain a lethal. So the major part of the inactivation of haploid yeast seems to be through a mechanism other than production of recessive lethals. MAGNI's experiments [1956] allow one to reject the hypothesis that lethals in heterozygous condition are eliminated by mitotic crossing-over and selection in the divisions taking place between irradiation and sporulation. But one must mention that the possibility of a recovery mechanism operating in the zygote or in the diploid clone cannot be excluded by these experiments. As suggested by Mortimer and by Magni, it seems probable that at least part of the lethal damage induced by ionizing radiations in haploid yeast is of cytoplasmic nature.

### 3.1.2. *Nature of the lethal damage in diploid and polyploid cells*

Yeasts with ploidy higher than haploid exhibit sigmoidal survival curves, although no clear relation exists between zero-dose extrapolation number and ploidy. There is a decreasing resistance with increasing ploidies beyond diploid [MORTIMER, 1958]. To account for this increased radiosensitivity it has been assumed that dominant lethals increase in frequency with ploidy. The existence of dominant lethals was demonstrated through a procedure utilizing micromanipulative techniques. Mortimer has proved that dominant lethal mutations occur in addition to recessive lethals even in haploids, the proportion of the two types of lesions being 1 to 15. But as the ploidy increases the majority of the inactivation arises through induced dominant lethals. It has been shown by LASKOWSKI [1962] that in diploid cells heterozygosity (aα) for mating types, as compared with homozygosity (aa or αα), affects the response to X-rays: the aα cells are much more resistant than the aa or αα clones. As these strains are completely isogenic this means that only one locus may influence the radiosensitivity, the role of this genes is not yet understood.

It is generally admitted that there is an increase in resistance to radiation-induced DNA damages with increased genome complexity [TERZI 1961; KAPLAN and MOSES, 1964]. If this is true, the observations made on haploid and polyploid yeast series show that one has to be very careful in any generalization of this assumption. As we shall see in the next section, haploid mutants have been induced which are more resistant than diploid cells.

### 3.2. A MUTATION TO RADIORESISTANCE IN *Saccharomyces cerevisiae*

Mutants which are more resistant than the wild type cells to the lethal action of ionizing radiations have been isolated.

### 3.2.1. *The induction of radioresistant mutants (xr)*

The survival curve of haploid yeast to $^{32}$P decay is exponential. As the $^{32}$P lethal effect is not modified by starvation, which decreases the phosphate and the RNA contents of the cells, the sensitive site to

$^{32}$P disintegrations might thus be the DNA. One can observe that during the decay, the surviving population becomes more and more resistant to the lethal effect of X-rays. The clones derived from the survivors to $^{32}$P decay are stable as regards their resistance to X-rays.

As the survival curve to $^{32}$P decay of the radioresistant (xr) and radiosensitive (XS) cells are exponential, and superimposable when the two populations are equally labelled, one can deduce that $^{32}$P decay induces a mutation and does not select preexistant spontaneous xr cells. The efficiency of induction of this mutation by $^{32}$P decay is unusually high. After a decay which leaves about $10^{-2}$ living cells, nearly 50% of them yield resistant-type clones. Assuming that the coefficient of efficiency for mutation is the same as that for killing in yeast ($a = 0.01$), it can be calculated that the maximum size of the structure which controls radioresistance is about 1/22 nd of the whole genome.

Like $^{32}$P decay, UV light, X- and $\gamma$-rays, and chemical agents such as nitrous acid or mustard gas, induce the xr mutation with high efficiency if compared to the rate of reversion of other nutritional characters [MOUSTACCHI and MARCOVICH, 1962; MOUSTACCHI, 1964].

One may note that acriflavine [EPHRUSSI et al., 1949] and 5-fluorouracil [MOUSTACCHI and MARCOVICH, 1963], which are potent inducers of the cytoplasmic mutation "petite colonie", are unable to induce the xr mutation.

### 3.2.2. *Characteristics of the xr mutants*

The survival curves of most of the resistant mutants are sigmoidal, though some mutants with exponential survival curves are always found. The final slope is smaller by a factor of two or three than that of the sensitive strain (fig. 8). With $\alpha$-rays the difference in the slopes is the same as with X-rays, but for some unknown reason the curves are exponential. It must be noted that the resistant character concerns only ionizing radiations (X, $\gamma$, $\alpha$-rays) but not ultraviolet light or $^{32}$P decay (fig. 9). This last remark emphasizes one of the differences between this system and the *Escherichia coli* B and B/r one. As shown by Witkin in her early studies, the B/r resistance, as compared to that of B, exists both for X-rays and ultraviolet light [WITKIN, 1946].

An oxygen effect and a protection by cysteamine (fig. 10) of the same magnitude are observed for the xr and XS cells. The hypothesis of a mechanism of radioresistance related to the primary effect of ionizing radiations is ruled out by these observations and by the fact that the

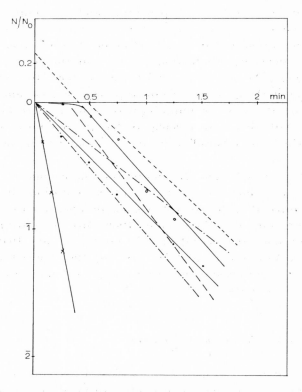

Fig. 8. Comparison of the X-ray sensitivity of XS and xr mutants.
×  Wild type strain (XS)
o  xr mutants (sigmoidal survival curve)
●  xr mutants (exponential curve)
The dotted lines indicate the experimental limits of the survival curves of different mutants [from MOUSTACCHI and MARCOVICH, 1962].

induced resistance to X-rays appears with the same efficiency whether [32]P decay occurs before or after irradiation of the cells. (In the latter case the X-ray irradiation is given immediately after labelling the cells with [32]P. Decay is then allowed to occur at 0°C).

According to their normal DNA content, the resistant mutants are haploid. Genetic analyses involving segregation of several markers located on different chromosomes allow one to eliminate the possibility of an aneuploidisation of the xr strains. Incidently such analyses have shown a new characteristic of these strains: abnormal segregations are observed, which are explained by an extra mitosis occurring during the meiotic process. This point will not be developed here; for more details see MOUSTACCHI [1964].

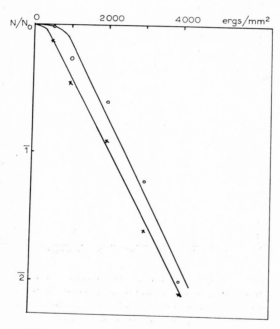

Fig. 9. Survival to UV light of a wild type XS strain ( × ) and of an xr mutant ( ● ) derived from XS [from MOUSTACCHI and MARCOVICH, 1962].

Radiosensitivity XS is dominant over radioresistance xr in diploid cells XS xr resulting from the corresponding cross. These diploids are less resistant than the resistant haploid wild type parent. Their survival curve is identical to that of the diploid wild type. The test of allelism with xr xr diploids shows that at least 3 different loci control the radio-resistant character.

In order to detect a biochemical difference which could account for the difference in radiosensitivity in the two types of cells, the RNA content of the xr strains has been compared to that of the XS strains in the exponential and stationary growth phase. It was found that the xr strains contain two to three times more RNA than the XS strain. The profiles in sucrose gradient show that the ribosomal and soluble RNAs are increased in the same proportion. This technique did not reveal any abnormal peak in the xr strain, as compared with the XS.

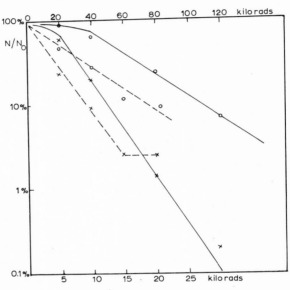

Fig. 10. Protection by 0.4 % cysteamine. The strains are cultivated for 5 days in complete medium, then washed and resuspended in buffer ($10^6$ cells/ml). Half of the culture is treated with cysteamine for 30 minutes at 30°C. The suspensions are then irradiated.

Dotted line: Strain N123XS (lower abscissa)
Full line: Strain N4 xr (upper abscissa)
× : Controls    o : with cysteamine.
[from MOUSTACCHI, 1964].

### 3.2.3. Mechanism of radioresistance

One may ask whether any correlation exists between radioresistance and the surplus RNA. To check this possibility, cells have been treated with 5-fluorouracil (5-FU) an analogue of uracil which blocks DNA synthesis [Bosch et al., 1958] and is incorporated into RNA [Cohen et al., 1958]. This last effect is antagonized by uracil. As is well known, only purine and pyrimidine analogues incorporated into DNA have a radiosensitizing effect. In only one known case has 5-FU a similar effect: that is when it is incorporated into TMV, which is an RNA virus

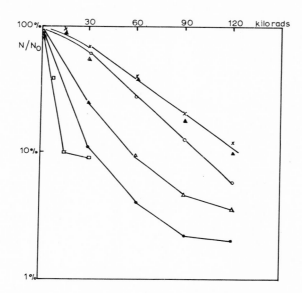

Fig. 11. Effect of 5-FU on the X-ray survival of an xr mutant.

×  Control xr culture in synthetic medium.
▲  Culture in synthetic medium supplemented with 10 μg/ml of 5-FU and 100 μg/ml of uracil.
△  Culture in synthetic medium supplemented with 1 μg/ml of 5-FU.
o  Culture in synthetic medium supplemented with 10 μg/ml of 5-FU. 2 hours of contact with the analogue.
●  Culture in synthetic medium with 10 μg/ml of 5-FU. 8 hours of contact with the analogue.
□  Control XS culture in synthetic medium.

[from Moustacchi, 1964].

[Becarevic et al., 1963]. When XS and xr strains are grown in the presence of 5-FU it can be seen (fig. 11) that:

—a concentration of 5-FU of 1 μg/ml sensitizes the xr strain N4 to X-rays. The radiosensitivity increases with the 5-FU concentration; it reaches a maximum for 10 μg/ml, yielding approximately the same sensitivity as that of the XS strain. The radiosensitivity of the wild type strain (XS) N123 is unaffected by different concentrations of the analogue.

—when uracil is added to the medium together with 5-FU there is no increase in the radiosensitivity of the xr strain.

—for a concentration of 5-FU of 10 $\mu$g/ml the radioresistance starts to decrease after two hours of contact. The maximum radiosensitivity is reached after 6 to 8 hours.

—this sensitization of the xr strains is phenotypic; when 5-FU treated xr cells are seeded in normal growth medium the radioresistance is restored.

—FUDR does not influence the response of xr cells to radiation. This substance has one of the effects of 5-FU: it blocks DNA synthesis, by acting on thymidilate synthetase. Its conversion to 5-FU does not seem to play a role here, since it cannot induce the "petite colonie" mutation which is detectable even with 0.5 $\mu$g/ml of 5-FU. So it seems probable that 5-FU exerts a radiosensitizing effect by its action on RNA. One may ask if the sensitization is due to the formation of abnormal RNA or to the synthesis of aberrant proteins formed in consequence of this abnormal RNA. In other words is the excess RNA by itself responsible for the resistance of the xr strains or does the resistance result from some protein characteristic of these mutants?

Two sorts of experiments have been done in order to answer this question.

1) Starvation for uracil or adenine of the xr strain auxotrophic for these substances decreases the RNA content per cell. This treatment has no influence on the survival curve of these populations. This experiment allows one to eliminate a possible non-specific quantitative role of total RNA. It can be noted that an increase of total RNA in *E. coli* due to thymine starvation of a thymineless strain [BILLEN, 1963] or to methionine starvation of a "relaxed" strain [MOUSTACCHI and KOHIYAMA, unpub.] is not followed by an increase in radioresistance.

2) xr cells have been treated with parafluorophenylalanine (PFPA), an analogue of phenylalanine, which is incorporated into protein. Fig. 12 shows some degree of radiosensitization by this compound. The shape of the curve is modified but it can be noted that PFPA is not as effective as 5-FU even at high concentrations (100 $\mu$g/ml). This experiment shows that proteins have a role to play in the mechanism of radioresistance.

To account formally for the survival curve of haploid radioresistant cells one can admit that the genetic lesions induced by radiations (20 to 30 % according to Mortimer's and Magni's results) and a fraction of the cytoplasmic damage are suppressed in these strains. The hypothesis of a protection of the cells by a mechanism comparable to that of anoxia or SH-compounds has been previously discussed and is not able to explain the experimental results. Some recovery process acting after irradiation seems more probable. One must note that the xr character is recessive; in other words the majority of the lethal lesions are of a genetic nature in a diploid XS xr or $xr_1$ $xr_2$. The ability

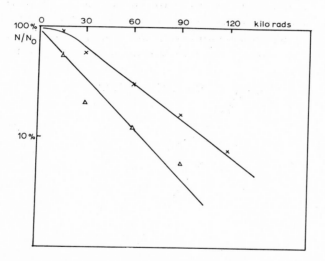

Fig. 12. Effect of the incorporation of PFPA on the X-ray sensitivity of an xr mutant.

× Population cultivated in normal medium.
△ Population having incorporated PFPA at concentration of $10^{-2}$ M.
[from MOUSTACCHI, 1964].

to undergo a recovery process introduced into the zygote by the xr mutation is abolished. To explain this fact it can be suggested as a working hypothesis that the system for restoration is inhibited (or repressed) in wild-type XS strains. $^{32}$P decay and other mutagens may suppress this inhibition and the repairing mechanism then becomes operative. In the heterozygote XS xr, the synthesis of the inhibitor is effective and the recovery process does not function. The hypothetical "inhibitor" may act on the transcription of the genetic information for repairing enzyme(s) (repressor) or on the enzyme(s) itself. This model is actually under investigation.

3.3. INFLUENCE OF THE DIVISION CYCLE ON RADIOSENSITIVITY

In one of the early studies on radiation effects in yeasts LACASSAGNE and HOLWECK [1930] observed that dividing cultures were more resistant than stationary ones. BEAM et al. [1954] have demonstrated that the young budding cells are 10 to 100 times more resistant than interdivisional ones. In yeasts of the species *Hansenula amonala* BEAM [1959] has shown that budding cells are refractory to recessive lethal damage, only dominant lethals being induced in these cells.

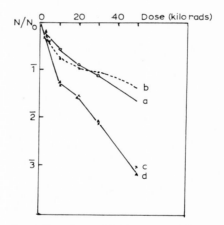

Fig. 13. Influence of uracil and methionine starvation on X-ray survival of a population containing 10 % budding cells.
(a)  □  uracil starvation.
(c)  ×  methionine starvation.
(d)  △  uracil and methionine starvation.
(b)  ●  control unstarved culture.
[from MOUSTACCHI, 1963].

This large shift in radiosensitivity seems to be related to the variations in the composition of the free amino-acid pool and in protein synthesis in the budding cells (fig. 13) [MOUSTACCHI, 1963]. As a matter of fact, the radioresistance is decreased or disappears after nitrogen starvation [ELKIND and BEAM, 1955], or after being deprived of the amino-acid corresponding to an auxotrophy of a given strain [MOUSTACCHI, 1963]. The qualitative and quantitative modifications of the composition of the free amino-acid pool in cells grown in a lactate medium, or in the presence of amino-acid analogues such as parafluorophenylalanine or 5-methyl-tryptophan, are accompanied by a decrease in the radioresistance of the budding cells. These treatments do not affect the radiosensitivity of interdivisional cells.

Phosphorus starvation or uracil or adenine deprivation of auxotrophic strains decreases the RNA content per cell. The biological function of RNA can also be affected by adding 5-fluorouracil to the growing medium [BUSSARD et al., 1960]. These different treatments are without effect on the radioresistance of budding cells. The decay of $^{32}P$ incorporated in yeast does not modify the structure or the biosynthetic process responsible for radioresistance. In other words there is no correlation between the radioresistance of budding cells and the composition of the free nucleotide pool or the RNA content per cell. On the contrary, protein synthesis and/or the amino-acid pool composition seem to be important for the radioresistance of budding cells.

A radioprotective mechanism acting, for instance, through the action of SH-compounds seems improbable: the different treatments mentioned would modify only the final slope of the survival curve of the budding cells. On the contrary the shape of the curve is changed from sigmoidal to linear.

One can assume for the moment that a protein which appears specifically during the process of division is involved in the mechanism of radioresistance of budding cells. One of the enzymes implicated in the replication process may favour a repair of the radiolesions responsible for recessive damage. Or if this hypothetical protein is linked to the genetic material it may reduce the probability of transfer of energy along the nucleoprotein chains as observed in some *in vitro* experiments [ALEXANDER et al., 1961].

## 4. Summary

Thanks to the techniques of conjugation, it has been possible to go one step forward in the knowledge of the primary effect of radiation in microorganisms.

In *Escherichia coli* K12, though it has not been possible to detect any localized lethal lesion on the chromosome, radiation induces damage which prevents the transfer of the male genetic material, or the integration of the recipient one, in the zygote, when each of the parents is irradiated respectively. These results are discussed in the light of actual hypotheses concerning DNA replication during conjugation.

An indirect mechanism of killing occurs through the induction by radiation of lysogenic cells. A direct action on repressor molecules is improbable for both X-rays and UV. The possibility of cross-induction is also contradictory to this hypothesis. The facts that UV, and not X-rays, cross-induce, and that this effect is mediated only by episomic elements, is discussed.

The mutagenic action of radiation in *E. coli* has been shown to be a direct modification of the genetic locus when X-rays are used, and a cytoplasmic mediated one after UV irradiation.

The results concerning the characterization of the damage induced by radiations in yeast of different degrees of ploidy are recalled. The fraction of non-genetically transmissible damage seems to be important in haploid cells. But as ploidy increases the major part of the lethal action is related to the appearance of recessive and dominant lethal mutation.

Mutants which are resistant to the lethal action of ionizing radiations have been induced by $^{32}P$ decay and different mutagenic agents. According to their normal DNA content these mutants (xr) are haploid. However, the xr strains contain two to three times more RNA than the wild type radiosensitive strains. 5-FU has a radiosensitizing effect on xr cells; this effect is inhibited by uracil. This indicates that some correlation exists between radioresistance and the excess RNA. The xr character is controlled by several loci.

The influence of some metabolic factors on the radioresistance of budding yeast has been determined. In this case protein synthesis seems to have an important role in this transitory radioresistance.

## References

ALEXANDER, P., LETT, J. T. and ORMEROD, M. G. 1961. Biochim. et Biophys. Acta **51** 207.
BEAM, C. A., MORTIMER, R. K., WOLFE, R. G. and TOBIAS, C. A. 1954. Arch. Biochem. and Biophys. **49** 110.

BEAM, C. A. 1959. Rad. Res. suppl **1** 372.

BECAREVIC, A., DJORDJEVIC, B. and SUTIC, D. 1963. Nature **198** 612.

BILLEN, D. 1963. Biochim. Biophys. Acta **72** 608.

BOREK, E. and RYAN, A. 1958. Proc. Nat. Acad. Sci. **44** 374.

BOREK, E. and RYAN, A. 1960. Biochim. et Biophys. Acta **41** 67.

BOSCH, L., HARBERS, E. and HEIDELBERGER, C. 1958. Cancer Res. **18** 335.

BURGI, E. and HERSHEY, D. 1963. Biophys. Journ. **3** 309.

BUSSARD, A., NAONO, S., GROS, F. and MONOD, J. 1960. Compt. Rend. Acad. Sci. **250** 4049.

BUTTIN, G., JACOB, F. and MONOD, J. 1960. Compt. Rend. Acad. Sci. **250** 2571.

CAIRNS, J. 1963. Journ. Mol. Biol. **6** 208.

CAMPBELL, A. 1959. Virology **9** 293.

COHEN, S. S., FLAKS, J. G., BARNER, H. D., LOEB, M. and LICHTENSTEIN, J. 1958. Proc. Nat. Acad. Sci. **44** 1004.

DEVORET, R. 1963. Intern. Journ. Rad. Biol. **6** 385.

DEVORET, R. and GEORGE, J. 1964a. Compt. Rend. Acad. Sci. **258** 2227.

DEVORET, R. and GEORGE, J. 1964b. Compt. Rend. Acad. Sci. **258** 5287.

ELKIND, M. M. and BEAM, C. A. 1955. Rad. Res. **3** 88.

EPHRUSSI, B., HOTTINGUER, H. and CHIMENES, A. M. 1949. Ann. Inst. Pasteur **76** 351.

HAYES, W. 1953. Cold Spring Harbor Symposia Quant. Biol. **18** 75.

JACOB, F. 1962. Ann. Inst. Pasteur **82** 433.

JACOB, F. 1954. Compt. Rend. Acad. Sci. **238** 732.

JACOB, F., BRENNER, S. and CUZIN, F. 1963. Cold Spring Harbor Symposia Quant. Biol. **28** 329.

JACOB, F. and CAMPBELL, A. 1959. Compt. Rend. Acad. Sci. **248** 3219.

JACOB, F., SUSSMAN, R. and MONOD, J. 1962. Compt. Rend. Acad. Sci. **154** 4214.

JACOB, F., RYTER, A. and CUZIN, F. 1965. Mendel Centenary Symposium - London. In the press.

JENSEN, A. J. and HAAS, F. 1963. Proc. Nat. Acad. Sci. **50** 1109.

JOSET, F., LOW, B. and KRISCH, R. 1964. Biophys. Res. Comm. **17** 742.

JOSET, F. and WOOD, T. H. 1965. In the press.

KADA, T. and MARCOVICH, H. 1963. Ann. Inst. Pasteur **105** 989.

KAPLAN, H. S. and MOSES, L. E. 1964. Science **145** 21.

KELNER, A. 1953. Journ. Bact. **65** 252.

KORN, D. and WEISSBACH, A. 1962. Biochim. et Biophys. Acta **61** 775.

KOROGODIN, V. I. and MALUMINA, T. S. 1959. Priroda **48** 82.

LACASSAGNE, A. and HOLWECK, F. 1930. Compt. Rend. Soc. Biol. **104** 1221.

LASKOWSKI, W. 1962. Zeitschr. für Naturf. **17b** 93.

LATARJET, R. and EPHRUSSI, B. 1949. Compt. Rend Acad. Sci. **229** 306.

LATARJET, R. 1951. Ann. Inst. Pasteur **81** 389.

LWOFF, A., SIMINOVITCH, L. and KJELDGAARD, N. 1950. Ann. Inst. Pasteur **79** 815.

MAGNI, G. E. 1956. Compt. Rend. Lab. Carlsberg **26** 273.

MAGNI, G. E. 1959. Rad. Res. suppl. **1** 347.

MANNEY, T. R. and MORTIMER, R. K. 1964. Science **143** 581.

MARCOVICH, H. 1956. Ann. Inst. Pasteur **90** 303.

MARCOVICH, H. 1961. Thesis, Faculté des Sciences, Paris.
MARCOVICH, H. 1961. Ann. Inst. Pasteur **101** 660.
MARCOVICH, H. and KAPLAN, H. S. 1963. Nature **200** 487.
MARMUR, J., ROWND, R., FALKOW, S., BARON, L. S., SCHILDKRAUT, C. and DOTY, P. 1961. Proc. Nat. Acad. Sci. **47** 972.
MELECHEN, N. E. and SKAAR, P. D. 1962. Virology **16** 21.
MORTIMER, R. K. 1955. Rad. Res. **2** 361.
MORTIMER, R. K. 1958. Rad. Res. **9** 312.
MOUSTACCHI, E. 1959. Biochim. et Biophys. Acta **36** 577.
MOUSTACCHI, E. and MARCOVICH, H. 1962. Ann. Inst. Pasteur **103** 841.
MOUSTACCHI, E. 1963. Ann. Inst. Pasteur **105** 757.
MOUSTACCHI, E. and MARCOVICH, H. 1963. Compt. Rend. Acad. Sci. **256** 5646.
MOUSTACCHI, E. 1964. Thesis Faculté des Sciences, Paris.
NAONO, S. and GROS, F. 1960. Compt. Rend. Acad. Sci. **250** 3527.
OTSUJI, N., SEKIBUCHI, M., TIJIMA, T. and TAKAGI, Y. 1959. Nature **184** 1079.
PATRICK, N. H. and HAYNES, R. H. 1964. Rad. Res. **23** 564.
ROMAN, H. L. and JACOB, F. 1958. Cold Spring Harbor Symposia **23** 155.
RYAN, A. 1962. Biochim. et Biophys. Acta **60** 455.
TERZI, M. 1961. Nature **191** 461.
WOLKIE, D. and LEWIS, D. 1963. Genetics **48** 1701.
WITKIN, E. M. 1946. Proc. Nat. Acad. Sci. **32** 59.
WOOD, T. H. 1959. Rad. Res. suppl. **1** 332.
WOOD, T. H. and MARCOVICH, H. 1964. Genetics **49** 779.
ZIRKLE, R. E. and TOBIAS, C. A. 1953. Arch. Biochem. Biophys. **47** 282.

# VI

# RADIOPATHOLOGY OF EXTRACELLULAR STRUCTURES

R. BRINKMAN and H. B. LAMBERTS

*Radiopathological Institute, University of Groningen, The Netherlands*

# CONTENTS

# 1. Introduction

When we say that biological macromolecular complexes "live" in water, this statement should be greatly amplified. Firstly, of course, it has to be realized that water is not only the environment, but that structured water is a vital part of the living system [SZENT-GYORGYI, 1960]. And secondly that extracellular tissue water is not just a balanced salt solution but is built into a matrix environment, many properties of which are not well enough known. One would like to know more about the function of this ground substance as a diffusion medium for small molecules, as a barrier to large molecules, and about its formative properties with regard to fibres and basement membranes*. Biochemically, due to the pioneer investigations of Duran Reynolds and Karl Meyer, much is known of its chiefly mucopolysaccharide structural part, its enzymic resistance or sensitivity, and the turnover of its macromolecules under the influence of endocrine regulation [DORFMANN, 1963; DZIEWIATOWSKI, 1964].

But it is to be expected that the functional significance of the interplay between the cells, their outer surface (BENNETT's [1963] glycocalyx) and their matrix environment will prove to be more fundamental than appears from the words "diffusion medium" and "cementing substance". The biophysical chemistry of the ground substance, as initiated by GERSH and CATCHPOLE's [1960] research on its "two phase" system, may develop into an important directive field of physiological and pathological significance. For radiation biology, the attractive properties of the extracellular medium abundantly present in young connective tissue are its great radiation sensitivity and the accessibility of these relatively simple structures, allowing the study of immediate or very early effects at low levels of X-irradiation.

# 2. Water permeability of sub-epidermal membranes

As an example we shall describe the very simple direct measurement of water filtration through sub-epidermal peeled-off membranes of

---

* See: Connective Tissue Intercellular macromolecules [1964] Little and Brown, Boston; also: The Biochemistry of Mucopolysaccharides of Connective Tissue [1961]. Biochem. Soc. Symp. No. 20.

the rat's skin dermis, and the immediate effect of X-irradiation on this. It was well known to older histologists and has recently been described again by DAY [1959] that the dermal connective tissue essentially consists of a complex of membranes, stuck together by the imbibing matrix mucopolysaccharides, which fill up the interstices of the interlaced very fine fibrils. A thin experimental membrane is still built up of five or more separate layers, connected by transverse ridges [BRINKMAN et al., 1961]; from a freshly exposed skin inner surface it can easily be peeled off and fixed to a 10 mm bore lucite tube. If, from a small side tube, salt solution (Tyrode) is filled into this tube, at a pressure of 10 cm of water, it slowly passes through the membrane at a constant rate, which at once increases on X-irradiation. Fig. 1 gives the average of many experiments, and it can be

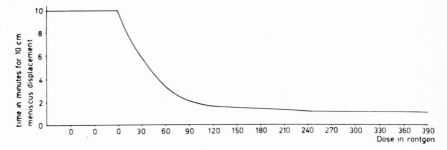

Fig. 1. Effect of X-ray irradiation on water permeability of connective tissue membranes, peeled from the inner surface of the rat's skin.

Vertical:   Time (min) for 10 cm displacement of meniscus in indicating capillary tube.

Horizontal: X-ray dose (60 kV, 10 mA).

seen that a sensitivity to 1 to 2 r is present at room temperature. If membranes are taken from young rats, this phenomenon is regularly reproduced and may serve to demonstrate some further observations, which in our opinion have general importance. If the precautions described in BRINKMAN et al. [1961] are taken, two factors can be traced which have great influence on X-ray sensitivity; mechanical tension and temperature. Tension, resulting in a small stretching of the dermis' membrane, is caused by a pressure of 10 cm of water; if this pressure is much lower, or if elastic deformation is prevented by a very tight sub-layer of non-elastic nylon gauze, the rate of filtration, and especially the X-ray sensitivity, are much diminished. If, in the two phase system, as described for ground substance by GERSH and CATCHPOLE [1960], one wants to think of "pores", they might be "stretchable pores", as suggested by MAYERSON [WASSERMAN et al., 1955]. And increased X-ray sensitivity might have its cause in the immediate distension of the gaps in macromolecules, produced through scission by OH radicals (see section 7), thus preventing immediate recombination. One is inclined to speculate whether the factor tension may be important for intracellular membranes under irradiation also.

Osmotically produced membrane tension in red cells (section 4), in mitochondria, and in "vesicles" has often been observed; if as suggested by H. S. Bennett basement membranes should be considered here too, direct mechanical tension, e.g. of capillary walls, also comes into this field [MAJNO and PALADE, 1961].

The second factor, temperature, appears to be important also for irradiation sensitivity of the mucopolysaccharide matrix. This might have been expected from the large temperature coefficient of synovial radiosensitivity (section 7), but it is also very obvious in the dermal membranes. The possible cause of this unexpectedly large temperature effect will be discussed in the section on synovial radiosensitivity.

The above-described connective tissue matrix phenomenon was studied in a dead membrane. It may be compared to analogous findings in living ones in the intact animal, or in man. The methods here are the increased resorption of weals [BENSLEY, 1934], increased capillary permeability depending on the basement membrane, and the registration of subcutaneous injection pressure, all under the influence of low-level X-irradiation. The first method has been known for a long time; here we mention only the latest investigation on man by Pape and collaborators [ALTH et al., 1964]. These authors made small depots, labelled with [131]I, by intramuscular or subcutaneous injection, and demonstrated increased resorption rates caused by 2 r if two conditions were fulfilled: non-optimal circulation and definitely hypotonic solutions. The X-ray effect could be called immediate, and was stronger than that evoked by hyaluronidase. The resorption of colloidal [198]Au was not increased, showing that the barrier against larger particles was still intact.

In this connection the increased permeability of the capillary wall after X-irradiation, permitting the passage of trypan blue and other pigments, must also be mentioned; JOLLES' (1963) striking experiments should be cited, although the necessary dose here is very much higher. He showed that a localized irradiation with 800 r, on the rabbit's depilated flank, caused leakage of intravenously injected pontamine blue exactly at the irradiated spots (lead sieve irradiation), one hour or earlier after exposure. This must be an effect on the ground substance enclosing the capillaries, which according to MAJNO and PALADE [1961] is the real barrier layer. A preceding total body irradiation (except for head and hind quarters) with 600 r will protect against this localized damage for the time from a few hours after total body irradiation to six days later. Jolles' interpretation is the absence of "immune response" during this time; we would suggest that the liberation of a bioamine mixture by total body irradiation [VENINGA, 1965] may result in chemical protection of the pericapillary sheath during this time. It will not be difficult to test this hypothesis.

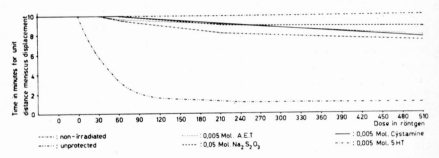

Fig. 2. Chemoprotection against X-rays of membrane permeability for water by cystamine, AET, serotonin, and thiosulphate.

Vertical:     Time (min) for 10 cm displacement of meniscus in indicating capillary tube.

Horizontal: X-ray dose (60 kV, 10 mA).

Further, we want to add two more observations on the irradiated connective tissue membrane experiments, their excellent suitability for demonstrating chemical protection in dead tissue (excluding anoxia) and their aptness for studying the irradiation effect caused by the mucopolysaccharide binding of $^{140}Ba$, a short-lived $\gamma$- and $\beta$-emitter.

With regard to the first, fig. 2 shows how effectively this membrane is protected against X-irradiation if very low concentrations of serotonin, AET or cystamine are added to the permeating solution. It is obvious, and has been carefully verified by BACQ and collaborators

[1959], that in this case anoxia cannot be the explanation; we shall later show that for matrix protection oxygen can even be a protector. An interesting but not much studied protecting substance found in this way is thiosulphate; this is not a chemical defense against total body irradiation, because it cannot enter into cells, but extracellularly it appears to be an important one, because it can be given in large concentrations. It has found application in the radioprotection of the vascular intima (section 6), and will be considered further in analysing synovial chemoprotection (section 7). The increase just mentioned in

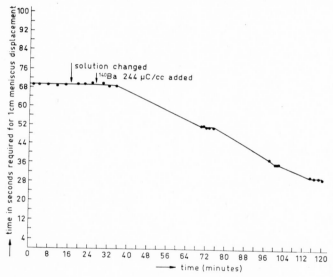

Fig. 3. Effect of $^{140}$Ba on the permeability of a connective tissue membrane.

Vertical:          Time in seconds for meniscus displacement per unit distance.
Horizontal:     Duration of experiment in minutes.
First arrow:     Solution changed;
Second arrow: 244 $\mu$C $^{140}$Ba/cm$^3$ added.

membrane permeability due to dissolving 244 $\mu$C of $^{140}$Ba in the per-meating solution is seen from fig. 3. As mucopolysaccharides, sulphated or not, have a high affinity for alkaline earth ions, especially for Ba [DUNSTONE, 1962], the interesting possibility arises that even this short-lived isotope, the most abundant in fall-out, might be pathoge-nous in very small concentrations if it is deposited in the radiosensitive macromolecules themselves. In fig. 3 we see a distinct effect in one hour, very probably to be ascribed to the isotope's β-radiation. Of course, the concentration used here is very high, but what will occur if small concentrations are acting for weeks, and in places where the breakdown of matrix barriers may have vitally important consequences, such as in the intima of large arteries? This is not just a suggestion but has some foundation. LAMBERTS and VAN ANDEL [1965] have shown that after one injection of $30\mu$C of $^{140}$BaSO$_4$ subcutaneously into rats, their aortic wall becomes loaded with radioactivity from 5 weeks after injection onwards. If $^{140}$Ba was injected, the aortic radioactivity showed periodic falls in the course of weeks,

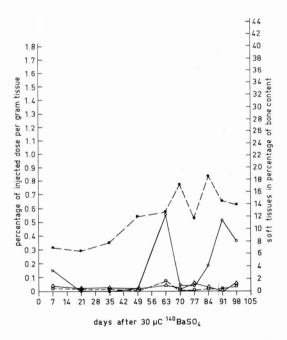

Fig. 4. Bone and soft tissue activity in 100 rats, at various times after 30 $\mu$C of subcutaneous $^{140}$BaSO$_4$.

Vertical left:   Percentage of injected dose in bone.
Vertical right:  Percentage of bone content in soft tissues.
Horizontal:      Days after injection of 30 $\mu$C $^{140}$BaSO$_4$.

> ●----● bone
> ○——○ aortic wall
> □----□ skin
> △——△ lung

presumably by the degrading effect of irradiation on the binding mucopolysaccharides (fig. 4). With $^{85}$Sr, a pure $\gamma$-emitter, this binding was also found, but not the periodicity (fig. 5). Much more work will have to be performed in this field, but the possible significance of the short-lived $^{140}$Ba atoms in fall-out for decreasing the barrier function of the intima of large arteries, thus facilitating the onset of atheromatosis, cannot be ruled out.

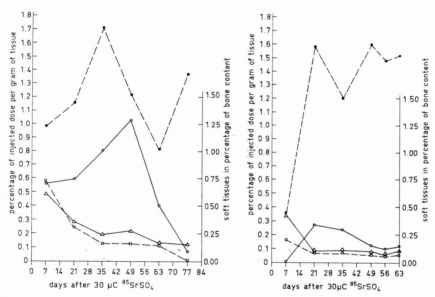

Fig. 5. Bone and soft tissue activity in $2 \times 30$ rats at various times after 30 $\mu$C of subcutaneous. $^{85}$SrSO$_4$.

Vertical left:    Percentage of injected dose in bone.
Vertical right: Percentage of bone content in soft tissues.
Horizontal:      Days after injection of 30 $\mu$C $^{85}$SrSO$_4$.

        ●----●   bone
        ○———○   aortic wall
        □----□   skin
        △———△   lung

## 3. Intradermal injection pressure

We would now like to mention one more way of displaying the connective tissues' great sensitivity to X-irradiation, which was most suitable for demonstrating the immediate effect, not after but during irradiation. This is the registration of a decreasing intradermal injection pressure during irradiation, shown in plate 1. It can be shown in any animal or man still possessing a sufficient amount of ground substance in the dermal compartment, can be repeated and varied many times, and is well suited for demonstrating efficient extracellular chemical protection. The principle of this type of investigation is that a very slow intradermal injection of saline will meet the flow resistance of the macromolecular gel of the ground substance, which may be overcome either by filtration with small molecules or by pushing it away *in toto* if large molecules are to pass through. In both cases a weal will be formed on the dermis' inner side [BRINKMAN et al., 1961]. The flow resistance will cause an injection pressure, which in this case has usually been set at 100 mm Hg by input accommodation and by an overflow outlet. The injection is made through two fine needles attached to two syringes, and the pressure is registered electronically. If the insertion point of one needle is X-irradiated locally, the pressure will drop nearly at once to a low value. The twin injection is used as a control or can be irradiated at a later time. Several observations have been made which have a bearing on matrix radiosensitivity.

a) In old animals, or in men over 60 years of age, the measurements very often cannot be made, because not enough or not suitable ground substance is present in the dermis.

b) The preliminary development of pressure, giving rise to mechanical tension at the injection locus, is again essential. If X-irradiation is given before the ground substance is under tension, no pressure drop can be found with doses up to 500 r. The probable mechanism of this observation has been analysed by BRINKMAN et al. [1961].

c) Again the temperature coefficient of this phenomenon is large; raising the temperature to 40°C will increase radiosensitivity to 1 r for a distinct drop in pressure.

d) In the living animal the fall in flow-resistance is reversible. If injection pressure is stopped, the original resistance will have been restored in two to three hours. In dead animals no restoration occurs.

e) The pressure values mentioned above are valid for the abdominal skin in young rats. If the injections are made in the skin of the back, much higher injection pressures develop, otherwise the observations described are unchanged. Injection pressure in the aortic intima is very high; this will be discussed later (section 6).

f) The preparation is well suited for demonstrating chemical X-ray protection; the usual protectors and also thiosulphate are very active, and again independent of anoxia [BACQ et al., 1959].

## 4. The outer layers of the erythrocyte cell wall

We now want to say a few words on the transition layer between the real barrier, the plasma membrane, and the ground substance, the outer layers of the cell wall, H. S. Bennett's glycocalyx. This is mucopolysaccharide in composition, acts as a filter for compounds approaching the plasma membrane, and is similar to the structures mentioned in the foregoing chapters. In many epithelial tissues this tenuous structure is tightened to a basement membrane, and then its impermeability is much more evident [MAJNO and PALADE, 1961].

In vertebrate cells the glycocalyx often is not easily demonstrable by electron microscopy, but in erythrocytes many clear pictures have been given (plate 2), and functionally the evidence is abundant; one has only to think of the enzymes and the numerous blood-group antigens on the surface. DAMON and PERK [1962] showed in preparations of "ghosts" that in man and in many animals the outer erythrocyte covering is thick, rough and easily folding concentrically in young cells, but thin, smooth and radially folding in old cells; both types will be present in a sample. If glass slides are used, the rough layer disappears and crenation is observed, but on parlodion film it is retained and the ghosts keep their discoid shape [POLIVODA and VINETZKII, 1959].

Chemically, SEAMAN et al.'s [1960] investigations show that this red cell outside layer is a polyanionic structure, its charges resulting from carboxylic groups of N-acetylneuraminic or sialic acid. The maintainance of the disk shape is a dynamic process, demanding energy; in stored human blood the cells sphere in a few days, but this can be reversed by the addition of ATP or by adenine sulphate and inosinmonophosphate, from which the cell envelope can build up its ATP [NAKAO et al., 1959, 1960]. In species where this property is deficient, the tendency to sphering is greater. Much more evidence for the necessity of ATP energy for keeping up the platycyte form could be cited [PRANKERD, 1960]. This process can be blocked by small concentrations of sodium azide, preventing ATP synthesis; it can be used for preventing restoration of sphered cells, if sphering is caused by X-irradiation.

By analogy with X-ray depolymerization in connective tissue, we have tested the red cell's glycocalyx for a similar reaction. The expected results were sphering, and loss of substances present in this outer layer. Sphering was considered a probable reaction because of the rise in interfacial tension to be expected if the outer layer comes off. It has been known for 40 years [BRINKMAN and VAN DAM, 1920] that washed red cells lose their outer layer (the "antisphering" substance) by contact with glass and with many other foreign surfaces; electron-microscopically this has been demonstrated by POLIVODA and VINETSKII [1959]. If the lipid or protein layers of the plasma membrane are denuded in this way, the interfacial tension at the red cell surface must go up from its necessarily very low value, and a tendency to sphering will be present. We have shown [BRINKMAN, 1962] that sphering is a regular consequence of X-irradiation of a red cell suspension in saline, and that this effect might be used for studying human individual X-ray sensitivity. Some precautions have to be taken, but they are simple and this "eryformtest" might become useful in radiation biology. It is not much applied as yet; one of the interesting constant findings is that the resistance against X-ray sphering of human red cells invariably increases three to four hours after therapeutic irradiations for a period of some hours, as capillary permeability also does. The cause of this is not known. Pictures of the sphering reaction are given in plates 3, 4 and 5. The reaction is very well suited for demonstrating the action of the usual chemical protectors, and has also been used for studying chemical sensitization in man [BRINKMAN et al., 1964]. Serotonin is a powerful protector in a concentration of $1\gamma/ml$, and, curiously enough, the most effective sensitizer, also at $1\gamma/ml$ appeared to be taurine, known to be liberated by X-irradiation in the same way as serotonin.

It will have been remarked that the X-ray dose used for very early sphering is rather high, at least 5000 r. Compared to the amount necessary for early, or even delayed, haemolysis due to loss of K-ions from the cells [LAMBERTS, 1958] it is not high at all, but still we have tried to attack the red cell surface with much lower doses and searched for an effect.

## 5. Enzyme liberation

Here we come into the field of enzyme liberation, often mentioned but not often detected in radiation biology. Of course, compared to the detection of the liberation of intracellular enzymes, the study of enzyme liberation from the red cell envelope (its only membrane) appears relatively simple, and especially so if the enzyme can be easily traced and measured quantitatively. As an example of such an enzyme we found the very potent carbonic anhydrase well suited; its chief location is in the inside structure of concentrated haemoglobin, but the envelope also appears to contain a certain amount. Many other enzymes, like ATP-ase,

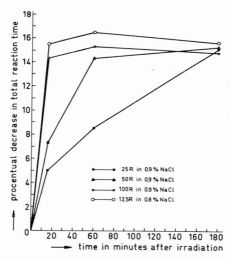

Fig. 6. Carbonic anhydrase release from erythrocytes irradiated with different doses of X-rays and measured according to BRINKMAN [1933].

acetylcholinesterase, DPN-ase, etc. have been demonstrated in the surface membrane [PRANKERD, 1960, p. 79], but carbonic anhydrase is the easiest to measure [BRINKMAN, 1933]. The occurrence in a bound state is indicated by its complete absence in the surrounding saline of a washed suspension, even after many hours. If no haemoglobin is detectable here, the anhydrase is equally absent if the cells have not been subjected to a liberating agent.

Release from a washed red cell suspension after X-irradiation is evident from fig. 6, which shows the concentration of the liberated enzyme in the saline, up to 180 minutes after X-irradiation. It may be seen that 12.5 r is sufficient for the release of an easily measurable enzyme effect, and that increasing the dose up to 100 r does not cause much further liberation. Compared to the total amount in the red cell, the released portion is very small indeed, about 0.1 per cent of the total, so we think the inside concentration is not continuous with the membrane depot. Only a trace of haemolysis can be found in the irradiated suspension, and the depot is thought to be present in the outermost envelope.

It can also be seen that a slight osmotic stretching of the membrane increases the radiation release. This effect possibly is comparable to the sensitizing by membrane stretching mentioned in section 2.1.

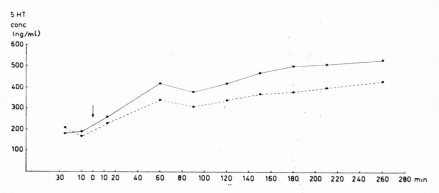

Fig. 7. Concentrations of serotonin (ng/ml) in the bathing solution of non-irradiated and X-irradiated uterine horns, at various times before and after 1000 r (↓)

——— irradiated.      − − − − − non-irradiated control.

With regard to the question of release from a bound state, either by membrane damage or from some kind of attachment, the liberation of biogenous amines by X-irradiation must be briefly discussed. The phenomenon is quite general; X-irradiation of living tissues or of whole animals is followed by liberation of a mixture of amines in the first few hours.

Most of the work on liberation of bio-amines in our laboratory has been done by Dr. T. S. VENINGA [1965]. It can be summarized in the following short survey, which concerns the actual release and its possible significance. The release by moderate doses of X-irradiation (1000 r) was studied in the frog's skin and in the rat's uterine horns. In both tissues considerable amounts of biogenous amines are present in the bound state, and it can be shown that the granules and vesicles, containing serotonin, catecholamines or histamine, will have released amines a few hours after irradiation; fig. 7, 8 and 9 give examples. It

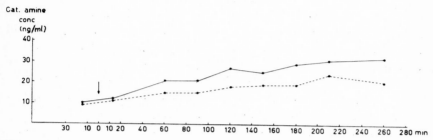

Fig. 8. Concentrations of adrenaline (ng/ml) in the bathing solution of non-irradiated and X-irradiated uterine horns, at various times before and after 1000 r ($\downarrow$)

———— irradiated.        ----- non-irradiated control.

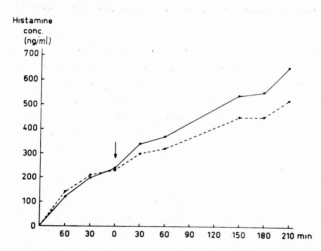

Fig. 9. Concentration of histamine (ng/ml) in the bathing solution of non-irradiated and X-irradiated uterine horns at various times before and after 1000 r ($\downarrow$)

———— irradiated.        ----- non-irradiated control.

was also found that X-ray release was always multiple; the three bio-amines mentioned were liberated simultaneously. So, if some signifi-cance is to be attached to amine release, a constellation of at least three amines, but probably of more, is to be reckoned with. This may reflect a physiological situation; in pharmacology the amines are mainly studied separately, and that may be unphysiological. We found that X-ray phenomena, such as darkening of the hypophysectomized frog's skin [VENINGA, 1965] or temporary paralysis of the rat's stomach [LAMBERTS and DIJKEN, 1961] always demand multiple bioamine action for their development. Thus quantitative measurement of amine release after X-ray liberation cannot be made by pharmacological methods, but must be done separately for each amine by fluorimetry [VENINGA, 1965]. For radiation biology it is interesting that with certain amine mixtures a summation in chemical protection may be obtained which cannot be had from any single amine.

Unfortunately in our experience the most protective mixture of amines also was the most toxic. Further research may come up with more suitable combinations, which could also contain released enzymes.

## 6. The importance of matrix mucopolysaccharide damage

The low level matrix and cell surface X-ray effects may have radia-tion biological interest, but they probably have no direct vital impor-tance. If one looks for locations where X-ray depolymerization of mucopolysaccharides might be more pathogenic, the large arteries come into account. Here their presence under hydromechanical tension is obvious, and depolymerization might break down the function of artery walls in gel filtration to form a barrier against infiltration by macromolecules from the blood.

The first question: can this breakdown be demonstrated by one of the methods described in the previous sections? can be answered posi-tively provided that the experimental set-up is adapted to the much more dense and strong network of fibres present in the arterial intima. The interstices filled with ground substance are so small, especially if the elastic network is tightened by arterial wall pressure, that the apparatus registering injection pressure must be very rigid if an imme-diate drop after X-irradiation is to be observed (plates 6 and 7).

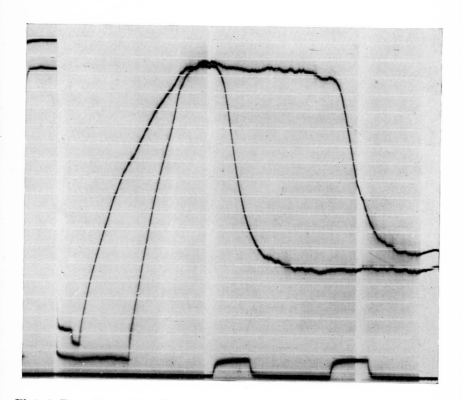

Plate 1. Recording of the effect of X-irradiation on the injection pressure in the rat's dermal connective tissue.

Calibration signal corresponding to 100 mm Hg is followed by the injection. The lower curve gives the irradiation signals. In both needles the irradiation causes an immediate drop in the injection pressure.

Plate 2. An electron micrograph of a portion of an air-dried erythrocyte ghost, shadowed. This is typical of the un-treated control specimens. Noteworthy here is the plaque structure which covers the surface of the ghost. The distri-bution is apparently random, with the size varying only slightly over the entire surface. At the left is seen the edge of the cell and a portion of the supporting collodion film. Large masses such as the one appearing in this micrograph

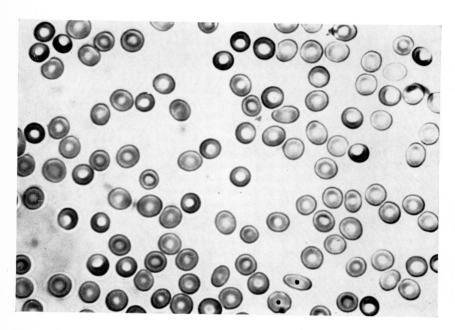

Plate 3. Erythrocytes on a treated glass slide. The dotted cells show the beginning of a sphering reaction. Normal picture.

Plate 4. Increasing number of cells show sphering (dotted cells).

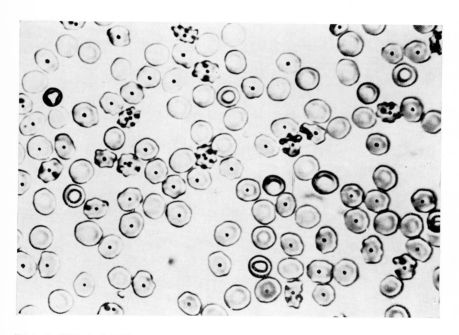

Plate 5. Effect of 5000 r on the shape of erythrocytes. More than 50 % of the cells are in different phases of sphering.

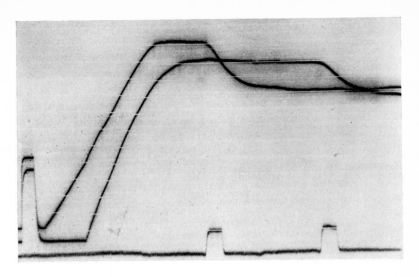

Plate 6. Effect of irradiation with 500 r on the injection pressure in the medial portion of a cow aorta. On the left is the calibration signal corresponding to a pressure of 100 mm Hg. The lower line gives the irradiation signals for both needles.

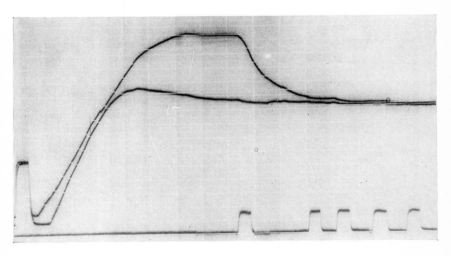

Plate 7. Same as plate 6, but here a solution containing $Na_2S_2O_3$ was injected through one needle. Repeated irradiations here caused no drop in injection pressure.

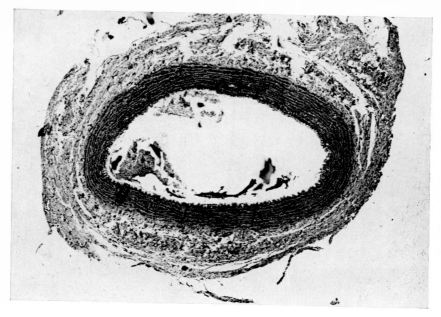

Plate 8. Control carotid artery of a rabbit. No lesions apparent.

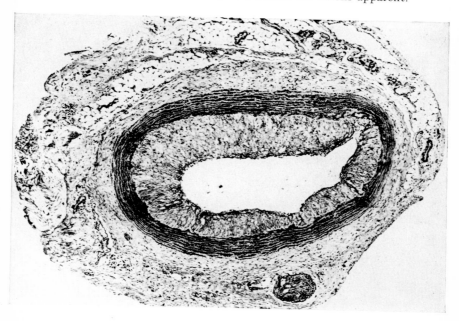

Plate 9. Irradiated artery of the same rabbit as plate 8. Radiation dose 500 r. The animal was killed six weeks after the irradiation. An enormous atheromatous plaque has developed, causing considerable narrowing of the lumen.

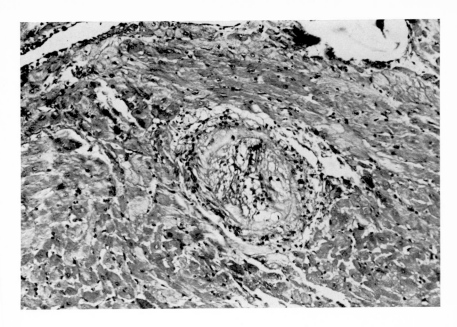

Plate 10. Coronary occlusion in a rabbit, one month after irradiation of the
heart with 2000 r.

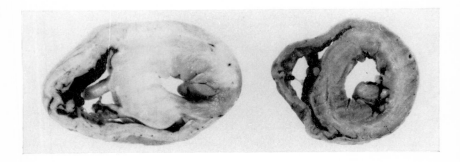

Plate 11. Two rabbit's hearts, the left one of a rabbit twenty-five days after
irradiation of the heart with 2000 r, showing an infarct and enormous dilatation;
the right one of a non-irradiated rabbit of the same age and size.

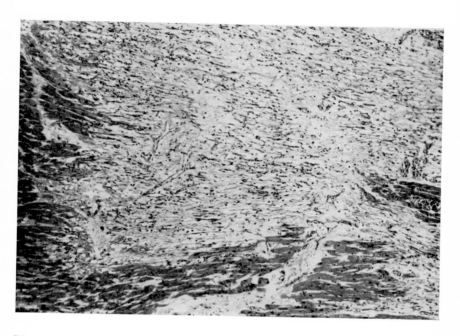

Plate 12. Myocardial fibrosis in a man of 27 years, who was irradiated for a mediastinal metastasis of an embryonic carcinoma of the testis.

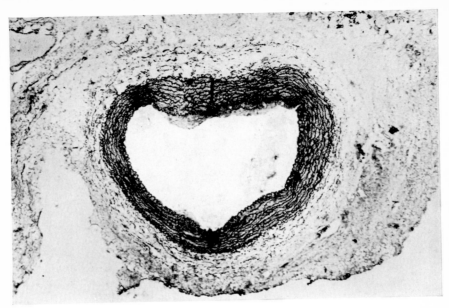

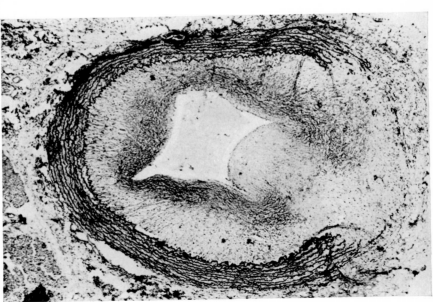

Plate 13. Carotid arteries of a rabbit.
Both were irradiated with 1000 r; one before (lower) and the other (upper)
after intravenous injection with sodium thiosulphate (1 g/kg body weight).

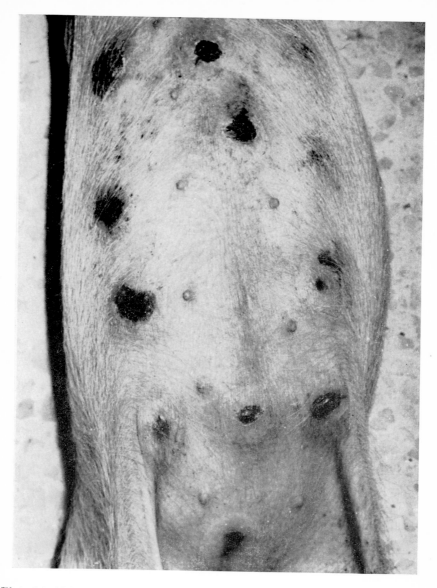

Plate 14. Abdominal skin of a pig. The skin was irradiated in three longitudinal rows of three areas each with 2000, 2500 and 3000 r from cranial (upper part) to caudal.
Left row at 40°C, middle row at normal skin temperature and right row at 0°C skin temperature. The lesions at 0°C are much less than the others.

Still, this result encouraged us to look for analogous effects in living animals, or rather for their pathogenic consequences.

Lamberts, who carried out this work in the last three years, gives the following survey [LAMBERTS and DE BOER, 1963]: "In order to form an idea about pathological effects of vascular irradiation, we designed the following experimental set-up. In hypercholesterolaemic rabbits both carotid arteries were mobilized surgically for a length of approximately 5 cm. One of the arteries was X-irradiated with different doses (200–3000 r) while shielding the other parts of the body. The opposite artery was then sham-irradiated and was used as a control. From other experiments it is known that hypercholesterolaemia itself does not cause early pathological changes in the carotid arteries in rabbits. The rabbits were killed at different time intervals after the irradiation, but mostly an interval of 4 weeks was used. The carotid arteries were examined histologically using different staining techniques. In all irradiated arteries the following pathological changes were found:

1) Deep infiltration of lipids into the arterial wall.
2) Deposition of lipophages (foam cells) on the intima, leading up to plaque formation.
3) Degenerative changes in the elastic tissue.
4) Degenerative changes in the smooth muscle cells.

The control arteries were not affected (plates 8 and 9). As the radiation effects in arteries cause an appreciable occlusion of the vascular lumen, it became interesting to see what would happen to vital organs which were functionally dependent on their blood supply. The heart is a good example of such an organ, and in ten rabbits we irradiated the heart with a single dose of 2000 r. In all animals the coronary arteries showed the same lesions as the irradiated carotid arteries, and in three out of these ten rabbits we could demonstrate myocardial infarcts by electrocardiography, confirmed at necropsy (fig. 10; plates 10 and 11).

In the meantime we started to study autopsy material from patients who had received radiotherapy during life. Here too we found, in all of the twenty-five cases examined, extensive atherosclerotic changes in the arteries in the irradiated parts of the body. These are particularly illuminating in the few younger patients of this series. In these cases the vascular lesions may well have contributed to the death of the patients, mainly from pulmonary and myocardial fibrosis (plate 12).

In rabbits it is possible to protect blood-vessels against radiation damage to a certain degree by an intravenous injection of $Na_2S_2O_3$, in amounts of 1 mg/g body weight or even more. This substance is completely non-toxic and eventually may find clinical application. The experimental results are very promising (plate 13).

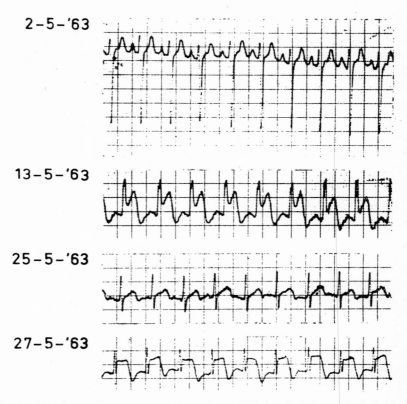

Fig. 10. Electrocardiogram recording of a rabbit irradiated on the heart with 2000 r. The first recording was taken one day before irradiation.

## 7. Radiation-induced chemical changes in synovia and hyaluronic acid

The previous section has demonstrated the importance of matrix mucopolysaccharide radiation damage for some aspects of radiation biology. It may be interesting to know more about the radiation chemical changes caused by X-irradiation. We present here some observations on synovia and on solutions of purified hyaluronic acid.

Synovia, freshly taken from a joint, has the great advantage of containing a mucopolysaccharide mixture resembling the connective tissue matrix, and it is not subjected to preparation damage. We collected synovia mostly from the tibiotarsal joints of recently slaughtered cattle; not every sample can be used. A spontaneous drop in viscosity over 24 hours indicates the presence of depolymerizing agents; these samples must be discarded. OGSTON and STANIER, [1951] conclude from viscosimetric sedimentation and electrophoretic studies that the synovial hyaluronic acid-protein complex is a chain polymer with random flexibility, with a molecular weight of $10^7$ and nearly spherical solvated particles of 140 m$\mu$, giving a high viscosity in low concentrations. In the tibiotarsal joint of cattle the concentration is about 0.05 %, giving a relative viscosity of 2 to 4. The protein part is about 30 %; the proteins are plasma proteins and the binding seems to be ionic. We have measured synovial viscosity with an Epprecht rotation viscometer and with Ostwald pipettes. Structural effects are present, but for comparison purposes, determination with Ostwald pipettes is sufficient. The effect of X-irradiation (220 kV, 900 r/min) on the relative viscosity of fresh synovia can be studied from fig. 11. Obviously, in this type of experiment without mechanical tension, the X-ray effect is not as sensitive as in the membrane exposure. On the other hand, it is more suited for quantitative measurement, also of the after-effect, and for studies on chemoprotection and sensitization.

Light scattering measurements on pure hyaluronic acid dissolved in 0.2 M sodium chloride at 22°C [LAMBERTS and ALEXANDER, 1964] or on synovia [LAMBERTS, 1958] have shown that the primary effect on the macromolecule is a main chain scission, about halving the molecule. No cross linking can be observed. Lamberts and Alexander ascribe the scission to OH radicals, formed by water radiolysis. But, while a clean break by OH radicals in a number of organic macromolecules has often been observed [ALEXANDER and FOX, 1952; CHARLESBY, 1962], some complications must be mentioned here. Firstly, the chloride ions of the physiological medium play a role, because in their presence a large after-effect is observed, especially at low temperatures. In salt-free water, in fluoride or in perchlorate solutions, the mucopolysaccharide viscosity decreases to its final value nearly at once, but in 0.2

M NaCl or KCl, the same final value is reached only after one hour at room temperature or after about 20 hours at 1°C. Lamberts and Alexander's explanation is that OH radicals at once react with the chloride ion, giving rise to a product which still can cause main chain scission, but at a much slower rate. One fact sustaining this hypothesis is the powerful protection by thiosulphate, not only for the immediate effect (thiosulphate added before X-irradiation), but also for the

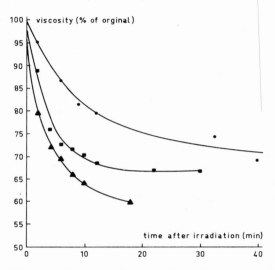

Fig. 11. Effect of 2000 r of X-rays on the viscosity of the sodium salt of hyaluronic acid (20 mg/100 ml) dissolved in 0.1 M NaCl (all solutions in equilibrium with air).

▲, irradiated and measured at 30°;
■, irradiated and measured at 22°;
●, irradiated and measured at 1°C.

after-effect (added at once after irradiation in 0.2 M NaCl). Under irradiation of saline, chlorine atoms are known to be formed [DEWHURST, 1957; KURIEN, PHUNG and BURTON, 1959] and the OH radicals react with them preferentially in the presence of organic molecules. Fluoride and perchlorate ions do not react in this way, and their presence does not introduce a post-irradiation effect. Since the extent of the degradation of hyaluronic acid is the same in solutions of chloride, fluoride or perchlorate ions, it would seem that the intermediary compound is as efficient in producing breaks as OH radicals.

According to LAMBERTS and ALEXANDER [1964], the greater drop in viscosity in the presence of electrolytes compared to that in pure water is due to the electrostatic repulsion between the charged groups of the macromolecular polyelectrolyte and the salt ions. One observation which, in our opinion, is not explained by the presence of chloride ions during irradiation, is the large influence of temperature, not only observed in the viscosity of hyaluronates (plate 14) but also in membrane experiments. One reason might be the maintainance of the ice structure of water at lower temperatures, especially in contact with the non-polar parts of the macromolecules, giving a somewhat greater local rigidity to those structures and thus favouring immediate repair of breaks. If this hypothesis gets more support, it may become interesting for radiation therapy, since the skin might be protected by cooling. Some papers can be found which point in this direction, and plate 14 shows the effect of cooling on the X-radiation sensitivity of pig's skin.

A discussion of the importance of structured water as an integral part of biological membranes can be found in KAVANAU'S, [1964] monograph. Also the much increased radiation sensitivity of macromolecules, if completely dry, as compared to the same structures containing hydration water [WEBB, 1963; WEBB et al., 1963] might contribute to this way of thinking. A second point, which has to be mentioned although no distinct explanation is forthcoming, is the reverse oxygen effect for X-ray degradation of hyaluronic acid. Not only is X-ray sensitivity increased in anoxic solutions, but oxygen protection can be added to the protective action of, for example, AET. This has been found by LAMBERTS [1958] and now is confirmed in his paper with ALEXANDER [1964]. It may be relevant to note that a strongly reducing substance like dithionite will decrease synovial viscosity and open up connective tissue membranes, just as X-irradiation does, and that also here the usual protectors are active [BRINKMAN et al., 1961]. Although further analysis of this reverse oxygen effect cannot be given, the very distinct phenomenon might be interesting for X-ray therapy under high oxygen pressure.

## 8. Ozone as a radiosensitizer

Before ending this survey of our work on the effect of X-irradiation on extracellular or external cell surface structure, we would like to add one other group of observations, which does not strictly belong here because it probably concerns intracellular damage too. This is the sensitizing effect of very low concentrations of ozone. In radiation pathology the role of radicals originating from the internal milieu, water, is fundamental, but why is there little interest in active molecules created by irradiation in the external milieu, air? The formation of ozone by UV, by high voltage apparatus, and by electron beams, is quite common, and the stability of this active oxygen is large compared to that of radicals produced by water radiolysis. It has been known

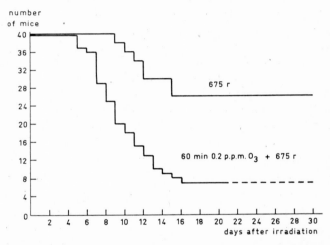

Fig. 12. Summation of the effects of ozone exposure and a sublethal irradiation with 675 r. The "controls" have been irradiated only. The other mice were exposed during 60 minutes to ozone immediately before irradiation. The ozone treatment alone had no killing effect.

for some years that exposure of seeds, human cell structures and mice to low ozone concentrations is radiomimetic [BRINKMAN, LAMBERTS and VENINGA, 1962], and we have now found a distinct sensitizing effect to X-irradiation. Concentrations of 0.1 to 1 part per million of this active gas in accelerator rooms, in high flying airplane cabins, in badly ventilated rooms with UV apparatus, and also in patients' rooms furnished with "ozonizers", are frequently found and often considered to be beneficial. In fig. 12 we show the time of death of four month old mice exposed to ozonized air and then X-irradiated, compared with a group of mice which received X-rays only. We have made many experiments of this type, and always found considerable sensitizations. One circumstance to be thought of is the fact that exposure of mice and rats to ozone in higher concentrations or for longer times rather rapidly evokes an anti-oxidant response [STOKINGER, 1954, 1956], and this protects not only against ozone intoxication but also against irradiation [HATTORI et al., 1963]. The work on ozone sensitization will be continued; it might be a substitute for high pressure oxygen therapy, and a protection against its sensitizing action must be searched for. Our mentioning the effect here is just to bring attention to an interesting and little-studied subject.

## Acknowledgment

All experiments by Brinkman, Lamberts and collaborators, mentioned in this paper, were made under contracts with the International Atomic Energy Agency.

## References

ALEXANDER, P. and FOX, M. 1952. Nature **169** 572.

ALTH, G., MOSTBECK, A., PAPE, R. and SIEDEK, H. 1964. Strahlentherapie **125** 524.

BACQ, Z. M., CICCARONE, P. and RENSON, J. 1959. Experientia **15** 175.

BENNETT, H. S. 1963. J. Histochem. and Cytochem. **11** 14.

BENSLEY, S. 1934. Anat. Rec. **60** 93.

BRINKMAN, R. and VAN DAM, E. 1920. Biochem. Z. **108** 52.

BRINKMAN, R. 1933. J. Physiol. **80** 171.

BRINKMAN, R., LAMBERTS, H. B., WADEL, J. and ZUIDEVELD, J. 1961. Int. J. Rad. Biol. **3** 205.

BRINKMAN, R., LAMBERTS, H. B. and ZUIDEVELD, J. 1961. Int. J. Rad. Biol. **3** 509.

BRINKMAN, R. 1962. In: Biological Effects of Ionizing Radiation at the Molecular Level. (I.A.E.A. Monograph, Vienna) p. 307.

BRINKMAN, R., LAMBERTS, H. B. and VENINGA, T. S. 1962. In: Biological Effects of Ionizing Radiations at the Molecular Level. (I.A.E.A. Monograph, Vienna).

BRINKMAN, R., LAMBERTS, H. B. and VENINGA, T. S. 1964. The Lancet **133**.

CHARLESBY, A. 1962. Atomic Radiations and Polymers (Pergamon Press, Oxford).

COOK, G. M. W., HEARD, D. H. and SEAMAN, G. V. F. 1960. Nature 188 1011.

DAMON, D. and PERK, K. 1962. J. Cell. Comp. Physiol. 59 117.

DAY, T. D. 1959. Quart. J. Exp. Physiol. 44 182.

DEWHURST, H. A. 1957. J. Chem. Phys. 19 1329.

DORFMANN, A. 1963. J. Histochem. and Cytochem. 11 2.

DUNSTONE, J. R. 1962. Biochem. J. 85 336.

DZIEWIATKOWSKI, D. D. 1964. In: Connective Tissue: Intercellular Macromolecules. Proceedings of Symposium sponsored by the New York Heart Association. p. 215. Little, Brown & Co. Boston.

EDGERLEY, R. H. 1952. Amer. J. Physiol. 171 668.

GERSH, J. and CATCHPOLE, H. R. 1960. Perspectives Biol. and Med. 3 282.

HATTORI, K., KATO, N., KINOSHITA, M., KINOSHITA, S. and SUNADE, T. 1963. Nature 198 1220.

HILLIER, J. and HOFFMAN, J. F. 1953. J. Cell. Comp. Physiol. 42 222.

JOLLES, B. and HARRISON, R. G. 1963. Nature 198 1216.

KAVANAU, J. L. 1964. Water and Solute-Water Interactions. (Holden Day Inc. S. Francisco, London, Amsterdam).

KURIEN, K. C., PHUNG, P. V. and BURTON, M. 1959. Rad. Res. 11 283.

LAMBERTS, H. B. 1958. Thesis, Groningen.

LAMBERTS, H. B. and DIJKEN, B. G. 1961. Int. J. Rad. Biol. 4 43.

LAMBERTS, H. B. and DE BOER, W. G. R. M. 1963. Int. J. Rad. Biol. 6 343.

LAMBERTS, H. B. and ALEXANDER, P. 1964. Biochem. Biophys. Acta 88 642.

LAMBERTS, H. B. and DE BOER, W. G. R. M. 1964. Int. J. Rad. Biol. 8 359.

LAMBERTS, H. B. and VAN ANDEL, J. G. 1965. In the press.

MAJNO, G. and PALADE, G. E. 1961. J. Biophys. Biochem. Cytology 11 571.

NAKAO, M., NAKAO, T., TATIBANA, M., YOSHIKAWA, H. and ABE, T. 1959. Biochem. Biophys. Acta 32 564.

NAKAO, M., NAKAO, T. and YAMAZEE, S. 1960. Nature 187 945.

OGSTON, A. G. and STANIER, J. E. 1951. Biochem. J. 51 585.

POLIVODA, A. L. and VINETZKII, Y. P. 1959. Biofisika 5 85.

PRANKERD, F. A. J. 1960. The red cell. (Blackwell, Oxford).

STOKINGER, H. E. 1954. A.M.A. Arch. Industr. Hyg. 9 366.

STOKINGER, H. E. 1956. A.M.A. Arch. Industr. Hyg. 14 158.

SZENT-GYORGYI, A. 1960. Introduction to a Submolecular Biology, (Academic Press, New York, London) p. 93.

VENINGA, T. S. 1965. Thesis, Groningen.

WASSERMAN, K., LOEB, L. and MAYERSON, H. S. 1955. Circulation Res. 3 594.

WEBB, S. J. 1963. Nature 198 785.

WEBB, S. J., BATHER, R. and HODGES, R. W. 1963. Canad. J. of Microbiology 9 87.

# VII

# RADIATION BIOLOGY AS APPLIED TO RADIOTHERAPY

J. F. FOWLER

*University of London Postgraduate Medical School, Hammersmith Hospital, London W 12*

# CONTENTS

# 1. Introduction

Radiotherapy has grown empirically, as an art not a science. If therapists had waited for a fully scientific basis before treating the first patient, radiotherapy would not have started yet. But the important questions are becoming clearer, and the formulation of relevant questions is an essential step to discovering useful answers. This chapter is written at a time of rapid change in the field of radiobiology applied to radiotherapy. It is therefore difficult to write a balanced account, but perhaps an attempt at stocktaking should be made now because the picture appears likely to change even more rapidly in the next few years.

Radiation biology is sometimes said to have impinged sharply on radiotherapy in the last five years, since mammalian cell survival curves have been available. Before this time, some radiotherapists had felt that radiobiology could not help them: men, mice, bacteria and fruit-flies were far too different from each other. But this was not altogether true: radiobiology has over many years laid the essential foundations for the present work in radiation biology. For example, the oxygen effect was observed in radiotherapy (but not explained) as early as 1909 [SCHWARZ] when compression of skin was found to be associated with smaller skin reactions. In addition an intimate connection between radiation effects and processes of cell replacement was recognized very early in the history of radiobiology. In 1906, Bergonnié and Tribondeau proposed that X-ray sensitivity varied directly with the rate of proliferation and the number of future divisions, and inversely with the degree of morphological and functional differentiation. It is only in recent years that more precise interpretations are becoming possible.

The thinking of pioneer radiotherapists has certainly been influenced, consciously or unconsciously, by radiobiological findings. It is clear that for radiobiologists and radiotherapists to collaborate fruitfully, very frequent discussions and the efficient transfer of information in both directions are necessary. It appears that radiotherapy will now improve mainly insofar as biological factors can be exploited. It must not be forgotten that a great deal of valuable information passes through radiotherapists' hands in their day-to-day work. This information may be inaccurate, or difficult to retrieve, but it is the most relevant information that it is possible to obtain. At the present time radiobiology is undergoing a change from its preoccupation with individual cells to an attempt to deal with populations of cells in organized tissues. It is therefore timely to remember that the widest possible range of experiments has to be considered, from chemical experiments with sensitizing and protective compounds, through enzymes, bacteria, and mammalian cells, to animal experiments. And there the range extends from quantitative clone-counting experiments in spleens of mice to "clinical" observations on the skin of pigs. The importance of cell population kinetics is becoming very much clearer, but good experimental systems representing slow-growing tumours or normal tissues in animals as long-lived as man have yet to be found.

## 1.1. THE QUESTIONS OF CLINICAL RADIOTHERAPY

The following questions are as old as radiotherapy, but they have not been answered yet. Does radiation affect tumour cells differently from normal cells? Or tumour masses differently from normal tissues? What factors determine optimum doses in radiotherapy? How can rational fractionation regimes be devised? Is the presence of anoxic cells in tumours an important factor in the success or failure of treatment? How can radiotherapy be improved? It is essential that normal tissues should not be damaged too much, yet the tumour must be destroyed. How can this be achieved?

The special value of radiobiology to radiotherapy is that these questions can be rephrased so that there may be a chance of answering them. We must now think and experiment in terms of the survival or sterilization of individual cells, in terms of radiosensitivity which depends upon the presence of oxygen and other compounds or upon the phase of cell cycle, and in terms of partial recovery from intracellular injury. Further, we must consider populations of cells rather than individuals and ask how the response to radiation of the whole tumour or tissue depends upon the number of proliferating cells, upon differentiation rate, upon vascular supply and nutritional deficiencies. If we knew the way in which these complex processes varied with time over several days after radiation doses of various sizes given to different tissues, then we should have much of the information needed to plan rational radiotherapy. We also need to know the long-term effect of radiation on function of normal tissues which unavoidably have to be irradiated. We do not know how these processes work, but we are beginning to ask the questions which may bring useful answers.

Since about half the new cases of cancer seen are treated by radiotherapy, the other half being treated by surgery, any improvement in the results of radiotherapy would affect very large numbers of people.

Two of the most important aspects in which radiobiology may help to improve radiotherapy are

1) Dealing with anoxic cells in tumours, and
2) Finding rational regimes of fractionation.

## 2. Cellular theories of radiosensitivity

The proliferation or sterilization of individual cells, however profoundly modified in its manifestation through population growth, is obviously central to the question of malignant disease. The effect of radiation in modifying cellular proliferation will be described in this section in degrees of increasing complexity.

### 2.1. CELL SURVIVAL CURVES

Cell survival curves have been a great aid to clearer thinking in this field. There are, as has already been mentioned, major modifications to the simple theories which must never be forgotten, but even with these limitations, cell survival curves are extremely useful. It was immensely stimulating when in 1959 Hewitt and Wilson found that mouse leukaemia cells irradiated *in vivo* or *in vitro* and assayed *in vivo* showed a relationship between the proportion of cells surviving and the radiation dose which was almost identical to that shown by cells derived from hamster lungs and grown as clones in cell culture dishes by PUCK and MARCUS [1956]. Other mammalian cells were soon found to follow rather similar survival curves, as in fig. 1. The ordinate axis is a logarithmic scale, but the dose scale is linear. "Survival" means the special property of an individual cell of continuing to proliferate indefinitely so as to form a clone of cells, or eventually to regrow a tumour. Such cells have been called "clonogenic". A cell may instead live in differentiated or sterile form, and may carry out a function in the organ for the normal lifespan of the cell, but by this definition it is not counted as "surviving" unless it continues to divide. This distinction between the number of clonogenic cells in a population

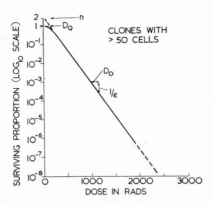

Fig. 1. Typical cell survival curve, obtained *in vitro* or *in vivo* by counting the number of clones. Each cell surviving with its reproductive integrity intact grows into a clone. Important parameters are $D_0$, $n$ and $D_Q$. Some survival curves continue to bend over downwards at high doses.

and the total number of cells in a population at a given time is extremely important. Very much higher doses are required to impair the function of already differentiated cells than appear to be needed to sterilize proliferating cells. This is shown by the comparatively high doses given to the pituitary or thyroid glands to reduce their function: 10 000 to 100 000 rads delivered over several days by $^{131}$I or $^{90}$Y.

The property of indefinite proliferation is obviously essential to tumour cells, so that if all the cells in a tumour are sterilized, the patient is cured. If one cell survives it may regrow the tumour. In terms of fig. 1, if a tumour containing $10^9$ cells is irradiated to reduce the proportion of survivors to $10^{-10}$, then there is 1 chance in 10 that a viable cell will remain in the tumour. In a series of such tumours, a cure rate of 90 % would be observed. If immunity response is present, then the number of surviving cells need not be reduced to less than one, but only to a number where the immune reaction can kill the remainder. (The only convincing evidence for this in human cancer appears to be the lymphocytic or round cell infiltration in medullary carcinoma which constitutes about 5 % of all breast cancer [BLOOM, 1965].) If encapsulation by fibrous tissue occurs, with isolation of viable tumour cells from nutritional supplies and from phagocytic action, again the tumour need not be reduced to less than one viable cell. Whether the number of survivors is one or several thousand, a curve like fig. 1 which defines this number is an essential starting point.

A slope of $1/D_0$ where $D_0 = 140$ rads is common. $D_0$ is called the *mean lethal dose*, less commonly the 37 *per cent dose slope*. It is the dose required to reduce the proportion of surviving cells from 1 to 0.37 on the straight exponential part of the semilogarithmic cell survival curve. It is also the dose which on the average produces throughout an irradiated specimen one lethal event in every unit of volume equal to that of a sensitive "target" region in a cell [ZIMMER, 1961]. Details of the lethal processes are not known, but such sensitive regions may be of the order of 5 to 100 nm in diameter, and it may be necesssary to deposit energy equivalent to several ionizations in order to cause lethal damage [BARENDSEN et al., 1963; FOWLER, 1964a].

The intercept of the straight tail in fig. 1 produced back to the zero dose axis at $n$ is known as the "extrapolation number" [ALPER et al., 1960], so as not to be committed to the particular multi-target model of cell death [ZIMMER, 1961]. Extrapolation numbers of 2 or 3 are common, but higher values are also frequently found, as described below. There are some biophysical reasons to expect that the higher the extrapolation number, the more likely the semilogarithmic survival curve is to continue with a downward curvature instead of becoming straight even at high doses [FOWLER, 1964c, BARENDSEN, 1964, FOWLER, 1965a]. For some time it was half believed that all mammalian cells may have sufficiently similar survival curves to allow quantitative predictions to be made about the number of cells surviving after various doses of radiation (as if mammalian cells all had similar biophysical target volumes, which is not really unreasonable). In fig. 1, for example, the dose required to reduce the number of cells surviving from $10^9$ to $10^{-1}$ is about 3000 rads. This would give a 1-in-10 chance of regrowing the tumour, i.e. a 90 % cure probability. The dose required to give a 1-in-2 chance of regrowth, i.e. a 50 % chance of cure, is only 300 rads less. MUNRO and GILBERT [1961] and GRAY [1961] drew useful conclusions from this approach, and stated their assumptions and the limitations of the model quite clearly. It is now apparent that cell survival curves are found with differing shapes and that doses to produce the same survival are certainly not the same in all cells. The variations are of course a limitation in applying numerical results too literally to practical situations unless the relevant data are well known; they will be described in the next section. The fact of numerical variation between cell strains or between differing cell cycle times does not prevent the concept of a cell survival curve from being one of the most useful aids to rational thinking about radio-therapy, provided that the subsequent modifying factors and especially population kinetics are taken into account.

## 2.2. VARIATIONS IN CELL SURVIVAL CURVE SHAPE

### 2.2.1. *Different cell strains*

Slopes varying from $D_0 = 47$ or 58 rads [CELADA and CARTER, 1962] to 280 rads [TILL, 1961] have been found in different strains of mammalian cells [review by WHITMORE and TILL, 1964].

### 2.2.2. *Differences throughout the mitotic cycle*

A variation in sensitivity in different phases of the cell cycle has been found [TERASIMA and TOLMACH, 1963; SINCLAIR and MORTON, 1963; DEWEY and HUMPHREY, 1963; WHITMORE et al., 1964]. The number of cells surviving a given dose varied up to a factor of ten with time after mitosis, but the doses required to produce a given proportion of surviving cells varied by only about 50 per cent. The experimental data were reviewed by WHITMORE and TILL [1964] who pointed out that since $D_0$ and the extrapolation number were found to vary in opposite directions with increase of time in the cell cycle, the observed time of maximum sensitivity will depend upon the dose given. This factor would contribute to the apparently different results from different cell lines. The only generalization that can be made is in favour of a minimum cell survival just before the DNA synthesis phase begins. A maximum in cell survival during the DNA synthesis phase appears to occur somewhat earlier if large doses ($> 1000$ rads) are given.

TERASIMA and TOLMACH [1963] showed that the summation of surviv-al curves obtained with synchronized cell populations did coincide with the gross survival curve obtained from a randomly dividing population. The gross survival curve would, however, have a lower extrapolation number than the average of the extrapolation numbers of the component phases.

### 2.2.3. *Shapes of survival curves*

Shapes of survival curves very different from fig. 1 have been found. Extrapolation numbers up to 10 or more are fairly common [WHIT-MORE and TILL, 1964] and some investigators have obtained survival curves *in vitro* that continue to bend over downwards with increasing dose instead of becoming straight exponential lines [BARENDSEN, 1962; ELKIND, SUTTON and MOSES, 1961; SINCLAIR, 1964]. The significance of survival curve shapes in terms of 'multi-hit' or 'multi-target' concepts is open to doubt, but has been discussed recently in relation to the sub-microscopic distribution of energy dissipation [ROSSI, 1962; BARENDSEN, 1964; FOWLER, 1964a, 1964c].

No trend of differences has been observed between cells derived from malignant as compared with normal tissues. The three types of variation listed above are all factors affecting the survival of individual cells as measured in clone-counting experiments. Nothing has been said about any possible degrees of sub-lethal injury to the cells which are counted as survivors. The next section deals with this aspect.

### 2.3. DIFFERENCES BETWEEN CELL SURVIVAL CURVES AND FUNCTIONAL DOSE-RESPONSE CURVES *in vivo*

Observations of radiobiological effect which depend upon the *total number of cells in a population*, or on the number of differentiated cells, must be sharply distinguished from *clone-counting experiments*. Most functional effects such as intestinal death, moist desquamation of skin, or size of tumour depend upon the total number of cells in all the clones. "Clone-counting" experiments however include those with cells plated out in dishes (Puck and Marcus; Elkind and Sutton) and *in vivo* dilution experiments (Hewitt and Wilson) or spleen colony counting experiments [TILL and McCULLOCH, 1961, 1963]. It is correct to refer to their results as "cell survival curves" because each clone arises from one surviving cell. "Total population" results, on the other hand, are better described in terms of "dose-response curves", and we have to seek the relationship between such dose-response curves and the cell survival curves for individual cells present in the tissue.

Large discrepancies have been observed between cell survival curves obtained *in vitro* [HEWITT and WILSON, 1959; PUCK and MARCUS, 1956] and those deduced from functional studies *in vivo* in some tissues, especially intestinal epithelium [HORNSEY and VATISTAS, 1963], skin of pigs, mice and men reviewed by FOWLER et al. [1963c], and cure of squamous cell carcinoma [FOWLER and STERN, 1963]. These discrepancies have been recently clarified by Wither's confirmation of a large shoulder in the dose-response curve for moist desquamation of the skin in mice (an end-point which is a function of cell depletion), whereas a clone-counting experiment in skin of the same mice showed a smaller shoulder [WITHERS, 1965]. (See also section 4.3.3.) This observation goes to the root of the arguments about the possible relevance of cell survival curves in predicting curves relating functional response to dose. The two types of dose-effect relationship must indeed be distinguished clearly.

This difference can, in principle, be explained by variations in the rates of growth of different clones arising from those cells that survive irradiation. This concept is most important and will be described here, although it should be emphasized that its formulation is too recent for it to have been fully evaluated yet [WHITMORE and TILL, 1964]. Together with other aspects of population kinetics, it may be found to explain the well-known failure of survival curves like that shown in fig. 1 to explain quantitatively several aspects of radiotherapy, for example why squamous cell carcinoma is curable with surprisingly low doses [COHEN, 1960], or quantitatively how the total dose increases with number of fractions in fractionated therapy [FOWLER and STERN, 1963]. The explanation is however tentative at the present time.

It is well known that some clones which "survive" in clone-counting experiments are slower-growing and therefore smaller than others [SINCLAIR, 1964; BARENDSEN, private communication]. The proportion of small clones increases with dose. Therefore curves of "total number of cells in the population" *versus* dose would bend downwards with increasing dose, even if the corresponding curve for "number of clones surviving" in the same population were a straight exponential line. WHITMORE and TILL [1964] pointed out that this variation in clone size can be explained by the assumption that radiation reduces the probability $p$ of successful mitotis in a cell, and that the probability remains at a reduced level of $p$ for all the subsequent daughter cells, through successive generations. This model is described very clearly in the latter part of WHITMORE and TILL's excellent review [1964]. It is assumed that $p$ is reduced more by larger doses of radiation, so that a larger proportion of small clones at high doses is predicted (fig. 2).

Now cell systems in which a high proportion of mitoses lead to differentiated cells (possibly after a long latent period) instead of to proliferating cells have, by definition, a lower probability $p$ of producing a pair of proliferative cells at each division than populations which are dividing and not differentiating. In other words, the value of $p$ in a differentiating tissue is low even before irradiation, and irradiation

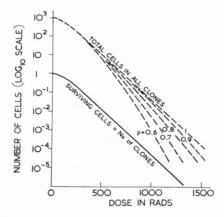

Fig. 2. Cell survival curve as modified by reduced probabilities $p$ of successful mitosis (see text). It is assumed that $p$ decreases with increasing dose, reaching the values shown. Full line: clone-counting cell survival curve. Dotted lines: total number of cells in all the clones, after about 10 cell divisions. The "total population" curves show more divergence from the shape of the "clone-counting survival curve" if $p$ is low. (The actual shape depends upon the time at which the count is made.)

reduces $p$ still further. If $p$ is brought down close to the critical value of $p = 0.5$ below which the whole population will become sterile, we should expect to see very large discrepancies indeed between "clone-counting" experiments and "total-population" experiments (fig. 2). This would be most marked in tissues where a high proportion of mitoses leads to differentiated cells rather than to repopulating the

stem cell compartment. The requirements of such a population are as
follows.

   (a) large number of differentiated cells present relative to the
       number of dividing stem cells;
   (b) long stem cell cycle time (intermitotic time);
   (c) long lifetime of stem cells compared with stem cell cycle time.
   In tumours, we may read "tumour cells" for "stem cells", and "differentiated or other non-dividing cells" to allow also for nutritional failure.
The more completely these requirements are fulfilled, the larger the
divergence between "clone-counting" cell survival curves and "total-
population" dose response curves, in the direction observed by Withers
of greater curvature on the latter. We may therefore expect rapidly-
growing anaplastic tumours to behave more nearly according to cell
survival curve predictions (provided that impaired vascular supplies
in the unirradiated tumour were not causing a large proportion of
cell death by nutritional failure, which would lead instead to a divergence due to condition (a) above). On the other hand, well-differentiated
tumours, and certain organs including skin, may be expected to show
a divergent response.
   This concept is a special case of the population kinetics considerations
which follow in the next section. It depends particularly on the *decrease
in survival probability with increasing dose*. It is too early yet to assess
its full value in explaining differences between cell survival curve
results and functional tests, but there is no doubt that population
kinetics play a predominant part in the response of organs or whole
animals. We will therefore turn from considering how many individual
cells survive a given dose of radiation (section 2.2.) and how these
may increase in number subsequently (this section) to more general
questions of the total cell population in organs.


2.4. ORGAN RADIOSENSITIVITY AND POPULATION KINETICS

   "Cellular radiosensitivity" described by cell survival curves has
been distinguished in the previous section from "total population
radiosensitivity" as measured at any given time after irradiation by
some functional test which depends upon the number or mass of cells
present. Both these concepts depend upon the number of cells, or the
number of clones, present at a particular time after irradiation, and

both depend basically on how many cells are sterilized by a dose of radiation. Therefore survival curves are always basic, whatever happens during subsequent growth. The "total population radiosensitivity" introduces growth rate and cell turnover, i.e. population kinetics.

Radiosensitivity has often been described clinically in terms of the severity or rapidity of appearance of a radiation effect, such as reduction in size of a tumour or organ. This "organ radiosensitivity" depends upon the turnover rate of cells in the organ, i.e. upon the lifetime of the cells in the organ before their removal by normal processes. Fig. 3 illustrates the way in which this is related to proliferative

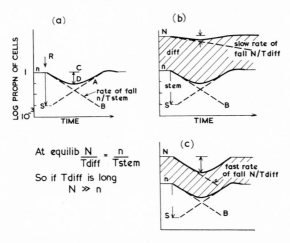

Fig. 3. Organ radiosensitivity. (a) Stem cells (or all cells dividing) only. At irradiation $R$, the number of stem cells $n$ is reduced to the proportion $S$ which after a mitotic delay repopulates the organ (A). The sterile proportion $1-S$ is removed (according to B) the physiological turnover rate being $n/T_{stem}$, where $T_{stem}$ is the average lifetime of a stem cell. The critical reduction of organ size (mass) is at CD. (b) Stem and differentiated cell compartments. Stem cells as before. $N$ is reduced at rate $N/T_{diff}$ where $T_{diff}$ is the average lifetime of the differentiated cells. When the stem cells have repopulated enough to contribute significantly to $N$ again, $N$ will increase. (c) As in (b) but with a faster removal of differentiated cells due to a faster physiological turnover rate, i.e. a shorter $T_{diff}$ than in (b). The critical reduction in organ size is greater than in (b).

survival of cells. Let us first consider tissues consisting entirely of proliferative cells, e.g. the stem cell compartment of an organ, or an anaplastic tumour. At irradiation the surviving proportion of these cells is reduced to, say, $10^{-3}$ (fig. 3a). These survivors will now prolif-

erate at a rate inversely proportional to their cell cycle time, giving
the rising curve A of new cells as shown. (Their growth is exponential
so the line in the semilogarithmic plot of fig. 3a is straight.) At the
same time, the damaged 0.999 of cells are removed by lysis or phagocytosis. To the extent that their destruction is a consequence of abor-
tive division, the rate of removal will be equal to the repopulation rate,
provided that lysis or phagocytosis can remove the damaged cells
sufficiently rapidly. In fig. 3a, it has been assumed that the removal
rate (curve B) is the same as the repopulation rate (curve A). In
tumours it is not likely that the repopulation rate will be controlled
by the usual tissue growth factors. In non-neoplastic tissues, however,
the repopulation could be speeded up in response to damage, so that
the rising curve A in fig. 3a could be steeper than B. In any case, a
minimum number of proliferating cells occurs at approximately
the time of crossover of the rising and falling curves in fig. 3a. The
extent of this reduction in cell number is smaller if the radiation dose
is small, and if repopulation occurs at a faster rate than normal. For
stem cells with different turnover rates, the time axis can be adjusted.

We must now consider the effect of such a deficiency of proliferating
cells on the total size of an organ or tumour. The total size of an organ
is determined by the rate of generation of differentiated cells from the
stem cell compartment, and by the lifetime of these differentiated
cells before their removal by the usual physiological processes. If $N$
is the total number of differentiated cells in the organ and $T_{diff}$ hours
is their average lifetime, then the normal repopulation rate from stem
cells is $N/T_{diff}$ cells per hour. If the lifetime $T_{diff}$ is very long, i.e. in
organs with a slow cell turnover such as liver, or (an extreme case
where no turnover occurs) in neurones, then the number of cells
provided from the stem cell compartment per hour or per day is a very
small proportion of the total number of cells in the organ. It is then
obvious that even large changes in this small repopulation rate will
cause very small changes in the total number of cells in the organ,
provided that the repopulation rate returns to normal in a time which
is short compared with the lifetime $T_{diff}$ of the differentiated cells
(fig. 3b). These organs will show little change after irradiation, and
would be classed as "radioresistant".

For organs with rapid turnover, however, where $T_{diff}$ is short and
may be comparable with the time during which stem cell replacement is
deficient, there will obviously be a much bigger loss of differentiated

cells from the organ before repopulation takes effect. The same reduction in stem cell numbers as in the previous case will be followed by a much larger reduction in total cells in the organ (fig. 3c). This organ would then be classed as "radiosensitive", although the same proportion and number of proliferative stem cells survive the irradiation as in the "radioresistant" organ. The lifetime of the differentiated cells $T_{diff}$ is short enough to show up the damage.

In the event that $T_{diff}$ were shorter than the lifetime of the stem cells, the reduction in number of differentiated cells would follow very closely the reduction in proportion of surviving stem cells shown in fig. 3a. The reduction in "organ size" will therefore be greatest for organs with

(a) short lifetime of differentiated cells, and

(b) small total numbers of differentiated cells relative to stem cells.

In tumours, we may read "clonogenic cells" for "stem cells" and "differentiated or other non-dividing cells" for "differentiated cells". The more nearly the conditions just described are fulfilled, the more nearly will the response of the total population follow predictions from simple cell survival curves. They are the inverse of conditions (a)–(c) necessary for deviations from simple cell-survival curve predictions as described in section 2.3 above.

The organs with rapid turnover rates in mammals include intestinal epithelium and bone-marrow, and these are certainly classed as "radiosensitive". Should the organ need a minimum number of cells for the animal to survive (e.g. leucocytes in the blood, or intact villi per square centimetre in the gut), then the animal would be expected to die as a result of injury to the organs with rapid rates of cell turnover. This is found to be so: intestinal epithelium and marrow are the critical organs for death after whole body irradiation of mammals, and the respective times of death can be related to the cell population kinetics of the organs [PATT and QUASTLER, 1963]. Other organs in the same irradiated animals will also have had their stem cell populations reduced considerably by the same irradiation, but the damage will appear much more slowly, if ever.

A tumour with rapid cell turnover rate (e.g. anaplastic) may show a rapid decrease in size soon after irradiation, but if the number of clonogenic cells was not reduced sufficiently by the irradiation, the tumour might regrow. Such tumours have been misleadingly termed "radiosensitive". Conversely, a tumour with a slow turnover rate might

show only a very slow reduction in size, and may loosely be described as "radioresistant", whereas its cells might have been sterilized by irradiation so that it does not regrow. This example emphasizes the difference between the "number of individual cells or clones surviving", which matters in cure of cancer, and the "total number of cells in the organ"; a description of radiosensitivity based on the latter is therefore not adequate. Fig. 4 illustrates this difference in rate and magnitude of

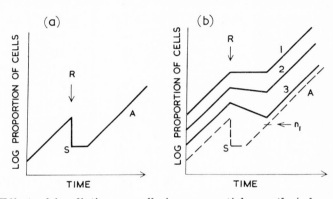

Fig. 4. Effect of irradiation on cells in exponential growth (schematic). (a) Dividing cells only (stem or tumour). Irradiation $R$ reduces the surviving proportion to $S$ which after a delay continues dividing as at A. (b) Full lines: total population including differentiated or other sterile cells. Dotted lines: dividing cells. (Growth of the *total* population will be logarithmic provided that the same *proportion* of divisions leads to sterile cells throughout.) Full lines 1, 2, 3, show alternative assumptions of successively faster removal rates of sterile cells. The total population grows again as soon as dividing cells start contributing significantly to it, i.e. when the dividing cell population has grown to $n_1$ (corresponding to CD in fig. 3). When sterile cells remain present in the tissue (curve 1) the ultimate proportional decrease in size for a given $S$ will be less than when sterile cells are absent as in (a) or rapidly removed as in (b) [after LAJTHA and OLIVER, 1962].

decrease in size of irradiated tumours in which various proportions of differentiated or other sterile cells are produced, when the number of clonogenic cells surviving the irradiation is assumed to be the same in each case.

It may be noted that in fractionated radiotherapy, it is not only the number of clonogenic cells surviving each dose (as given by survival curves) that matters, but the number of clonogenic cells to which these survivors have proliferated at the time of the next fraction.

The differences in population kinetics described above for fast and slow growing tissues can readily explain the differences in "organ radiosensitivity" or "tumour radiosensitivity" known to every radiotherapist, without invoking unreasonably large differences in the sterilizing effect of radiation on individual cells. The differences in survival curve shape described in section 2.2 of course contribute also. It should be emphasized that no consistent difference in cellular radiosensitivity or survival curve shape has been observed for cultures derived from malignant or normal tissues.

This section has attempted to describe without mathematical notation some of the consequences of population kinetic studies, and is therefore extremely inadequate in indicating the scope of these ideas [LAJTHA et al., 1962; LAJTHA, 1964]. It must be remembered that many of the parameters required if population kinetic studies are to give useful results are unknown. At the present time, therefore, it is important not to stop at theoretical predictions, but to carry out experiments on animal systems which are as similar as possible to human beings, for example on pigs; and also to record very carefully the results of radiotherapy on human patients.

## 2.5. THE LIMITING DOSES IN RADIOTHERAPY

It is obvious that even if there is no difference in *cellular radiosensitivity* between tumour and normal cells, it may be possible to find differences in *organ radiosensitivity* which can be exploited to minimize the relative damage to normal tissues. This will be explored further in the section on fractionation. In the present section the importance of good physical distributions is re-affirmed, but it does not seem likely that further major gains will follow from better and better distributions of X-ray or electron doses fitted more precisely round the prescribed treated region. This is, of course, largely because very good dose distributions are now readily available using supervoltage radiation. Physical developments to this state have probably constituted the main improvements in radiotherapy over the last two decades, but the next improvements are likely to be due to biological factors.

The limiting doses are determined by the maximum dose tolerated by such normal tissues as must be irradiated. Now that good dose distributions are available, *the limiting normal tissues are within the prescribed*

*treated region*. The example of a tumour encircling the oesophagus is a good one, but in every radical treatment the associated normal tissues limit the maximum tumour dose. Even for a well-localized tumour the radiotherapist must treat a somewhat larger volume than the known tumour, not because of poor localization but because of the possible presence of infiltrating tumour cells. Therefore the response of *normal* tissues is of prime concern to the radiotherapist, so that he can give the maximum possible dose to the treated region consistent with survival of the patient. If improvements are to be made, the relative response of tumours and normal tissues must be known for many sites. Too little is known about them at present.

We said above that physical improvements to X-ray and electron beams are unlikely to bring major gains in radiotherapy; the main objectives were achieved when high doses outside the treated volume were eliminated. Developments in physics are more likely to be in the direction of new types of particle, for specific biological purposes. Of course a great deal of effort and attention is still needed in practice to maintain the good standards of dose control that exist in many centres, and whoever underestimates this does so at his, or the patient's, peril.

The two aspects of radiotherapy which are ripe for improvement at the present time are:

1. The elimination of the effect of anoxic cells in tumours,
2. Fractionation, i.e. the implications of giving treatments by regimes other than 5 times per week.


## 3. The problem of anoxic cells in tumours

It is well known that X-ray doses 2 to 3 times larger are required to produce the same damage in anoxic systems as when irradiation takes place in the presence of oxygen [GRAY et al., 1953]. In order to obtain the same degree of damage in experiments which result in cell survival curves, both *in vitro* and *in vivo* [HEWITT and WILSON, 1959a], the X-ray or gamma ray doses must be multiplied by about $2\frac{1}{2}$ for any level of damage (fig. 5). The extrapolation numbers remain the same; the effect is usually assumed to be that of a simple dose-modifying ratio. No change in shape of the survival curves has been

confirmed due to the presence or absence of oxygen. The ratio of doses is called the oxygen enhancement ratio (OER). It should however be mentioned that REVESZ and LITTBRAND [1964] found a lower extrapolation number for Ehrlich ascites tumour cells in anoxic conditions,

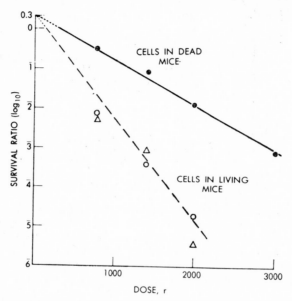

Fig. 5. Survival curves of mouse leukaemia cells taken from the liver after whole body radiation with $^{60}$Co gamma rays under the following conditions: ● anoxic; ○ mice breathing air; △ mice breathing oxygen at atmospheric pressure [from HEWITT and WILSON, 1959b].

and also that HALL, BEDFORD and OLIVER [1965] found reduced extrapolation numbers for HeLa and hamster cells but only after more than 12 hours in anoxic conditions before irradiation. It is likely that cells exist in an anoxic or hypoxic state for many hours before irradiation of a tumour, so the question of the shape of the response curves in tumours must be left open.

The variation of radiosensitivity with oxygen concentration is shown in fig 6; it is similar in many biological systems [GRAY, 1961]. The outstanding feature is the rapid rise of sensitivity to a plateau level with increasing oxygen tension. Therefore if the oxygen tension were doubled or trebled, there would be only a small increase in radiation response of tissues at sufficiently high oxygen tension to be

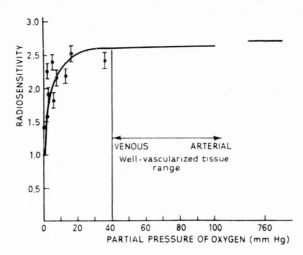

Fig. 6. Curve relating radiosensitivity of mouse Ehrlich ascites tumour cells to oxygen tension around them at the time of irradiation. It is a typical relationship for mammalian cells and many other biological systems. Increasing the partial pressure from 3 to 10 mm would approximately double the radiosensitivity; but the corresponding increase of well oxygenated cells from 100 to 300 mm would be only a few per cent in radiosensitivity [from CHURCHILL-DAVIDSON, 1964, and DESCHNER and GRAY, 1959].

on the plateau, but the radiosensitivity of tissues at very low oxygen tension would be greatly increased.

## 3.1. ANOXIC CELLS IN TUMOURS

The question is whether the very low radiosensitivity of anoxic cells matters in radiotherapy. THOMLINSON and GRAY [1955] suggested that cells situated more than about 180 microns from capillary vessels would receive no oxygen, and would eventually die. Capillaries may be pushed more than 360 microns apart during tumour growth, depending upon the cohesion of the tumour cells. It is found histologically that necrotic regions are indeed present in tumours more than a few millimetres in diameter, both in man and in rats; and that the healthy tumour cells are found surrounding capillary vessels, but not at distances greater than about 200 microns from them. In relatively "healthy" tumour tissues, multiple small necrotic foci were seen in the regions

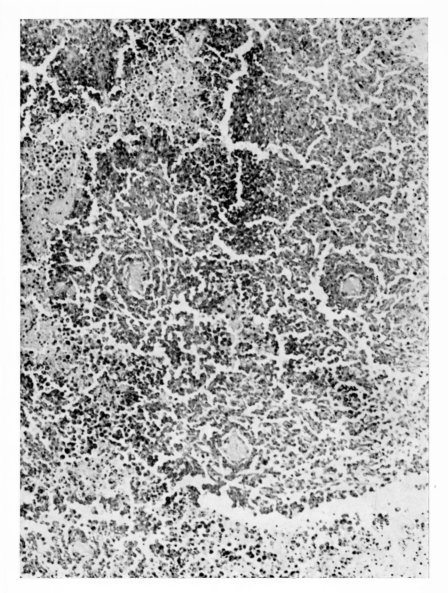

Fig. 7. Section of fibrosarcoma, showing circular areas of "healthy" tumour cells extending outwards about 180 microns from the three capillary vessels, and a necrotic region midway between them [from THOMLINSON, 1961].

midway between several capillaries (fig. 7). This is an important observation, as it is relevant to small tumours without macroscopically necrotic volumes. In tumours larger than about a centimetre, where significant volumes of necrotic tissue may occur, "sleeves" of healthy tumour cells were seen surrounding capillary vessels. These findings were common to tumours of different types, both in animals and man.

It is suggested that cells at the edge of necrotic regions, deficient in oxygen but not yet dead, are the ones that are radioresistant but capable of regrowing the tumour after irradiation, which changes the environment by killing many cells and so diminishing the demand for the available nutrition and oxygen. From fig. 1, the proportion of well-oxygenated cells surviving after a dose of 300 rads is about 10 %, so the remaining 90 % are sterilized and, in tumours, may later be lysed or phagocytosed. The proportion of anoxic cells surviving the same dose would, however, be as high as 80 %. From Thomlinson's histological sections, the proportion of cells lining the borders of necrotic volumes to a depth of one cell thickness was estimated to be about 1 % of the intact cells in the tumour [THOMLINSON, 1961]; this proportion would only be reduced from 1 to 0.8 % by a dose of 300 rads.

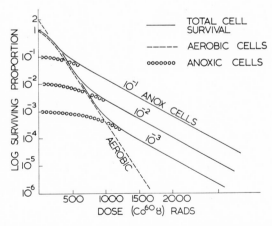

Fig. 8. Calculated cell survival curves for various proportions of anoxic cells, from the data in fig. 5 [HEWITT and WILSON, 1959b].

HEWITT [1959] has calculated cell survival curves resulting from a mixed population of anoxic and oxygenated cells (fig. 8), based on the experimental survival curves shown in fig. 5. It is clear that the oxygenated cells are readily killed as dose increases, leaving the anoxic cells in the "anoxic tail" as those with which we have to deal. If the dose necessary to produce a given cell survival in fully oxygenated cells is 4000 rads, the dose required in 99 % oxygenated and 1 % of anoxic cells is 7000 rads (single dose of $^{60}$Co). The doses required to produce the same level of cell survival in populations containing respectively 0.1 %, 1 % and 10 % of anoxic cells are 6630, 7000 and 7370 rads (fig. 5). The presence of even these small proportions of anoxic cells will therefore nearly double the single dose required to sterilize the same number of well-oxygenated cells.

## 3.2. FURTHER EVIDENCE FOR THE IMPORTANCE OF ANOXIC CELLS IN TUMOURS

GRAY [1961] has discussed the evidence from *in vitro* systems in a very comprehensive review. In this section we shall discuss further evidence from *in vivo* solid tumours.

One set of experiments is that of POWERS and TOLMACH [1963]. They irradiated mouse lymphosarcoma tumours *in vivo*, growing as solid tumours 1–2 cm in diameter, then minced them up and injected successively smaller aliquots into batches of similar mice. The dilution necessary to give 50 per cent "takes", expressed as a ratio of the dilution for 50 per cent takes from unirradiated tumour, gave the proportion of cells surviving a given dose. They were thus able to find the proportion of cells surviving single doses of 200 to 2500 rads of X-rays. This experiment was of course a clone-counting cell survival determination. Their resulting curve (fig. 9) shows two components, just as predicted by Hewitt (fig. 8). Further, the resistant component has a slope (i.e. cellular radiosensitivity) 2.5 times less than the initial component. The interpretation of oxygenated and anoxic cell components seems inescapable. The resistant component extrapolates to a survival proportion of 1 %, suggesting that 1 % of the cells were anoxic in agreement with THOMLINSON's [1961] prediction for rat fibrosarcoma which was mentioned in the previous section. In later experiments they showed that when the animals breathed high pressure oxygen instead of air during irradiation, the resistant component extrapolated to about 0.1 % instead. This experiment is an excellent example of a theoretical prediction based

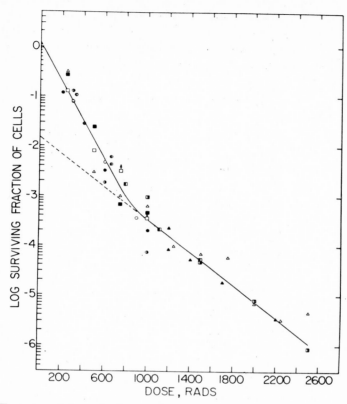

Fig. 9. Experimental survival curve for mouse lymphosarcoma cells irradiated *in vivo* as solid tumours 1–2 cm in diameter, then minced, diluted, and injected into a series of similar mice. The ratio of dilution which gave 50 % 'takes' was proportional to the fraction of cells surviving. When unirradiated, 2–5 cells were required for 50 % takes. Each point represents one tumour given one dose
[from POWERS and TOLMACH, 1963].

on one radiobiological system [HEWITT, 1959] which was later confirmed in a different tumour system. It concerns strictly the proportion of clonogenic cells which survived single doses.

A very comprehensive series of experiments is due to THOMLINSON [1961, 1965]. These experiments are not simply clone-counting experiments since observations were made on the gross growth rate of solid tumours in rats. Thomlinson used a transplantable fibrosarcoma which was infiltrating and metastatic. The implantation technique gave spherical tumours with reproducible growth rates in the

unirradiated controls. Irradiation was carried out at 8–10 mm diameter, and the average diameter was plotted against time in days.
Fig. 10a shows the progressively greater delay in growth caused by
increasing doses of X-rays, with the rats breathing oxygen at 45 psi.

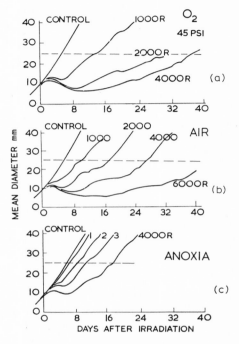

Fig. 10. Growth curves of rat fibrosarcoma R.I.B.5 after single doses of 250 kV
X-rays. Top: rats breathing oxygen at 45 psi. Centre: rats breathing air.
Bottom: tumours made anoxic by clamping the blood vessels. The time delay
in re-growing to a given diameter can be read off (dotted line, 25 mm) [from
THOMLINSON, 1961].

Fig. 10b shows that if the irradiation was carried out with the rats
breathing air at atmospheric pressure, the delays in growth were less.
They were still less if the blood supply to the tumours was clamped
during irradiation (fig. 10c). The full anoxic/oxygen dose ratio (OER)
was 3.4 (fig. 10c), and the air/oxygen dose ratio (representing the gain
in effective dose with 45 psi oxygen compared with a treatment given
in air) varied with the magnitude of the dose. At low doses in air, the
gain was small, showing that the in-air response was close to that in

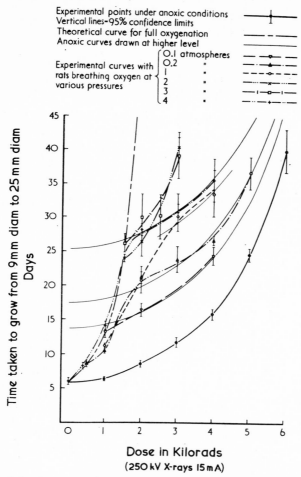

Experimental points under anoxic conditions
Vertical lines-95% confidence limits
Theoretical curve for full oxygenation
Anoxic curves drawn at higher level

Experimental curves with
rats breathing oxygen at
various pressures
{ 0.1 atmospheres
0.2 "
1 "
2 "
3 "
4 "

Time taken to grow from 9 mm diam to 25 mm diam
Days

Dose in Kilorads
(250 kV X-rays 15 mA)

Fig. 11. Time delay in re-growing tumour R.I.B.5 to a given diameter (25 mm) *vs* dose, in different conditions of the rat breathing air or oxygen, or with the tumour clamped off. Since growth is logarithmic until large volumes are reached, the time delay is proportional to the logarithm of the volume reduction caused by the radiation. Therefore the ordinate axis, if plotted downwards, would represent log (proportion of cells surviving) so that this diagram represents approximate cell survival curves inverted. They are not exactly cell survival curves because the effect of mitotic delay is unknown, and also the growth ceases to be logarithmic at large volumes [by kind permission of THOMLINSON, 1965].

oxygen. At higher doses the gain was approximately a factor of two, showing that the in-air response was closer to the nitrogen response.

This change of the response in air from being close to the oxygen response at low doses towards the nitrogen response at high doses (fig. 11) is entirely consistent with expectations from the cell survival model derived from figs. 5 and 8. An estimate based on fig. 11 of the proportion of anoxic cells present in this tumour in air gave a value about 1 per cent [THOMLINSON, 1965], in good agreement with his earlier prediction based on histological evidence.

It should be noted that this tumour is rapidly growing (fig. 10), the volume of each control tumour being doubled in approximately one day, so that the proportion of mitoses leading to differentiated or sterile cells instead of to cells which divide further is likely to be low. This was the criterion given in section 2.4 for good agreement between the "total population" dose-response curve and the associated cell survival curve. Similarly, it can also be seen from fig. 10 that the reduction in growth rate begins only 1 or 2 days after irradiation, so that the lifetime of the cells sterilized by radiation, or of pre-existing non-dividing or differentiated cells, is short. This was the condition mentioned in section 2.4 for the total number of cells in a tumour to correspond closely to the changes in the number of surviving cells. It would therefore be expected that this tumour, in common with other very rapidly growing tumours, should conform reasonably well to predictions based on simple cell survival curves. An unknown factor at present is the contribution of mitotic delay to the observed delays in tumour growth shown in figs. 10 and 11.

There is thus a considerable body of evidence that the anoxic component in tumours would be expected to determine the response when large individual doses of X-rays are given. But what happens when many small doses are given? Is there still the same disadvantage to tumour cure? Reference to figs. 8, 9 and 11 shows that anoxic cells are relatively less important if a small dose is given: the cell survival curve is determined predominantly by the oxygenated component. This would be true for subsequent small fractions, provided that *the same cells did not themselves remain anoxic throughout the course of fractionated radiotherapy*. It is conceivable that fractionated X-ray doses have always been overcoming the potential disadvantage of anoxic cells in just this way! On the other hand, LAJTHA and OLIVER [1961] pointed out that if the same anoxic cells *do* remain anoxic throughout the series of fractions, they would become even more predominant than after a single dose. This matter will be discussed further in the section on fractionation.

The only experimental evidence known to the author about the effect of anoxic tissues in a series of dose fractions is that of Du Sault et al. [1959]. They found improved cure of spontaneous tumours in C3H mice when the animals were treated breathing 95 % $O_2 + 5$ % $CO_2$ at atmospheric pressure, compared with in-air treatments. In this experiment 15 fractions of 400 r or 9 fractions of 667 r were given over 18 days. There was no increase in metastatic spread, which had been suggested as a possible disadvantage of better oxygenation in tumours. Du Sault [1963] later found that breathing oxygen at 45 psi increased the cure rate of these tumours from 9 % breathing air to 39 % (fig. 12), compared with 25 % cured when irradiated breathing

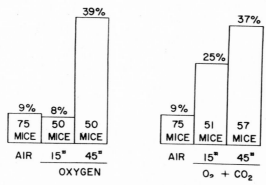

Fig. 12. Per cent of mice which completed the X-ray treatment and showed no evidence of tumour by palpation up to the time of death; irradiated breathing air or oxygen at 15 or 45 psi. The doses were six fractions of 1000 r over 18 days [Du Sault, 1963].

$O_2 + 5$ % $CO_2$ at atmospheric pressure and 38 % breathing $O_2 + 5$ % $CO_2$ at 45 psi: there was no significant difference between the 25 % and the 37% or 39%. It was noteworthy that breathing oxygen at atmospheric pressure gave no gain in proportion of cures over breathing air. The doses in this experiment were 6 fractions of 1000 r over 18 days. Du Sault also found that the mice treated in oxygen showed greater early mortality after the treatment than those treated in $O_2 + 5$ % $CO_2$ and concluded that the latter gave a more favourable therapeutic ratio than high pressure oxygen. The mice in this experiment were kept at high pressure for only 3 to 4 minutes before irradiation, and this may not have been long enough to obtain full oxygenation in the tumours [CATER and SILVER, 1960; NAYLOR and EVANS, 1962]. Nevertheless, Du Sault's results suggest that there is good reason to continue investigating the anoxic problem in fractionated radio-therapy.

Direct evidence of the importance of the oxygen effect in human tumours is, of course, difficult to obtain, but measurements of oxygen tension in human tumours [CATER and SILVER, 1960; NAYLOR and EVANS, 1962] have shown that there are regions where the oxygen tension is very low and where it rises, sometimes after considerable delay, with the breathing of oxygen at higher pressures. There are now at least six radiotherapy centres in the United Kingdom, two in Australia, and at least two in the United States where high pressure oxygen tanks have been installed.

Only two centres have as yet had appreciable experience of treating patients in high pressure oxygen, so it will be several years before definitive results on cure rates are available. The Medical Research Council is arranging for the collection of data from centres in the U.K. Dr. Churchill-Davidson in his pioneering work at St. Thomas' Hospital, London [CHURCHILL-DAVIDSON, SANGER, and THOMLINSON, 1957] and Dr. Van den Brenk in Melbourne, Australia, have the most experience of high pressure oxygen, and are personally convinced of its superiority. Neither Churchill-Davidson nor Van den Brenk were able to treat a fully randomized series, but both treated a number of comparable patients to similar dosage in air at atmospheric pressure. CHURCHILL-DAVIDSON [1964] has summarized his results up to April, 1963. "Although not uniform, the overall response to treatment has been definitely better than would have been expected from conventional radiotherapy and in 15–20 % of cases it has been dramatically better".

"Moderate-sized tumours with a reasonably good blood supply, which had not caused excessive damage to the normal surrounding structure, have shown the greatest 'oxygen effect'. Especially good results have been obtained in treating tumours of the tongue, floor of mouth, tonsil, nasopharynx, larynx, and rather surprisingly in view of the high distant-metastasis rate, bronchus. The one tumour site in which the response has been disappointing has been the brain. The response of secondary squamous carcinoma in lymph glands, notoriously resistant to conventional radiotherapy, is very markedly improved."

VAN DEN BRENK [1962, 1963, 1964] reported six-month results of clinical disappearance, or post-mortem findings, of primary head and neck tumours up to November, 1964: "43/51 (84 %) primary tumours disappeared when treated in high pressure oxygen, compared with 11/24 (46 %) treated in air with the same dose (3 × 1000 rads over 21 or 28 days). At the same time, incomplete healing or necrosis occurred at 3–24 months in 32/51 (63 %) of the cases treated in oxygen, so the treatment was changed to 6 × 500 rads over 17 days and the necrosis rate fell to 2/13 (15 %), whilst the tumour disappearance rate remained at 11/13 (85 %)". Clinical disappearance at 6 months is of course not a final result, but if tumours do *not* disappear by this time a cure is unlikely.

### 3.3. WHAT CAN WE DO ABOUT ANOXIC CELLS IN TUMOURS?

There are at least seven ways of dealing with the problem:
1) High pressure oxygen during irradiation [GRAY et al., 1953].
2) Breathing 95 % $O_2 + 5$ % $CO_2$ at atmospheric pressure during irradiation so as to increase oxygen tension by hyperventilation and capillary dilation [DU SAULT, 1963].
3) Local infusion of $H_2O_2$ to increase oxygen tension in the tumour when the conversion to $2H_2O + O_2$ takes place [MALLAMS, BALLA, and FINNEY, 1964]. This technique is open to the same objection as the infusion of sensitizers such as the uracils or synkavit, namely that a poor oxygen supply exists in some parts of tumours and an associated poor nutritional supply must be presumed. It is therefore quite possible that the sensitizing drug will not reach those tumour cells which are most likely to be hypoxic and therefore radiation-resistant.
4) The use of radioprotective chemicals in combination with radiation has the advantage over the previous three methods of "failing safe" [OLIVER and LAJTHA, 1961]. In the earlier methods hypoxic cells with a poor nutritional supply would be likely to fail to receive a good supply of the protective drug. The use of nitrous oxide or other anaesthetic gases is an example [EBERT and HORNSEY, 1958; EVANS and ORKIN, 1962]. In addition, ALPER [1962] has found that some protective agents act more efficiently on bacteria in the presence of oxygen.
5) Complete anoxia of all tissues during irradiation would eliminate the differential radioresistance of the anoxic tumour cells. However, the symposium "Hypoxia in Radiotherapy" [GRAY

et al., 1962] showed that this method does not offer any immediate prospects, since the muscle store of oxygen in myohaemo-
globin is released slowly and maintains the oxygen tension significantly above the anoxic level in all tissues except brain. The
method is, however, being used by tourniquet in limbs, for distal
tumours.

6) The patient could be given oxygen to breathe at less than the
   concentration of air for, say 24 hours, and then irradiated breathing air or oxygen at atmospheric pressure. A proportion of the
   anoxic cells would die during the 24 hours and the anoxic boundary would move closer to the capillaries than the usual 180
   microns. Restoring the higher partial pressure of oxygen just
   before irradiation would push the anoxic boundary out again,
   and would include the formerly anoxic but just viable cells in
   the oxygenated region [THOMLINSON, 1963]. This method has
   two objections. One is the distress caused to ill patients during
   the long breathing period at low oxygen concentration; the other
   is the damage caused to some normal tissues (e.g. liver) by the
   partial anoxia.

7) Radiation of high LET (i.e. high ionization density) could be
   used, because it kills cells almost as readily in the absence of
   oxygen as in its presence. For example the oxygen enhancement
   ratio (OER) for a fast neutron beam (e.g. from the M.R.C.
   cyclotron at Hammersmith) is about 1.7, instead of 2.5 or 3 as
   it is for X-rays. This gives a gain factor of 2.5 to $3 \div 1.7$, i.e.
   1.5 to 1.8 in effective dose to anoxic cells, which is a very large
   percentage increase to obtain.

Only the first three and the last of these seven methods provide
any immediate prospect of application.

## 3.4. HIGH-LET RADIATION: NEUTRONS

Thermal neutrons from reactors have very poor penetration, and
were not successful in treating brain tumours after boron compounds
had been injected. This work with neutron capture therapy has recently
been reviewed [FOWLER, 1964]. Epithermal neutrons have a better
penetration, but sufficient flux is not available and further investigations are needed.

The use of a fast neutron beam to overcome the problem of anoxic cells was fully discussed by the author and colleagues [1963a]. They pointed out that the gain factor of 1.5 to 1.8 mentioned in the previous section could, at best, lead to a 90 % chance of cure in tumours 75 mm diameter, compared with only 3.3 mm in diameter using X-rays, γ-rays or electrons. This gain factor is achieved for *equal damage to well oxygenated tissues* from the two types of radiation and it could, therefore, never be achieved by improved physical distributions alone, as discussed in section 2.5. They also found, using pig skin, that Stone's long-term skin damage in patients treated by the fast neutron beams from the Berkeley cyclotrons in 1937–42 [STONE, 1948] could be explained largely on the basis of an increase in RBE when large numbers of small fractions were used, so that there is some possibility of avoiding such damage in a future trial. This increase of RBE is expected

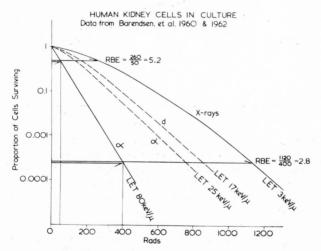

Fig. 13. Schematic representation of differences in mammalian cell survival curve shape for radiations of different LET. Cyclotron neutrons are similar to the deuteron and alpha particle curves of LET = 17 and 25 keV/micron shown dashed. The RBE for small doses is consequently greater than that for the larger doses [from FOWLER et al., 1963a].

from the known change in shape of cell survival curves with high-LET radiation (fig. 13) [BERRY and ANDREWS, 1963]. This is due to the larger probability of single-hit damage when the charged particle tracks include high-LET protons and other heavy particles.

There is a compromise between a better oxygen advantage using lower energy neutrons and a better depth dose using higher energy neutrons. An anoxic gain factor $G$ may be defined, where $G =$ OER for X-rays $\div$ OER for neutrons [ALPER, 1963]. This gives the effective increase in dose to anoxic cells when neutrons are used, for equal radiation damage to well oxygenated cells. If we multiply the depth dose of neutrons by the anoxic gain factor $G$, figs. 14, 15 and 16 are obtained. If inelastic

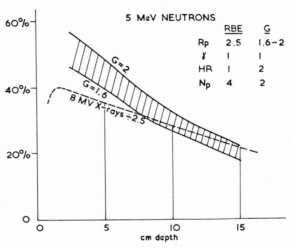

Fig. 14. Calculated 5 MeV neutron effective dose to anoxic cells versus depth in tissue. The dotted line is for 8 MV X-rays. The physical dose has been multiplied by the anoxic gain factor $G$. At the top right are given the values of RBE and $G$ which were assumed for four types of particle: Rp, recoil protons; $\gamma$, electrons released by gamma rays; HR, heavy recoil nuclei; Np, protons from the nitogen interaction. The width of the shaded area is due to uncertainties in $G$ (see fig. 17). Where the shaded area is above the dotted line, the neutron beam should be better for killing anoxic cells. The damage to normally oxygenated tissue is equal for neutrons or X-rays, at or near the surface [from FOWLER, 1964a].

collisions were more important than the present uncertain values indicate, then 14 MeV neutrons would be nearer the upper limit of the shaded area in fig. 16. Recent measurements of OER for neutrons [BROESE, 1964] suggest that the OER changes little with neutron energy, so that 14 MeV neutrons should be useful (fig. 17).

The gain factors $G$ given above are for single doses of neutrons. The use of fractionated doses is being investigated, and it would help if the way in which X-ray fractionation worked was known. But it is not.

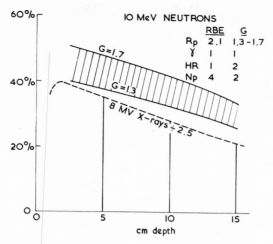

Fig. 15. Calculated 10 MeV effective depth dose to anoxic cells versus depth in tissue [from FOWLER, 1964a].

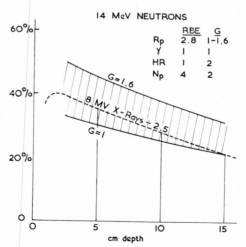

Fig. 16. Calculated 14 MeV effective depth dose to anoxic cells versus depth in tissue [from FOWLER, 1964a]. Recent results (see fig. 17) suggest that the upper border of the shaded area is more nearly correct.

It seems possible, however, that the tissue-sparing effect of repeated small fractions of X-rays will be reduced when small fractions of neutrons are used, as also may the anoxic gain factor (see figs. 8, 9 and 11). Fast neutron beams would probably be most appropriate

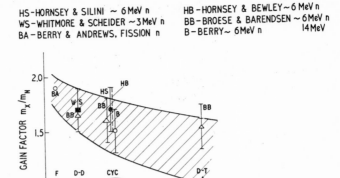

Fig. 17. Experimental oxygen enhancement ratios $G$ for mammalian cells versus neutron energy. F, fission neutrons; D-D, neutrons produced by accelerated deuterons on deuterium target; CYC, neutrons produced by 15 MeV deuterons on beryllium target in the MRC cyclotron; D-T, 14 MeV mono-energetic neutrons produced by accelerated deuterons on tritium target. The shaded area shows the limits of the assumptions about the values of $G$ made in figs. 14–16.

therefore for those cases which could be treated by fairly large fractions of X-rays with long intervals, i.e. of several days.

## 3.5. HIGH-LET RADIATION: NEGATIVE π MESONS

The use of negative π mesons was proposed by FOWLER (not the present author) and PERKINS [1961] because they would provide very good dose distributions (fig. 18). An additional advantage lies in the high LET of the particles released in tissue. $\pi^-$ mesons of 50 to 75 MeV travel 15 to 20 cm through tissue and then interact to give three α-particles of average energy 6 MeV each, i.e. of LET between 80 and 300 keV/$\mu$. A low oxygen enhancement ratio would certainly be expected from such particles, and consequently a high anoxic gain factor $G$.

However, nothing should be taken for granted in radiobiology, and recent results obtained by BARENDSEN and ALPER and BEWLEY (private communication) suggest that alpha particles (from the cyclotron) have a higher OER, and a smaller gain factor, than recoil protons

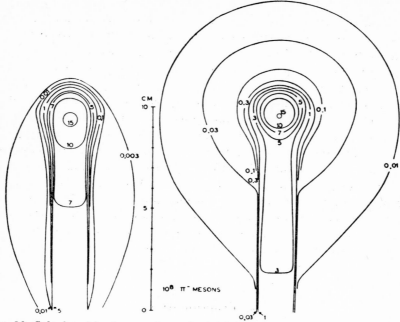

Fig. 18. Calculated isodose contours for initially parallel beams of protons and negative $\pi$ mesons of diameter 1.9 cm. Figures are doses in rads for $10^8$ incident particles [from FOWLER and PERKINS, 1961].

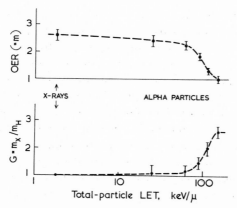

Fig. 19. Experimental oxygen enhancement ratios for human kidney T-cells irradiated by X-rays or by cyclotron alpha particles. Upper curve: OER. Lower curve: anoxic gain factor G. Here the value of G up to 80 keV/$\mu$ is less than 1.3, whereas for neutrons of energies 3–14 MeV (which have a spread of LET from 0.3 to over 100 keV/$\mu$) the values of G are all about 1.5–1.7. (by kind permission of Barendsen and Bewley).

from neutrons even at the same "average LET" (fig. 17 and fig. 19). It is likely that the alpha particles from the $\pi^-$ beam would have a sufficiently high LET to give a low OER, but radiobiological experiments with a $\pi^-$ beam will be necessary in order to make certain [FOWLER, P. H., 1965].

Beams of fast deuterons or alpha particles at 360 or 900 MeV respectively are used for pituitary ablation at Berkeley [LAWRENCE, 1965] and protons of 180 MeV are being investigated at Uppsala [FORS et al., 1964; LARSSON, 1958]. These particles are travelling so fast that they have only a low LET except in the terminal millimetre of their track; so scanning this Bragg peak backwards and forwards through a tumour 50 mm thick would diminish its contribution to one-fiftieth. These beams of deuterons or alpha particles would therefore give a negligible anoxic gain factor, so their use does not help in dealing with anoxic cells in tumours.

# 4. Fractionation

## 4.1. INTRODUCTION

DU SAULT, EYLER and DOBBEN [1959] pointed out that Churchill-Davidson's good results with high pressure oxygen could have been due to the use of a smaller number of larger fractions than the usual "5 fractions per week", rather than to the use of oxygen. They carried out an intercomparison of four fractionation regimes with C3H mice breathing air or 5 % $CO_2 + 95$ % $O_2$. The fractionation regimes were in two groups, 400 r "daily" or 667 r thrice weekly, with each group subdivided into either 6000 r in 18 days or 8000 r in 25 days. In all groups the proportion of spontaneous mammary tumours cured was greater for the gas mixture, although the difference was small (fig. 20). There was however a significant increase in proportion cured by the "48-hour" fractions compared with the "24-hour" fractions. The 48-hour group irradiated in air to 6000 r in 18 days showed a proportion of 13 % of tumours cured compared with 1 % for the 24-hour group. Those given 8000 r in 25 days improved from 13 % for "daily" to 26 % for 48-hours interval. The groups given 95 % $O_2 + 5$ % $CO_2$ showed little difference after 6000 r: 13 % for "daily" and 16 % for

"48-hour" fractionation. The groups given 8000 r however improved from 21 % to 42 %. These results showed that a change in fractionation produced somewhat larger improvements in cure rates than the

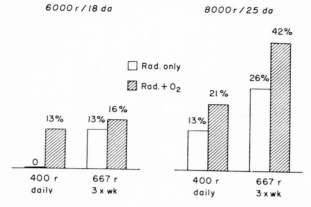

Fig. 20. Percentage of spontaneous mammary tumours cured in C3H mice: 400 r "daily" (i.e. 5f/wk) compared with 667 rat "48-hour intervals" (i.e. 3f/wk). White rectangles, irradiated breathing air. Crosshatched, irradiated breathing 5 % $CO_2$+95 % $O_2$ at atmospheric pressure. 30–40 mice in each group. 3×wk versus daily were different with $P = 0.002$. $CO_2$+$O_2$ versus air were different with $P = 0.01$ [from DU SAULT et al., 1959].

use of the gas mixture during irradiation. (The use of both gave still better results.) Unfortunately this experiment is ambiguous because the biological effect would be *expected to be greater* for a smaller number of larger fractions and the same dose and overall time (see section 4.3); the question of equal or greater damage to normal tissues is the important point. The objective in properly planned experiments should be to compare the doses or time-dose distributions which produce the *same* biological results. But this result was suggestive, both in confirming the importance of anoxic cells in fractionated regimes, and in pointing the way to altering fractionation as a possible means of improving radiotherapy.

BARTH, BÖHMER and WACHSMANN [1959] also found that 48-hour intervals gave better tumour cure rates for inoculated Ehrlich ascites tumours in mice than intervals of ½, 1, 3 or 5 days (overall time 18 days). The total doses were adjusted to give "equal expective reactions at the healthy skin" based on previous experience with pigs [KLEIN, 1957]. Although the equality of skin reaction was not proved in the

mice used, the total doses given for the 1, 2 and 3 day intervals correspond closely to the doses that would be predicted from the results of
experiments on pig skin, on the skin of SAS/4 mice, and on published
radiotherapeutic data [FOWLER, 1965b, and fig. 26], so that those
results of Barth et al. may be valid. On the same basis, the $\frac{1}{2}$ and 5 day
interval total doses seem too low. Although this result agrees with that
of Du Sault et al., the data are of course only relevant to the rates of
tissue repair and tumour growth in two types of tumour in mice.

If the relative importance of cell survival following irradiation and
of rate of repopulation or repair in (a) normal tissues and (b) tumours
of different types in man were known, then optimum regimes of fractionation could perhaps be proposed. These questions are easy to state
but extremely difficult to answer. Sir Oliver Scott said "It is to be
hoped that schemes of fractionation in radiotherapy will ultimately be
based on a time scale of known radiobiological events in the tumour
and its surroundings rather than the speed of rotation of the earth on its
axis" [SCOTT, 1958]. There is the important possibility that we *could*
do better, if only we knew how. This is why existing fractionation
regimes are under active criticism and investigation now.


4.2. PRESENT FRACTIONATION REGIMES

Present treatment regimes are entirely empirical. The most common
regimes for carcinoma of the larynx, for example, are probably
15 fractions over 3 weeks to a total of 5000 to 5500 rads, or 30 to 40
fractions over 6 to 8 weeks to a total of 6000 to 7000 rads. Variations in
fractionation regime range from the longer overall times of COUTARD
[1930, 1932] and BACLESSE [1949] in Paris, to a very few centres
where two massive doses spaced apart by a few days are being tried.
Single doses are used for some skin cancers, but radiotherapists tend
to use larger numbers of smaller doses for less accessible tumour sites.
Between these extremes lie regimes of 3 large doses spaced apart by
one or two weeks, as in the Stockholm radium technique which has
been successful for cure of carcinoma of the cervix.

PATERSON [1952] gave results for the treatment of carcinoma of the
mouth and of the pharynx and larynx in terms of the percentage of
patients who were well after 3 years. In treatments with an overall
time of 3 to 5 weeks these were 44 % and 29 % respectively, but over

1, 4 or 8 days only 20 % and 3 % respectively. He quoted these as a justification for fractionation extended over several weeks.

Churchill-Davidson in London and Van den Brenk in Melbourne have used 3 doses of 800 or 1000 rads each over 2 to 3 weeks, for treating patients in high pressure oxygen tanks. It may be significant that both these centres have recently changed to 6 or 7 smaller fractions (of 700 or 600 rads). A few other centres are trying 800–1000 rad fractions given at weekly intervals to higher total doses, but their results are scanty. A number of centres are trying 3 fractions per week instead of 5 over the same overall time. This modest change has advantages of convenience to patients and of economies in the use of treatment machines. A few centres have used 3 fractions per week for some years for these reasons. It has not been established whether this regime (or any other) really gives better tumour cure rates relative to the damage to normal tissues. The British Institute of Radiology is currently organizing a prospective study to determine the extent of any difference in tumour cure or normal tissue damage, or to confirm that no significant differences are found [FRACTIONATION WORKING PARTY, 1963, 1964]. Some centres [SAMBROOK, 1962; SCANLON, 1960; HOLSTI, 1964] are investigating "split-course" techniques, where a 5-fraction per week regime is interrupted for more than 1 week during the course of the treatment. The rationale for splitting in this way is to take advantage of any "differential recovery or repair" which may allow more of the radiation damage to be "repaired" in normal tissues than in tumours. This may well be a sound philosophy, but the facts on which it should be based are not yet known. Preliminary results appear to be good [HOLSTI, 1964].

An interesting variant on "daily" fractionation regimes has originated at Bristol [HALE et al., 1963]. In patients given a tracer dose of phosphorus-32, Geiger counters implanted in tumours have shown, in about 10 per cent of all cases, a spontaneous periodic "peaking" of the counting rate. In about 70 % of the remaining cases, peaks of counting rate were induced by 4 to 6 daily doses of methotrexate or by the usual "daily" dose of X-rays, although the peaks were often not seen for a further 10 to 30 days. In about a quarter of the patients the peaks recurred at approximately 24 hour intervals. Some patients have been given their daily X-ray treatment during the peak instead of at a fixed time each day. The results are reported as being favourable, but it is too early to draw definite conclusions. There is as yet no explanation or rationale for this procedure, but the effect of induced cell synchrony is being investigated.

WINTZ [1938] tried large single doses, and PATERSON [1952] said this had "never been proved to be wrong", although his own results (quoted in this section) tend to prove that it is wrong. Large single doses for radical treatment are not used today (except for small skin tumours). The extended fractionation of COUTARD and BACLESSE, however, continues. One obvious advantage of a massive single dose is that metastatic spread is checked as soon as possible. But there are serious disadvantages of single doses which will be discussed in section 4.4. No other statement can be made about improved fractionation regimes at the present time. The best regime of fractionation might be any number of fractions between 2 and 200, or even continuous irradiation. The questions which should be asked are becoming clearer. They involve both the sterilization of individual cells by radiation and population kinetics, including those of differentiating tissues. Factors which affect both these aspects include vascular and nutritional supplies, hypoxia, the anatomical changes which alter these latter factors, the processes controlling cell division or differentiation, and immune responses. It is not to be expected that answers will be simple, although based on simple principles. At present we cannot give answers, but we can clarify some questions.

### 4.3. HOW DOES X-RAY FRACTIONATION WORK?

It is well known that the dose required to produce a given effect, say moist desquamation of skin over half the treated area, or 90 % cure rate of squamous cell carcinoma, increases from just over 2000 rads of X-rays in a single dose to nearly 4000 rads when delivered in equal daily fractions in 5 or 6 days, and to 5000 rads when 15 to 20 fractions are used [FOWLER and STERN, 1963; survey based on ELLIS, 1944; JOLLES and MITCHELL, 1947; HALE and HOLMES, 1947; MITCHELL, 1960; STRANDQVIST, 1944; and others]. The increase might be considered *a priori* to be due either to repopulation or other repair of the tissues as the overall time increased, or to a rapid intracellular recovery process acting before each successive fraction. DU SAULT [1956] has described this distinction between "rapid recovery", i.e. virtually complete in a few hours, and longer-term "repair" or repopulation over weeks.

An important observation was made by ELKIND and SUTTON [1959, 1960] when they found a rapid recovery of sub-lethal damage to individual cells *in vitro*. This recovery had a maximum value at 2–3 hours, followed by smaller recovery when tested at 5–6 hours, and then by a steady value between 10 and 16 hours, being complete within one cell cycle. Its magnitude was close to that of the extrapolation number (fig. 1): if the extrapolation number of the cell survival curve were 4, then 4 times as many surviving cells would be present 16–24 hours after a single dose as immediately after giving the dose. Sublethal damage is represented on a survival curve by the curving initial portion, before the straight part of the survival curve is reached. If it were supposed that several particle tracks contribute to cell damage and that their effect was cumulative, then sub-lethal damage would represent the net result up to the penultimate track. After this, one more particle track would provide enough energy to sterilize the cell; the contribution of these final tracks corresponds in the survival curve to the straight exponential part, or to the nearly straight high-dose part.

The importance to fractionated radiotherapy of the finding of rapid intracellular recovery is illustrated in fig. 21. A single dose of $D_1$

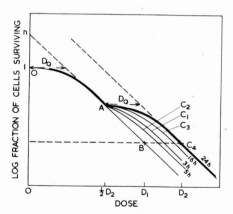

Fig. 21. Illustrating intracellular recovery. OAB is a cell survival curve, single dose $D_1$ being required to produce survival level B. If a single dose $\frac{1}{2}D_2$ is given, followed by a second dose $\frac{1}{2}D_2$ after intervals of (e.g.) 3, 5, 16 and 24 hr, the survival curves starting from A are successively $C_1$, $C_2$, $C_3$ and $C_4$. The shoulder has recovered completely by 24 hr. The total dose in two equal fractions $D_2$ is greater than $D_1$, and $D_2 - D_1 = D_Q$, provided that the survival curves have a straight exponential part at high doses.

reduces the survival to the level $B$, but if the dose were given in two equal fractions separated by various time intervals, some cellular recovery is seen at 3, 5, 16, hours etc., which can be represented by a reappearance of the initial shoulder. Therefore if two equal doses were given totalling $D_2$, this dose must be greater than $D_1$ if the same level of damage $BC_4$ is to be produced. The recovery is complete in these cells after about 16 hours. A typical time pattern of this recovery from sub-lethal injury, found by Elkind and Sutton *in vitro*, and later by other workers in mammalian cells *in vitro* and *in vivo*, is shown in fig. 22 [HORNSEY and VATISTAS, 1963]. ALPER et al. [1962] have designated the intercept of the straight exponential survival line (when present) with the horizontal line through 100 % survival as the quasi-threshold dose "$D_Q$" (fig. 1), so that here $D_2 - D_1 = D_Q$. This dose ap-

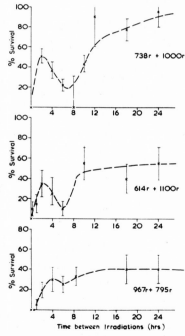

Fig. 22. Time course of recovery from sub-lethal injury of crypt cells in the small intestine of the mouse. Ordinates: per cent of mice surviving at four days after whole-body irradiation by two X-ray doses. Abscissae: interval between the two doses (hrs). The rapid recovery within about 2 hours, its subsequent decrease at 5–8 hours and full recovery by 16–24 hours has been observed in many cellular systems [from HORNSEY and VATISTAS, 1963].

pears as if "wasted" each time an additional fraction is given, provided that the intervals are greater than about 16 hours. This effect clearly shows that large numbers $n$ of small fractions, each one "wasting" $D_Q$ rads, will require a larger total dose $D_n$ than a single dose given within a few minutes in order to produce the same depopulation. If a given shape of survival curve (OAB in fig. 21) be assumed, the relationship between total dose and number of fractions to produce a given proportion of cells surviving can readily be calculated.

### 4.3.1. *Simple cell survival curve models*

In spite of the very simple nature of the cell survival curve model described in the previous section, and in sections 2.2, 2.3 and 2.4, it has given a tremendous impetus to thought and experimenting in the field of radiobiology applied to radiotherapy. Moreover it has great didactic value. LAJTHA, OLIVER and ELLIS [1960], in a series of stimulating papers, made use of cell survival curves and of the concepts of cellular recovery to put forward rational explanations of the bases of radiotherapy. They showed that the total dose required to kill a given proportion of clonogenic cells was smaller when given as few large fractions than when given as many small fractions. (In reaching this conclusion they assumed that the rate of cell repopulation was the same in the two cases.) They calculated some equivalent total doses, assuming an extrapolation number of 2 and $D_0 = 160$ rads. Similar calculations were made by WILSON [1961], and by ELKIND [1960] using a somewhat higher extrapolation number. These results, although showing an increase in total dose with number of fractions, were based on too simple a model to give good quantitative agreement with observed relationships of dose versus time, or dose versus number of fractions, in radiotherapy [ANDREWS and MOODY, 1956; DU SAULT, 1956; STRANDQVIST, 1944; FOWLER and STERN, 1963]. The contribution of cell population kinetics to the dose-time relationship is discussed in the next section.

OLIVER and LAJTHA [1961] pointed out that fewer and larger fractions might have the advantage of leaving a smaller proportion of anoxic cells surviving. They assumed here that *the same cells remained anoxic throughout the course of treatment.* The possible advantage of such a regime disappears if there is a significant decrease in the proportion of anoxic cells as the fractionated treatment proceeds, due to any anatomical rearrangements in the tumour. It has not been proved conclusively that such an improvement in oxygen status of the initially anoxic cells occurs, but four preliminary results in animal tumours suggest that it might happen [THOMLINSON, private communication; LINDOP, private communication; MAEDA and SUIT, 1965; VAN PUTTEN and KALLMAN, 1965]. Thomlinson's observation suggested a significant decrease in proportion of anoxic cells several days after a single dose of 2000 rads of X-rays, in the rapidly-growing fibrosarcoma RIB5 in rats. Maeda and Suit found that the ratio of the $TCD_{50}$ (dose yielding local control of half the irradiated tumours) in anoxia to that in air increased from 1.06 to 1.37 when treatment was given in 10 equal daily fractions instead of a single dose. They interpreted these results as indicating an increase in tumour tissue oxygen tension as radiation treatment progressed. Van Putten and Kallman, using C3H mouse tumours, found an increase in the proportion of anoxic cells from 15% to 30% after five daily fractions of 200 R of X-rays, measured by transplanting diluted suspensions of the cells into other mice. Had there been no change in the anoxic status of some of the cells, this proportion would have increased by a factor of about 100 instead of 2. These experiments suggest that it is most unlikely that cells which are anoxic at the start of fractionated treatment remain anoxic throughout, although more qualitative experiments are required. *There is therefore no case on these grounds for suggesting that a small number of large fractions would be better than present regimes.* Nevertheless, the empirical example of a successful radiotherapy regime such as the Stockholm radium treatment of carcinoma of the cervix should not be forgotten in this context. This consists of two or three massive doses with intervals of one to two weeks, although each dose was given slowly over 2–3 days.

If the assumption of the same cells remaining anoxic throughout were correct, there is no wrong prediction from survival curve theory. Indeed, the implication of survival curve data is that no single dose in a course of fractionated radiation should be so big that it will reduce the number of well-oxygenated cells to a value which is comparable with the number of anoxic cells present. This would be represented by doses big enough to give a total cell survival on the anoxic tail of the biphasic survival curve (figs. 8, 9 and 11). Individual doses should be kept smaller than this. The experiments of Du Sault which bear on this point were mentioned in section 3.2. If the proportion of anoxic cells is generally found to diminish between one fraction and the next, then this limitation on the dose of each fraction applies most strongly to the first fraction. When radiation of high LET is used this limitation would be less important since the disadvantage of anoxic cells is smaller.

Before further discussion of fractionation regimes it is necessary to consider the relative contributions of intracellular recovery between fractions, and of tissue repair and repopulation, to the well-known increase of total dose with overall time in radiotherapy.

### 4.3.2. *Differences between simple cell survival curve models and radiotherapy results*

The extent of the disagreement between radiotherapeutic results and calculations of equivalent total doses based on simple cell survival curve models was discussed fully by FOWLER and STERN [1963]. The largest differences occurred when the number of fractions considered was two to five. In these cases the calculated "wasting" of a dose $D_Q$ for each fraction after the first would lead to the prediction of an increase of only a few hundred rads in changing from one dose $D_1$ to a total dose $D_5$ in 5 fractions. The increases reported in the literature on radiotherapeutic effects were however, as large as 1500–2000 rads. [$D = 2000$ rads, $D_5 = 3500$–4000 rads, FOWLER and STERN, 1963]. A special point of difference was that the theoretical survival curves predicted a further large increase of total dose with numbers of fractions beyond five, whereas the clinical data showed a smaller increase at larger numbers of fractions. Fig. 23 illustrates these points. The dotted lines represent the clinical data reviewed by Fowler and Stern; the full lines are calculated assuming a survival curve with extrapolation number 2.8 and $D_0 = 130$ rads. It should be pointed out that cellular repopulation could not account for these differences. For it to do so would require the total doses to be even greater than those calculated, in which case the theoretical curves in fig. 23 would be even steeper at large numbers of fractions. The clinical data represent cure of squamous cell carcinoma, and "normal tissue tolerance reactions" probably mostly of skin or mucosa. They lie in a broad band as shown. The points marked 'F' refer to a series of 29 patients treated by FRIEDMAN and PEARLMAN [1955] for multiple breast metastases where each lesion in the same patient was given a different regime. These points lie

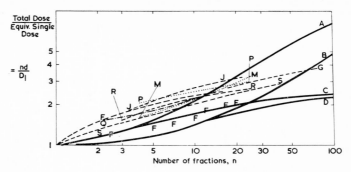

Fig. 23. Comparison of total dose to produce a given effect *vs* number of fractions calculated from cell survival curves (full lines) with published clinical data (broken lines). *n* is the number of individual doses of *d* rads each. The survival curve was assumed to have an extrapolation number of 2.8 and $D_0 = 130$ rads. A and B are for a sharply bent "shoulder' at low doses; C and D for a shoulder with a finite slope at zero dose and a more gradual increase of slope with dose. A and C are for lower doses than normally given in radiotherapy ($D_1 = 1040$ rads equivalent single dose). B and D are for more realistic doses where $D_1 = 3180$ rads. A dose-response curve with an extrapolation number of 10 would fit the clinical data better, but not as closely as a curve which continues to become steeper with increasing dose [FOWLER and STERN, 1963].

below the main trend of radiotherapeutic results on a graph of total dose versus number of fractions, although the statistical precision was not great. If Friedman and Pearlman's data were more correct than the others, extrapolation numbers of 7 to 10 would be required to fit the observational data. If they are not, the extrapolation numbers would have to be as large as 30 to 50.

It has been argued that the results based on radiotherapy may not be reliable, especially as regards the first point of difference concerning the small number of fractions. The present author has never felt that they were grossly misleading, in spite of the known problems of their analysis. These results had been reported carefully: the proof of the pudding lies in the eating, that is, in the cure of cancer in patients. For example, the five-fraction and single-dose results had been determined for over 800 cases by HALE and HOLMES [1947]. Nevertheless further information was clearly needed, and a series of experiments was undertaken at Hammersmith Hospital to test the validity of the clinical observations, and to investigate further the relative contributions of short-term recovery and long-term repair or repopulation, using a full-scale biological system with differentiated cells and vasculature.

### 4.3.3. *Animal experiments with fractionated regimes*

Experiments to determine how great was the effect of short-term recovery or long-term repair (including repopulation) during fractionated irradiations of skin over several weeks were carried out by FOWLER and colleagues [1963b], using swine 4–9 months old on which realistic X-ray field sizes could be used. Pig skin is similar to human skin in structure, and it was established that the dose-time relationship for 5 fractions per week (5f/wk) was closely similar to that for human skin. Three dose levels were given for each fractionated regime tested, and results were expressed as doses required to produce equal skin reactions averaged over a period of up to 80–100 days after irradiation. Moist desquamation was produced in the high-dose fields. Since no simple relationship between gross functional effect and cell survival should be assumed, we shall discuss "dose-effect curves" instead of "cell survival curves", and instead of "$D_Q$" we shall discuss the observed doses to produce a given effect, e.g. $D_2 - D_1$, and the quantity $(D_n - D_1)/(n-1)$ which represents the rapid short-term recovery, without commitment to a particular cell survival model. ($D_n$ is the total dose required in $n$ equal fractions to produce the same effect as a single dose $D_1$). A total dose of 3600 rads in 5 fractions over 4 days was required to produce the same average reaction as 5500 rads in 21 fractions over 28 days (fig. 24). The first day is counted as day 0. The equivalent single dose was found to be 2000 rads [FOWLER et al, 1963b]. This confirms the first point of difference mentioned in the previous section: the total dose does indeed increase by a large amount on changing from a single dose to five fractions. Subsequent experiments on pigs have confirmed this finding with 5, 3 and 2 fractions, and there is now no reason to doubt the earlier radiotherapeutic results shown dotted in fig. 23. In addition, the rather shallow slope of the dotted curves in fig. 23 was in agreement with the pig skin results (fig. 24). It is an oversimplification to assume that the iso-effect lines in fig. 24 are straight and to express their slope as a 'recovery exponent' as is often done. For pig skin, $(D_n - D_1)/(n-1)$ was as large as 400-500 rads for 2 to 5 fractions. The dose-response curves would consequently

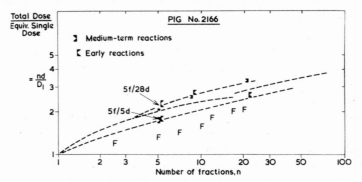

Fig. 24. Total dose to produce a given skin reaction (including moist desquamation ) *vs* number of fractions. Experimental results for pig No. 2166. *n* is the
number of individual doses of *d* rads each required to produce the same skin
reaction as a single dose. Three single doses ($D_1$) were used: 1750, 2000 and
2200 rads. The dotted lines are from the clinical data in the previous figure.
Medium-term reactions: 50–100 days; early reactions: up to 50 days after starting
irradiation. The results show general agreement between reactions in pig skin
and in patients. The difference between iso-effect doses for 5f/5 days and
5f/28 days is important [FOWLER et al., 1963b].

have extrapolation numbers higher than 10.

The experiment to investigate the effect of long-term repair or
repopulation was carried out as follows. Five equal fractions were
given in 4 days as one regime, and in 28 days as another regime.
In each case three dose levels were given so that the iso-effect dose
could be determined. The results are shown in table 1.

TABLE 1

| | |
|---|---|
| Single dose | 2000* rads |
| 5f/4d | 3600* rads |
| 5f/28d | 4200† rads |
| 21f/28d | 5500† rads |

* Average of 5 pigs. † Average of 2 pigs.
Standard deviation about ± 100 rads.

The increase between 4 and 28 days for the same number and size of
fractions was 600 rads. This is smaller than the increase on changing
from one fraction to 5 fractions in 4 days (1600 rads, i.e. an increase of

80 %) or from 5 to 21 fractions over 28 days (1300 rads). Therefore the size and number of fractions is the main factor determining the total dose required to produce a given effect, the short-term recovery of damage represented by the dose of $(D_n-D_1)/(n-1)$ being of major importance. The long-term repair, between 4 and 28 days, was equivalent to only 600 rads, i.e. to an increase of 17 % on the total dose in 5 fractions over 5 days. This increase is certainly not negligible, although it is a smaller effect than that of the size of individual fractions. If it were due to cellular repopulation, it would represent about a 100-fold increase in the number of surviving cells, i.e. 6 or 7 population doublings in 24 days: which would of course be a most important factor.

The magnitude of $(D_n-D_1)/(n-1)$ was found to decrease with decrease in size of each fraction $(D_n/n)$, as shown in table 2 [FOWLER et al., 1965a]. This confirms that the dose-response curve has a continuing curvature, at least up to doses of about 1000 rads per fraction.

Equally large values of $D_2-D_1$ were found for reactions of the skin of mice by FOWLER et al. [1965b] and by WITHERS [1965], and by HORNSEY and VATISTAS for intestinal death in mice [1963], as reviewed by FOWLER et al. [1963c]. These high values of 400–600 rads are significantly different from the lower values of 80–100 rads found for "$D_Q$" in many (but not all) clone-counting survival curve experi-

TABLE 2

Values of $(D_n-D_1)/(n-1)$

| Number of fractions /overall days | Size of individual fraction (rad) | $\dfrac{D_n-D_1}{n-1}$ (rad) |
|---|---|---|
| Pig No. 2154 | | |
| 2f/5d | 1300–1400 | 620–830 |
| 2f/2d | 1200–1480 | 450–700 |
| 3f/3d | 1100–1200 | 600–760 |
| 5f/5d | 750–850 | 460–540 |
| Pig No. 2166 | | |
| 5f/28d | 750–850 | 480–580 |
| 5f/5d | 650–750 | 350–450 |
| 9f/28d | 530–580 | 360–400 |
| 21f/28d | 250–290 | 150–230 |

ments, including *in vivo* dilution experiments [HEWITT and WILSON, 1959; POWERS and TOLMACH, 1963; BERRY and ANDREWS, 1963] and spleen colony experiments [TILL and McCULLOCH, 1961, 1963].

In order to investigate these large values of $D_2 - D_1$ in skin, and in particular to see whether they could be attributed to the intracellular type of recovery found by Elkind (fig. 22), split-dose experiments on skin damage were carried out to investigate the variation with time of the dose difference $D_2 - D_1$. ($D_2$ is the total dose in two equal fractions required to produce the same effect as a single dose $D_1$.) A series of intervals between the two equal parts of $D_2$ was used, 2–24 hours in pigs [FOWLER et al., 1965a] and 2–42 hours in mice [FOWLER et al., 1965b]. A rapid recovery was certainly observed with a similar time scale to that of Elkind and Sutton, but it was followed by a barely significant trough (fig. 25). It is not possible to say whether this rapid recovery in skin is partly or largely intracellular in origin; it may consist of a small intracellular component of about 100 rads, superimposed on other processes which make $D_2 - D_1$ very large.

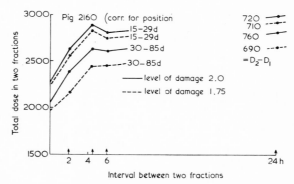

Fig. 25. Time course of "recovery" in pig skin reaction. Total dose needed to produce a given average skin reaction is plotted against the interval (hrs) between two equal doses. Skin reactions are shown averaged over 15–29 days or 30–85 days (8 MV X-rays). [FOWLER et al., 1965a and b].

It has been possible to eliminate hypoxia, either present during $D_1$ or induced by $D_1$ before $D_2$ was given, as an explanation of the large values of $D_2 - D_1$ in mouse skin [FOWLER et al., 1965b]. Neither repopulation nor cell migration are likely to explain the rapid rise in $D_2$ within 2 or 3 hours after $D_1$.

WITHERS [1965] has not only confirmed these large values of $D_2 - D_1$

for the macroscopic effect skin desquamation in mice, but has carried out a most ingenious clone counting experiment in mouse skin which yielded the $D_2—D_1$ value of only 150-350 rads of 250 kV X-rays for a 24-hour interval. Withers also showed that appreciable repopulation of epithelial cells occurs within 24 hours, at least after a dose as small as 700 rads. His value of 250-350 rads for "$D_Q$" in the survival curve for epithelial cells, together with nearly a population doubling in 24 hours, would account well for the large values of $D_2—D_1$ mentioned above in pig and mouse skin, which were for 8 MV X-rays, so that the equivalent $D_2—D_1$ for 250 kV X-rays was 400-500 rads. It remains to be explained why this recovery is almost complete at 5 hours, and to investigate repopulation and cell migration rates after a single dose as big as 2000 rads.

It was explained at the end of section 2.4 that *it is the clone-counting cell survival curve alone which matters when the last dose in a series of fractions is given* because the number of surviving cells must then be reduced below one (or a higher number if immunity is present). But for the other fractions, it is the total number of clonogenic cells present at the time, *including those which have grown up since the previous fraction* that matters; and it is this "total population" that is indicated by functional tests in animals. It is therefore more correct to use the animal results (and the radiotherapeutic data, since these agree with each other) when any predictions are made of the variation

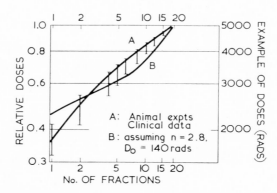

Fig. 26. Total dose *versus* number of fractions, matched for 5000 rads in 20 fractions. Curve A: Animal experiments and clinical data. Curve B: Assumed survival curve. A and B represent the dashed lines and the full line D respectively in fig. 23. [FOWLER, 1965b].

of total dose with number of fractions required to produce the same effect in skin (fig. 26), and possibly other epithelial tissues. It should be emphasized that a different relationship may be found for different tissues or tumours.

### 4.4. A POSSIBLE RATIONALE FOR FRACTIONATED THERAPY

This section consists of too many questions and too few answers to be safe or easy to write. Nevertheless, it is included with the intention of furthering discussion about these questions. It is only in this way that the many possible questions may be assigned some relative significance, so that investigations can be devised to answer them.

Some normal tissues in the absence of damage have only a small repopulation rate, whereas tumours have a large proportion of cells dividing and a rapid increase of population [REISKIN and MENDELSOHN, 1964]. The total rate of increase of tumour size will be the difference between the rates of the cell division and of cell death due, for example, to nutritional failure. Normal tissues can however repopulate extremely rapidly after damage, both by increasing the proportion of dividing cells and by shortening the cell cycle time. Tumours however are by definition under little if any control by the normal growth-limiting processes, so they do not increase their population growth rate correspondingly. So if an optimum amount of damage were caused by each irradiation, the normal tissues may be stimulated into more rapid repopulation than the tumour. Of course, intervals between

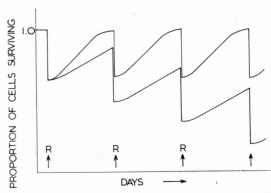

Fig. 27. A rationale for fractionated radiotherapy. Upper curve: normal tissues. Lower curve: tumour. Dose fractions given at R.

fractions must be allowed for this faster rate of repopulation to provide a greater normal population, so that the next irradiation can reduce the tumour population to a smaller proportion than the normal cells (fig. 27). Whether or not any therapeutic advantage is gained depends upon a delicate balance of cell survival and repopulation in normal relative to tumour tissues. Of course it should be easier to achieve this in slow-growing tumours. In moderately fast-growing tumours, the balance may be tipped in favour of normal tissues if there is a high rate of cell destruction due to nutritional failure. Very fast growing tumours will always be a bad proposition for therapy; in addition they metastasize rapidly. LAJTHA and OLIVER [1962] gave a number of examples of fractionated doses in "mixed populations" (fig. 28). Their illustrations are extremely valuable for didactic purposes, in considering the consequences of various combinations of repopulation

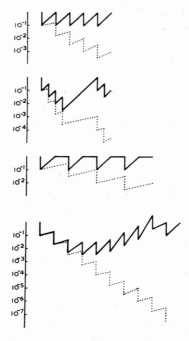

Fig. 28. As in the previous figure, for various combinations of time intervals and repopulation rates, for mixed populations. The lowest pair of curves represents two tissues in one of which repopulation rate increases with time [from LAJTHA and OLIVER 1962].

rates and sizes and spacings of fractions. In practice, almost nothing is known about the relevant repopulation rates of normal or tumour tissues, with or without irradiation. This is one of the most important fields of investigation, where the questions are now becoming clearer. It may well be that relevant answers will be obtained by radiotherapists before the detailed explanation of the behaviour of any one organ or cell system is obtained analytically.

There is nothing definite that radiobiology can yet offer in the way of suggested improvements to fractionation regimes, except to point out that quite different regimes are likely to be appropriate for different combinations of potentially fast and slowly repopulating tumours and normal tissues, whereas present regimes are often confined to 5 fractions per week for 3 to 7 weeks. There is no *a priori* reason why any number of fractions might be better than any other, from 2 to 200 fractions or even continuous irradiation [ELLIS, 1963; OLIVER and HALL, 1964]. The question of single massive doses for radical therapy is discussed below.

A good reason for speed in giving a fairly large total dose within, say, the first week is to prevent metastatic spread. Apart from this consideration, it will obviously be necessary to give fractions sufficiently large and often to cause the tumour to decrease in size. The rate of decrease will however be controlled both by the proportion of dividing cells which survive irradiation, and by the turnover time of the sterile or differentiated cells present, as described in section 2.4. As long as the quantitative aspects of these population kinetics are unknown, misleading conclusions may well be drawn concerning the number of surviving clonogenic cells. (This is where good analysis of the results of radiotherapy is eventually essential.)

As a general principle, it seems reasonable to propose two phases of any fractionated treatment: (1) when a fairly large dose is given over the first few days of the treatment so as to reduce the chance of metastatic spread; and (2) when treatment is continued at the maximum rate (i.e. dose per fraction and spacing between fractions) which the irradiated normal tissues can tolerate. Some normal tissues, such as lung tissues, may need more extended fractionation in phase (2) than other tissues, in order to avoid fibrosis. The extent to which this requirement can be met should be determined by the rate of growth of the tumour to be treated. In certain sites it may not be possible to devise optimum regimes of fractionation; but it is likely that improve-

ments can be made in some others. Provided that the spread of metastases does not become a worse problem, it may well be that *comparatively lengthy intervals* between groups of small fractions, or between
moderately large fractions, would allow better normal tissue healing
while still keeping the tumour size decreasing. From this point of
view the "split-course" regimes of SAMBROOK [1962, 1963], SCANLON
[1960] and HOLSTI [1964] are of considerable interest. DEELEY [private
communication] is also investigating a "maintenance dose" regime,
where doses of about 400 rads are given at monthly intervals to selected
cases. For these regimes, properly analysed results from patients would
give answers before radiobiology is likely to do so.

It should be obvious that the main considerations in phase (2),
that of minimizing the damage to normal tissues, are different from
the considerations in phase (1) where the prevention of metastases is
paramount; where subsequent anatomical changes in the tumour may
be initiated, in particular the possible improvement of oxygenation
and further where the problem of anoxic cells is likely to be more
serious than later in the fractionated regime, as pointed out in section
3.3. It is in phase (1) that the advantages of high-LET particles would
be most useful, if it is true that the proportion of anoxic cells becomes
smaller as fractionated treatments proceed. It should also be emphasized that answers to the latter question are not yet established.

If the proportion of anoxic or hypoxic cells in the tumour is progressively reduced by improved nutritional supplies, then two unwanted
consequences may arise: the repopulation rate (from the surviving
clonogenic cells) may be increased, and the rate of necrosis and cell
death due to nutritional failure may be decreased. There is little or no
evidence about these factors, except that in most reports of tumour
growth rate studies in patients [COLLINS et al., 1956; SPRATT, 1965;
BREUR, 1965] or in rats [THOMLINSON, 1965] there is no obvious
increase in growth rate after irradiation. Indeed, in some lung metastases the growth rates before and after irradiation are remarkably similar,
and similar also in some cases to the growth rate of another secondary
lesion in the same patient [BREUR, 1965]. This apparent constancy,
within statistical limits, suggests that neither nutritional changes nor
changes in immunity response are very important in some of these
metastatic fibrosarcomas in the lung. Immunity factors would of
course be more important if the critical number of viable cells, close
to the cure of a tumour, is reached, instead of a regrowth of the tu-

mour. Immunity factors do, however, seem to play a part in tumours of the lymphoid system [SZUR, 1964]. In other tumours changes in growth rate may occur, as  result of complex factors [COHEN, 1960].

Although nothing definite can be said about improved regimes of fractionation, a number of adverse comments can be made about single massive doses for radical treatments. Some small surface lesions, in particular rodent ulcers, are successfully treated by single doses of 2000–3000 rads, depending on the X-ray penetration and the area to be treated. But the deeper and more difficult to cure a tumour is known to be, the greater is the radiotherapists' tendency to fractionate the dose [VON ESSEN, 1963]. It was pointed out in section 4.2 that massive single doses for deep lesions were no longer in use, whereas the early method of extended fractionation was still used. It is clear that if there is any gain from differential repopulation rates in normal and tumour tissues, as suggested at the beginning of the present section, then more than one dose must be used in order to take advantage of it. The same point applies to the possible improvement of oxygenation due to improved nutritional supplies in the tumour: there is no gain if further fractions are not used. If, however, fractionation does not work by taking advantage of these two factors, then massive single doses might still be useful. Finally, most of the work on the problem of anoxic cells in tumours has been done with large single doses (figs. 9 and 11), and it is certainly a real problem for X-ray doses of the order of 1500 rads or more. The importance of the anoxic problem for smaller individual fractions is not yet clear, although it does not seem negligible. The obvious biological advantage of a large single dose is that metastatic spread is checked as soon as possible. Fig. 1 showed that comparatively small doses are required to reduce an oxygenated cell population to 1 per cent survivors, so that metastatic spread might be checked without using very large doses. This point requires further investigation. A practical advantage would arise from the saving of patients' time during treatment, but this cannot be contemplated if the results might be worse. Even though one massive dose cannot be recommended there is no firm argument against as few as two or three fractions (see end of section 4.2). Indeed, as has already been said, there are as yet no radiobiological grounds for suggesting any particular regime of fractionation between 2 and 200 fractions, or even continuous irradiation. ELLIS [1963] and HALL and BEDFORD [1964] have pointed out that at very low dose rates the intracellular sub-lethal recovery can keep pace with the rate of production of injury, so that sterilization is effected predominantly by single-hit events. In this situation the oxygen enhancement ratio may be smaller so that the problem of anoxic cells may be reduced by using continuous irradiation. Experimental evidence on this point is awaited with interest.

## 5. Conclusion

The most we can say is that the relevant questions are now becoming clearer. The radiotherapists and the radiobiologists together must answer them. In radiobiology, both fundamental investigations and full scale empirical experiments, for example with slow-growing tumours in pigs if this were possible, are required.

If we knew the amount of damage produced by doses of various sizes on tumour and normal tissues, and the subsequent variation with time of the expression of this injury and its recovery, we should have most of the knowledge required to plan rational radiotherapy. This is not one or two but many questions. Specific questions which could be investigated include the following. What are the growth rates of various types of tumour before and after irradiation? How much smaller do they become after irradiation and how rapidly? What is the relationship of this reduction in tumour volume to the magnitude and spacing of individual doses? In order to obtain a full description of a tumour it will be necessary to measure cell cycle times, proportion of cells dividing, and proportion of anoxic or hypoxic cells present. This has hardly been done in a single type of tumour as yet, although the work is beginning using techniques of autoradiography [MENDELSSOHN, 1963]. Then, what is the change of these parameters after doses of various sizes? What is the mitotic delay? Is synchrony induced, and does it change the radiosensitivity to subsequent doses? Do nutrition and oxygenation improve with time after irradiation? If so, how rapidly do they change? What is the effect of irradiation on capillaries and other blood vessels? All these questions not only have to be answered for a range of tumours, but for the wide variety of normal tissue which is also irradiated. The answers will vary for the different normal and tumour tissues. We must hope that certain broad principles may emerge, in order that we may deduce statistically better ways of treating cancer in certain sites without having to measure all the cell population parameters in each tumour individually. Or there may be no such easy answer.

A better understanding of the processes of repair and repopulation in normal tissues will require more knowledge of the way in which "differentiation" on the one hand or "triggering" into repopulating the stem cell compartment on the other hand are controlled in the intact animal. The processes following injury by irradiation are likely to be no simpler in tumours, except possibly in undifferentiated, very rapidly growing, anaplastic tumours. It is worth pointing out that even if one's interest is in the fundamental biological processes and not at all in radiotherapy, radiation is a most useful tool for reducing the viable cell number so that the kinetics of the populations can be investigated experimentally. It is in this direction that fundamental research is likely to make its greatest contributions to radiotherapy. Results will not be obtained quickly, but the next few years will be extremely interesting in the field of radiation biology applied to radiotherapy.

## Acknowledgments

I should like to express my great indebtedness to a number of colleagues and friends who have helped me over several years to any sensible views that may be found in this chapter but who can in no way be held responsible for my misconceptions: Dr. R. H. Thomlinson, who also read the script of this chapter and made many helpful comments, Miss Tikvah Alper, Mrs. Shirley Hornsey, Dr. D. K. Bewley, Dr. Patricia Lindop, Dr. R. J. Berry, Dr. G. W. Barendsen, Dr. T. J. Deeley, Sir Oliver Scott, Dr. L. H. Gray and many others.

I am grateful to those who have allowed me to quote from their private communications in the places acknowledged: Dr. R. H. Thomlinson, Dr. R. Withers, Dr. I. Churchill-Davidson, Dr. H. A. S. Van den Brenk, Dr. D. K. Bewley, Dr. G. W. Barendsen, Dr. R. F. Kallman, Dr. L. M. Van Putten, and Dr. H. Suit.

I am also most grateful for permission to reproduce the following figures, both to the authors mentioned in the legends and to the Editors of the following publications: British Journal of Radiology for figs. 4, 12, 13, 22, 23, 24, 26 and 28; British Journal of Cancer for figs. 5 and 11; Royal Society of Medicine for fig. 6; Brookhaven Symposia in Biology, Vol. 14, for figs. 7 and 10; Nature for figs. 9 and 18; I.A.E.A. Symposium on Biological Effects of Neutron & Proton Irradiations for figs. 14, 15 and 16; American Journal of Roentgenology and Radium Therapy for fig. 20.

# References

ALPER, T. 1961. Brit. J. Radiol. **35** 361.

ALPER, T. 1963. Brit. J. Radiol. **36** 97.

ALPER, T., FOWLER, J. F., MORGAN, R. L., VONBERG, D. D., ELLIS, F. and OLIVER, R. 1962. Brit. J. Radiol. **35** 722.

ALPER, T., GILLIES, N. E. and ELKIND, M. M. 1960. Nature **186** 1062.

ANDREWS, J. R. and MOODY, J. E. 1956. Am. J. Roentgenol. **75** 590.

BARENDSEN, G. W. 1962. Nature **193** 1153.

BARENDSEN, G. W. 1964. In: The Biological Effects of Neutron and Proton Irradiation. Vol II (IAEA Vienna) p. 379.

BARENDSEN, G. W., WALTER, M. H., FOWLER, J. F. and BEWLEY, D. K. 1963. Rad. Res. **18** 106.

BACLESSE, F. 1949. Brit. J. Radiol. Suppl. **3** 63.

BARTH, G., BOEHMER, D. and WACHSMANN, F. 1959. Strahlenther. **109** 599.

BERGONNIÉ, J. and TRIBONDEAU, L. 1959. Rad. Res. **11** 587 (Translated by G. Fletcher from: 1906. Comptes rendus. **143** 983).

BERRY, R. J. and ANDREWS, J. R. 1963. Brit. J. Radiol. **36** 49.

BLOOM, H. J. G. 1965. Brit. J. Radiol. **38** 227.

BREUR, K. 1965. Thesis. Leiden.

BROESE, J. J. 1964. Private Communication, also

BROESE, J. J. and BARENDSEN, G. W. 1964. In: The Biological Effects of Neutron and Proton Irradiation. Vol. II (IAEA Vienna) p. 309.

CELADA, F. and CARTER, R. R. 1962. J. Immunol. **88** 31.

CHURCHILL-DAVIDSON, I. 1964. Proc. Roy. Soc. Med. **57** 635.

CHURCHILL-DAVIDSON, I., SANGER, C. and THOMLINSON, R. H. 1957. Brit. J. Radiol. **30** 406.

COHEN, L. 1960. Am. J. Roentgenol. **84** 741.

COLLINS, V. P., LOEFFLER, R. K. and TIVEY, H. 1956. Am. J. Roentgenol. **76** 988.

COUTARD, H. 1930. Strahlenther. **37** 51.

COUTARD, H. 1932. Am. J. Roentgenol. **28** 313.

DESCHNER, E. E. and GRAY, L. H. 1959. Rad. Res. **11** 115.

DEWEY, W. C. and HUMPHREY, R. M. 1963. Nature **198** 1063.

DU SAULT, L. A. 1956. Am. J. Roentgenol. **75** 597 (Review paper).

DU SAULT, L. A. 1962. Am. J. Roentgenol. **87** 567.

DU SAULT, L. A. 1963. Brit. J. Radiol. **36** 749.

DU SAULT, L. A., EYLER, W. R. and DOBBEN, G. D. 1959. Am. J. Roentgenol. **82** 688.

EBERT, M. and HORNSEY, S. 1958. Nature **182** 1240.

ELKIND, M. M. 1960. Radiology **74** 529.

ELKIND, M. M. and SUTTON, H. 1960. Rad. Res. **13** 556.

ELKIND, M. M., SUTTON, H. and MOSES, W. B. 1961. J. Cellular comp. Physiol. **58** 113.

ELLIS, F. 1944. Brit. J. Radiol. **17** 335.

ELLIS, F. 1963. Brit. J. Radiol. **36** 153.

EVANS, J. C. and ORKIN, L. R. 1962. Nature **195** 822.

FORS, B., LARSSON, B., LINDELL, A., NAESLUND, J. and STENSON, S. 1964. Acta Radiol. Scand. **2** 384.

FOWLER, J. F. 1964a. In: The Biological Effects of Neutron and Proton Irradiation. Vol. II (IAEA Vienna) p. 393.

FOWLER, J. F. 1964b. In: The Biological Effects of Neutron and Proton Irradiation. Vol. II (IAEA Vienna) p. 185 (Review paper).

FOWLER, J. F. 1964c. Phys. in Med. and Biol. **9** 177.

FOWLER, J. F. 1965a. In: Report of Panel Meeting on Biophysical Aspects of Radiation Quality. (IAEA Vienna).

FOWLER, J. F. 1965b. Brit. J. Radiol. **38** 365.

FOWLER, J. F., MORGAN, R. L., WOOD, C. A. P. W., BEWLEY, D. K., THOMLINSON, R. H., ALPER, T., HORNSEY, S., TURNER, B. A. and SILVESTER, J. A. 1963a. Brit. J. Radiol. **36** 77–121.

FOWLER, J. F. MORGAN, R. L., SILVESTER, J. A., BEWLEY, D. K. and TURNER, B. A. 1963b. Brit. J. Radiol. **36** 188.

FOWLER, J. F., BEWLEY, D. K., MORGAN, R. L., SILVESTER, J. A., ALPER, T. and HORNSEY, S. 1963c. Nature **199** 253 (Review paper).

FOWLER, J. F., BEWLEY, D. K., MORGAN, R. L. and SILVESTER, J. A. 1965a. Brit. J. Radiol. **38**.

FOWLER, J. F., BERRY, R. J., ELLIS, R. E., KRAGT, K. and LINDOP, P. J. 1965b. Int. J. Rad. Biol., **9** 241.

FOWLER, J. F. and STERN, B. E. 1963. Brit. J. Radiol. **36** 163 (Review paper).

FOWLER, P. H. and PERKINS, D. H. 1961. Nature **189** 524.

FOWLER, P. H. 1964. Rutherford Memorial Lecture. Proc. Phys. Soc. **85** 1051.

GRAY, L. H. 1961. Am. J. Roentgenol. **85** 803.

GRAY, L. H., CONGER, A. D., EBERT, M., HORNSEY, S. and SCOTT, O. C. A. 1953. Brit. J. Radiol. **26** 638.

GRAY, L. H., WRIGHT, E. A., LINDOP, P. J., NUNN, J. F., ERNSTING, J. and ELLIS, F. 1962. Brit. J. Radiol. **35** 505.

HALE, C. H. and HOLMES, G. W. 1947. Radiology **48** 563.

HALE, B. T., BULLEN, M. A., FREUNDLICH, H. F., MARSHALL, D. H. and TUDWAY, R. C. 1963. Postgrad. Med. J. **39** 265.

HALL, E. J., BEDFORD, J. S. and OLIVER, R. 1965. Rad. Res. in the press; also HALL, E. J. and BEDFORD, J. S. 1964. Brit. J Radiol **38** 156 (Abstract).

HEWITT, H. B. and WILSON, C. W. 1959a. Nature **183** 1060.

HEWITT, H. B. and WILSON, C. W. 1959b. Brit. J. Cancer **13** 675.

HORNSEY, S. and VATISTAS, S. 1963. Brit. J. Radiol. **36** 795.

HOLSTI, L. and TASKINEN, P. J. 1964. Acta Radiol. Scand. **2** 366.

KALLMAN, R. 1964. Acta Union Int. Contre le Cancer **20** 1216.

KLEIN, L. 1957. Dissertation, Erlangen.

KOLSTAD, P. 1965. Brit. J. Radiol. **38** 216.

LAJTHA, L. G. 1964. In: Current Topics in Radiation Research. Vol. I. Ed. M. Ebert and A. Howard (North-Holland Publ. Co., Amsterdam) p. 139.

LAJTHA, L. G. and OLIVER, R. 1961. Brit. J. Radiol. **34** 252.

LAJTHA, L. G. and OLIVER, R. 1962. Brit. J. Radiol. **35** 131.

LAJTHA, L. G., OLIVER, R. and ELLIS, F. 1960. Brit. Radiol. **33** 634.

LAJTHA, L. G., OLIVER, R. and GURNEY, C. W. 1962. Brit. J. Haemat. **8** 442.

LARSSON, B., LEKSELL, L., REXED, B., SOURANDER, P., MAIR, W. and ANDERS-SON, B. 1958. Nature **182** 1222.

LAWRENCE, J. H. 1965. Nucleonics **23**(1) 48.

MAEDA, M. and SUIT, H. D., 1965. XI Congress of Radiology, Rome, Paper No. 980, Abstract book p. 460, and private communication.

MALLAMS, J. T., BALLA, G. A. and FINNEY, J. W. 1965. Amer. J. Roentgenol. **93** 160.

MENDELSSOHN, M. L., 1963. In: Cell Proliferation, Ed. L. F. Lamerton and Fry, R. J. M. (Blackwell, Oxford).

MUNRO, T. R. and GILBERT, C. W. 1961. Brit. J. Radiol. **34** 246.

NAYLOR, P. F. D. and EVANS, N. T. S. 1963. Brit. J. Radiol. **36** 418.

OLIVER, R. 1963. Brit. J. Radiol. **36** 178.

OLIVER, R. and LAJTHA, L. G. 1961. Brit. J. Radiol. **34** 659.

PATERSON, R. 1952. Brit. J. Radiol. **25** 505.

PATT, H. M. and QUASTLER, H. 1963. Physiol. Rev. **43** 357 (Review Paper).

POWERS, W. E. and TOLMACH, L. J. 1963. Nature **197** 710.

PUCK, T. T. and MARCUS, P. I. 1956. J. Exp. Med. **53** 653.

REISKIN, A. B. and MENDELSOHN, M. L. 1964. Cancer Res. **24** 1131.

REVESZ, L. and LITTBRAND, B. 1964. Nature **203** 742.

REVESZ, L. and LITTBRAND, B. 1964. Nature **203** 889.

ROSSI, H. H. 1962. Radiology **78** 530.

SAMBROOK, D. K. 1962. Clin. Radiol. **13** 1.

SAMBROOK, D. K. 1963. Brit. J. Radiol. **36** 174.

SCANLON, P. W. 1960. Amer. J. Roentgenol. **84** 632.

SCHWARZ, G. 1909. Münch. med. Wochschr. **56** 1217.

SCOTT, O. C. A. 1958. In: Advances in Biological and Medical Physics. Vol. VI (Academic Press, New York) p. 165.

SINCLAIR, W. K. 1964. Rad. Res. **21** 584.

SINCLAIR, W. K. and MORTON, R. A. 1963. Nature **199** 1158.

SPRATT, J. S. 1965. Cancer **18** 14.

STONE, R. S. 1948. Amer. J. Roentgenol. **59** 771.

STRANDQVIST, M. 1944. Acta. Radiol. Stockh., Suppl. **55**.

SZUR, L. 1964. Brit. J. Dermatol. **76** 10.

TERASIMA, T. and TOLMACH, L. J. 1963. Biophys. J. **3** 11.

THOMLINSON, R. H. 1961. In: Fundamental Aspects of Radiosensitivity. (Brookhaven Symposia in Biology No. 14) p. 204.

THOMLINSON, R. H. 1963. Brit. J. Radiol. **36** 89.

THOMLINSON, R. H. 1965. In: Scientific Basis of Medicine Annual Reviews.

THOMLINSON, R. H. 1965. Submitted to Brit. J. Cancer.

THOMLINSON, R. H. and GRAY, L. H. 1955. Brit. J. Cancer **9** 539.

TILL, J. E. 1961. Rad. Res. **15** 400.

TILL, J. E. and McCULLOCH, E. A. 1961. Rad. Res. **14** 213.

TILL, J. E. McCULLOCH, E. A. and 1963. Rad. Res. **18** 96.

VAN DEN BRENK, H. A. S. 1962. J. Coll. Radiol. Australia **6** 116.

VAN DEN BRENK, H. A. S. 1963. In: Proc. First Internat. Congress on Clin. Applic. of Hyperbaric Oxygen, Amsterdam. in the press.

VAN DEN BRENK, H. A. S. 1964. Private communication.

VAN PUTTEN, L. M. and KALLMAN, R. F., 1965, private communication.

VON ESSEN, C. F., 1963, Radiology. **81** 881.

WHITMORE, G. F., GULYAS, S. and BOTOND, J. 1964. In: Cellular Radiation Biology, Proc. 18th Ann. Symp. Fundamental Cancer Res. (Univ. of Texas, Houston).

WHITMORE, G. F. and TILL, J. E. 1964. Ann. Rev. Nucl. Sci. **14** 347.

WILSON, C. W. 1961. Radiology **77** 940.

WINTZ, H. 1938. Radiology **30** 35.

WITHERS, R. 1965. Private communication.

ZIMMER, K. G. 1961. Studies in Quantitative Radiation Biology. Translated into English by H. D. Griffith (Oliver and Boyd, London).

Fractionation Working Party of the British Institute of Radiology, 1963, Brit. J. Radiol. **36**, 382.

Fractionation Working Party of the British Institute of Radiology, 1964, Brit. J. Radiol. **37**, 562.

# AUTHOR INDEX

# SUBJECT INDEX

# M